A HISTORY OF BRITAIN'S HOSPITALS

A HISTORY OF BRITAIN'S HOSPITALS

G. Barry Carruthers M.D.
Lesley A. Carruthers B.Sc. (Hons)

Book Guild Publishing
Sussex, England

First published in Great Britain in 2005 by
The Book Guild Ltd
25 High Street
Lewes, East Sussex
BN7 2LU

Typesetting in Times by
Acorn Bookwork, Salisbury, Wiltshire

Printed in Bath by
CPI Bath

A catalogue record for this book is available from
The British Library.

ISBN 978 1 857769 05 0

Contents

Acknowledgements   vii

Imperial/Metric Conversions   ix

1   Earliest Hospitals: Monastic; Lazar Houses   1

2   The Royal Hospitals St. Thomas's & St. Bartholomew's;
Guy's   19

3   The Age of Hospitals: Voluntary Hospital System
18th Century; London and Provinces   57

4   19th Century London Voluntary Hospitals   105

5   Succour for the Sick Poor or Gateways of Death   133

6   First State Hospitals: Workhouses, Metropolitan Asylums
Board, Municipal Hospitals   153

7   Specialist Hospitals   183

8   Cottage Hospitals   219

9   Maternity Hospitals and Midwifery   227

10   Children's Hospitals   251

11   Mental Hospitals   279

12   Evolution of the Medical Profession   301

13   Development of the Nursing Ethic and Status   325

14   Background to the NHS   359

15   The Independent Sector   377

16   Money Matters   385

17   The First 50 Years   399

18   Hospitals in the Future   407

Bibliography   417

Index of Illustrations   421

General Index   423

Index of Hospitals   425

Acknowledgements

The authors wish to express their gratitude to the many people who have contributed information and advice during our eight years of research for this book. They have ranged from archivists and public relations or press departments of the Hospitals and Trusts concerned, to the publishers of relevant material and individuals with a personal interest in the background history of the medical, nursing and allied professions.

Nicholas Baldwin, Archivist, Great Ormond Street Hospital for Children NHS Trust.

Marion Rea, Archivist, St Bartholomew's Hospital Archives & Museum

Victoria North, Archivist, Royal Free Hospital Hampstead NHS Trust

Kevin Brown, Archivist, St Mary's Hospital NHS Trust

Alma Topen, Archivist, Yorkhill Division, NHS Greater Glasgow and the Medical Illumination Services, Glasgow Royal Infirmary

Jonathan Evans, Archivist, Royal London Hospital NHS Trust

Rob Baker, Archivist, Chelsea & Westminster Health NHS Trust

Stuart Anderson, President, British Society for the History of Pharmacy

London Metropolitan Archives, Corporation of London

Dr R.J. Taylor, Publications Manager, English Heritage; formerly RCHME

Wellcome Trust Centre for the History of Medicine

The Nuffield Trust for Research and Policy Studies in Health Services

The Librarian, Royal Society of Medicine

The Librarian, Royal College of Nursing

The Librarian, Edinburgh City Central Library

The Librarian, Royal Haslar Hospital

Press Office, The Royal Marsden Hospital

Mrs C. Goodall, Archivist, Sister Agnes Hospital for Officers

Chloe Hayward, Head of Communications, Royal Hospital for Neuro-Disability

Dr Foster, Independent Healthcare

Help the Hospices, Hospice House, London

Every effort has been made to contact our sources of information and illustration and the authors would wish to thank the following who have supplied or authorised illustrations for reproduction.

Great Ormond Street Hospital for Children NHS Trust: pages 256, 257, 258, 259, 260

St Bartholomew's Hospital Archives & Museum: pages 22, 50, 51, 53, 54

Yorkhill Division NHS Greater Glasgow: pages 267, 268, 269

Royal Free Hospital Hampstead NHS Trust: pages 107, 108, 109, 110

St Bartholomew's & London NHS Trust: pages 74, 76, 78

Royal Commission on the Historical Monuments of England: pages 101, 128, 221, 287, 363, 365

John C. Hughes, Chief Executive, Cygnet Health Care: pages 298, 299

HCA Hospitals: pages 381, 382

BMI Healthcare: page 380

Richard Carruthers: page 247

Garwood & Voigt Antiquarian Prints & Maps

Dr Johnson's Medical Books

Cover Design: L. A. Carruthers

Imperial/Metric Conversion Examples

Length

1 inch (1″)	= 25.4 mm
12 inches (12″) = 1 foot (ft)	= 305 mm
3 feet (3 ft) = 1 yard	= 0.91 m
1760 yards (yds) = 1 mile (1 m)	= 1.61 km

Area

144 square inch (sq. in) 1 sq ft	= 0.093 m^2
9 square feet (sq. ft) 1 sq yd	= 0.84 m^2
4840 sq. yards (sq. yds) 1 acre	= 4047 m^2

Weight

16 drams (dr) = 1 ounce (oz)	= 28 grams
16 ozs = 1 pound (lb)	= 0.45 kg
14 lbs = 1 stone (st)	= 6.35kg

Capacity

20 fluid ounces = 1 pint (pt)	= 568 ml
2 pints (pts) = 1 quart (qrt)	= 1.1 L
4 qrts = 1 gallon (gal)	= 4.546 L

(in USA 16 fluid ounces = 1 pint = 0.473 litre and US gallon = 3.785 litre)

UK Coinage Pre and Post Decimal

2 farthings	= 1 halfpenny	approximately	=	0.208p
4 farthings	= 1 penny (d)	approximately	=	0.417p
3d	= 1 threepenny bit	approximately	=	1.25p
6d	= 1 sixpenny piece	approximately	=	2.5p
12d	= 1 shilling (s) 'a bob'	approximately	=	5p
2s	= 1 florin	approximately	=	10p
2s/6d	= 1 half crown	approximately	=	12.5p

10s	= 1 ten 'bob' note	approximately	= 50p
20s	= 1 pound note	approximately	= £1
5 shillings	= 1 crown	approximately	= 25p
21 shillings	= 1 guinea	approximately	= £1.05p
4 pennies	= 1 groat	approximately	= 1.7p

Chapter 1

Earliest Hospitals: Monastic; Lazar Houses

The concept of hospitals that offered in-patient care and treatment was a relatively late entry onto the medical scene. In Britain the first to be established was a Roman field hospital at Inchtuthill in Perthshire in the first century AD.

Under Roman occupation Britain had been changed from a tribal patchwork of warring kingdoms to a disciplined country under central control for the first time. But the infrastructure did not survive the Romans' withdrawal and during the first part of the ensuing Anglo-Saxon period Britain reverted to its former state of separate warring kingdoms, with successive waves of invaders from Scandinavia and mainland Europe. In such an unsettled background there are no records of any established hospitals in Britain, although in both Europe and the Middle East centres for the sick were being established. Monasteries such as the French hôtels-dieu were founded in Lyons in AD 542 and established in Paris a century later. At best there was some charitable aid from the kings and lords for the sick or aged members of their household in the form of a smallholding or billet.

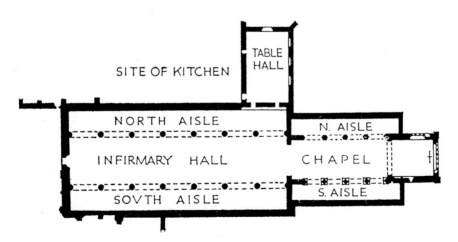

Monastic Infirmary, Canterbury Cathedral.

1

Christianity began to be effectively restored in AD 597 when St Augustine was sent with 40 monks by Pope Gregory to convert the pagan Anglo-Saxons. He established a base in Canterbury, where King Ethelbert's wife, Bertha, was already Christian. Augustine was to become the first Archbishop of Canterbury, which has remained the title of the head of the Anglican Church to this day. He was a Benedictine and gradually a network of some 200 monasteries was established across the country over the next 90 years, as in turn the kingdoms converted to Christianity. Whilst the regional kings continued their feuds, the tribal bishops became organised, paying allegiance to Rome through Canterbury.

While the rule of St Benedict imposed a strict pattern of self-discipline and worship, it allowed the monks and nuns to undertake local pastoral care and serve the local parish churches, called minsters; and the monasteries became centres of education and civil influence by

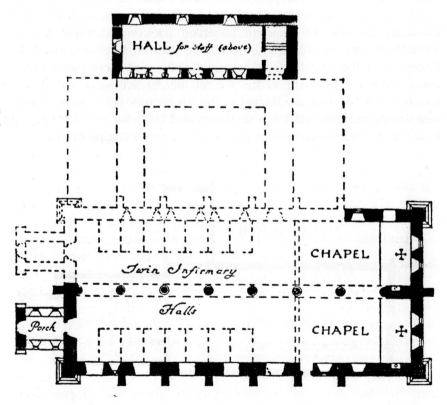

Later monastic infirmary, St Nicholas, Salisbury, divided to separate the sexes.

introducing organised methods of farming and trade. One of their services was to offer hospitality to passing pilgrims and travellers, alongside help to the local sick and poor.

In the documentation that exists, including the Domesday Book (1086), there is no clear-cut reference to independent hospitals before the Norman Conquest, although later several were to claim an origin from the Anglo-Saxon period. Amongst these were Flixton and St Peter's, founded by the canons of York, but probably these were only hospices. One of the difficulties is in terminology at the time. Hospital is a word derived from the Latin for reception of a guest, and the place a *hospitum*, or *hospice* in French. Only later was hospital to become a comprehensive word to include a permanent residence for the infirm – an almshouse – as well as a place for the temporary care of the sick – a spittle house.

There was one area for the elderly and infirm that began to develop during the 10th and 11th centuries. Both monasteries and royalty were faced with the problem of dependants who had outlived their useful working lives and needed sheltered accommodation. Benedictine rule dictated this should be provided and at the end of the 10th century the major monasteries and convents in England drew up an agreement, the *Regularis Concordia*, that cells should be set aside within the monastery for elderly monks and nuns, with novices assigned to look after them. All monasteries and nunneries established an infirmary to which their sick would be transferred when they could no longer sing in the choir. This would be a separate building of a standard format: a long hall containing up to 80 beds in two rows with their backs to the side wall and an altar at the eastern end. The infirmary was under the control of a priest called the *infirmarer*, primarily a finance officer who collected revenues from local land tenants and kept detailed accounts of expenditure on parchment rolls. The patients lived in relative luxury compared with their monastic life. Each would take their routine bedding, but flock and feather cushions might be added for their comfort, and had meat and fish in their diet. Records of the Westminster Infirmary established in 1049 for a prior and 50 monks are the most complete. They slept initially on a straw mattress with a blanket, coverlet and pillow. Later each had his own cubicle. They wore stockings, pants and a linen shirt with a black habit and leather cloak in winter. They were allowed two baths a year, at one time increased to four, and their linen was washed regularly. Water was supplied from local springs in Hyde Park and waste flushed downstream.

From sick records, the average age of death was about 51, similar to the national average, and their sickness pattern was similar to today's. The greatest demands on the infirmary came from about one third of the patients, whose health broke down at regular and frequent intervals, whilst some of the elderly *stagiarii* were long-stay cases. Admissions of novices under the age of 24, who broke down under the stress of the monastic atmosphere, were high, and special country houses were set up for the mentally sick. Treatment was largely 'loving care and attention' with the addition of abundant prayer, but there are some references to medical support. One of the monks would be trained to prepare medicines from herbs grown in the hospital garden, dispensed as pastes with honey or syrup to be taken by mouth, or as enemas or suppositories. Cupping was used, but blood-letting by monks was not allowed. Professional medical attention was expensive at the time, but there are references to visiting doctors – including one of a woman doctor who was paid 40 shillings for treating 10 monks.

Similar responsibilities towards their elderly and sick retainers was shown by some kings, particularly Alfred the Great and Edward the Confessor. Trade guilds were developing at that time and these began to finance almshouses for their elderly members. But all this residential accommodation was restricted to specific groups and there was nothing open to the average person.

After the Norman Conquest reliable records of free-standing hospitals began to exist, with details of their charters, possessions, endowments and staffing. There is little in their archives about the patients, who were probably a mixture of chronic sick and aged more than acute sick. The hospital would remain within the monastery complex and strict religious control was retained, with a chapel and resident priests. The first was established by Archbishop Lefranc after 1077, at Canterbury, outside the city walls, as part of his overall plans to reform the cathedral. It comprised a sizeable stone building divided into two halves, to separate men and women, who were not allowed to mix, even if husband and wife. There were outhouses with a chapel for the resident canons, who would pray for souls and bury the dead. At a safe distance were wooden huts where lepers were confined.

Land and tithes from the cathedral holdings were transferred to finance the hospital and this established a pattern that was to be created across the country. Some 68 hospitals were set up over the next 80 years, 23 under direct monastic control and the rest under the patronage of royalty, nobility or wealthy landowners, each retaining the rights to appoint staff and dictate occupancy.

The proliferation of monastic hospitals during the 12th century was independent of any central control, and Church involvement was through local bishops. It is difficult to determine the overall number of medieval hospitals and their function from the records that exist. The primary source is the Mappa Mundi, which lists the monasteries, castles and waterways that existed around AD 1200. This includes some hospitals, but is very incomplete. Only eight are listed in Kent and few elsewhere – in London only two houses of the Knights Templars and Knights Hospitallers are recorded and even St Thomas's and St Bartholomew's are omitted. It is known that over 250 existed by 1200 and the total had reached over 500 by the time of the Black Death of 1348, most too small and insignificant to be listed.

The residential hospitals fell into two main categories that offered care for protected groups or were almshouses for old-age pensioners. They often comprised a few cottages with a single master in charge, usually a priest. Larger centres based in towns might house over 100 long-stay inmates and were manned by a large clerical and domestic staff. The largest was St Leonard's, York, founded in the 12th century by King Stephen to replace St Peter's, which had been burned down, and for a long time symbolised the best of the hospital multifunctional system. It continued to house local travellers and distribute charity to the poor, whilst at its peak it could hold 240 long-term sick. The complex grew to include an orphanage and a school with 30 choristers, staffed by 34 clergy and a full complement of domestic and catering staff.

All hospitals were named after a patron saint and run primarily as religious establishments, with staff and patients equally obliged to comply with the strict prayer rituals of the clergy, and they were built to facilitate this. Patients and overnight guests were housed in a great hall dominated by a chapel at the eastern end so they could watch the seven daily services of the divine office. Alongside the less literate lay staff would have to repeat the Paternoster, Ave Maria and Creed up to 200 times in the day and might be woken at night by the dormitory bell to repeat them. Larger units might have a minstrel gallery or loft from which a priest could read or lecture.

The priests usually had separate quarters and kept aloof from day-to-day care, with some chantry priests confined to saying mass daily

5

The Boniface Hospital, Maidstone, 12th century.

for the souls of departed 'benefactors'. Any nursing care was entirely in the hands of the nuns attached to the monastery.

The background to hospital funding was complex and with time inevitably led to misdirection of funds and corruption. The majority were composed of one or more cottages built on a small parcel of land donated by a modest benefactor, with the inmates sustained by their own efforts and the support of their family and local charity. A larger scale required a patron of substance, usually a local bishop or royalty, who in return would expect the right to appoint senior staff and dictate occupancy. He would donate the land and fund the building cost and also grant endowments towards the support of the large number of clergy and other staff, who could outnumber patients. These endowments would include rents from local property, and tithes – a form of annual taxation levied by the parish church, amounting to one tenth of any man's property or produce. The hospital might also be entitled to a toll on local farmers or sales in the market, which could become a valuable, but unpopular, source of income. St Leonard's, York, was granted a thrave (20 sheaves) of corn from every ploughland in Cumberland and Westmorland known as 'Petercorn' and became the wealthiest hospital in England. Local grazing and forestry rights were common and in coastal towns hospitals might be granted a toll on customs duties or imported wine. There could also be exemption from property and other taxes imposed by the Crown and Church.

By themselves these endowments would be insufficient and had to be topped up by appeals to charity. Hospitals were often built alongside the main highways into towns, with collection boxes placed outside and offers of overnight board for passers-by. There would be annual local fête and fair days, whilst the larger foundations would send out warranted proctors to travel around the country to appeal for funds. The church establishments were not backward in taking full advantage of their religious influence. The wealthy were encouraged to endow a chantry off the main chapel where they would be buried and a priest would continue to pray for their souls. St Mary within Cripplegate, London, at one time would support six 'chancery' priests. A system of 'indulgences' was created, a form of pardon that could be purchased as a release from any penalties imposed when granted forgiveness at confession. Alongside the cathedrals, hospitals would send out 'pardoners', called proctors, to travel around and sell these indulgences.

The patients themselves became a source of funding. Hospitals could offer secure long-term care and began to copy the monasteries by selling beds to those who could afford them, known as corrody. The purchaser would be offered lifetime care for cash or for committing his assets on death. This could amount to a private room off the main hall with meals at the head chaplain's table, a servant and stabling. An ordinary patient could be charged an admission fee, even to a leper hospital, such as 100 shillings by Buckland at Dover. A maintenance charge from relatives became a common practice and later, even resident lay staff might be charged £5 for their post. All these practices were forbidden by the church authorities, but largely ignored at local level.

The pattern of hospital life was very disciplined. Between prayer times the able-bodied were expected to help with household chores or work in the garden. Outside, they would wear distinctive clothes or badges and were forbidden to beg or visit a tavern. Creature comforts were of variable standard, based on endowments. A basic quality of care was often laid down, although this might lapse with time. Wealthier establishments with staff would provide cooked meals with a generous allowance of beer, whilst the poorer would depend on the charitable donations of food which they prepared themselves.

In the early days beds were simple straw pallets, but by the end of the 12th century these had been replaced by wooden bedsteads often large enough to hold two or three patients. Bed linen was supposed to be changed between each new set of patients, but complaints of this being dirty and lousy became common later. There was still little or no central control of the hospitals. Technically, overriding responsibility rested with the King through his Chancellor, who had the right to inspect church and other hospitals, as well as those under his direct patronage. This was seldom exercised, except at times of disputes, which usually related to transfer of patronage of a well-endowed establishment. This left considerable power in the hands of the head warden appointed by the patron. In the larger units he would have his own house and staff as well as salary and expenses and he would have control of all income. Often the post became a sinecure and the warden, usually a clergyman, showed little or no interest in day-to-day management, which was left to deputies who would in turn 'milk the system'. The larger hospitals would often build up a large resident and outdoor staff, of whom half might be clergy with their sole function being prayer, and they absorbed an increasing proportion of the funds available at the expense of any charitable work. This led to mounting public resentment against the tithes they levied and the increased rents charged to their tenants. Meanwhile many smaller units became increasingly short of money and were forced to close down or be absorbed with their endowments into the hands of the larger ones.

Patrons equally abused the system. Royalty regarded the hospitals in their domain as free billets for their travelling households and tax collectors, whilst all patrons were faced with an increased number of ageing dependants as their retinue expanded. Retired monks and nuns would be retained as far as possible in their own monasteries or retirement homes. Wealthy parish priests were able to provide for themselves and fund curates to maintain their living. Many of the young men, however, attracted to the Church as a career, only held insecure posts as poorly paid curates or chantry priests and ended up dependent on charity. When royalty faced the same problem with their retired household and service personnel, the hospitals or almshouses in their patronage were natural sites for their dependants and they also had to create extra space which was often shared with the Church. Westminster Abbey at one time housed 500 monks, noble almsmen and 'poor knights', whilst Edward III established St George's Chapel, Windsor, as a residence when he instituted the Order of the Garter. Records of the occupants before the Reformation only refer to the more important, but the average expectancy of life in such sheltered accommodation had risen to 60, far above the national average, and this led to a blockage on beds.

Half the hospitals in the 12th century were lazar houses. Leprosy had established a social hysteria, akin to AIDS today, fanned by religious prejudice. Earliest medical records occur in Chinese literature around 250 BC, and it is thought to have been introduced into Egypt by the troops of Alexander the Great after his Indian campaign. It was brought into Greece, and later spread by the Roman army throughout Europe, where it became epidemic from AD 1000 to 1400. Victims had been isolated from earliest times because of their disfigurement and fear of contagion, and the Christian authorities played on these fears and the superstitions of an ignorant public. From dubious references in both the Old and New Testaments, leprosy was designated a curse inflicted as a penalty for sin, and the victims were to be cast out of society. A 'leper' mass was created at which the sufferers were excommunicated and isolated from any contact with the community, forced to wear distinctive clothing and carry a bell or rattle to warn of their presence. In extreme cases some were actually buried or burned alive. The true disease was incurable and produced facial and body decay, usually fatal, and was believed to make the leper sexually lustful, imparting the characteristics of a beast. It was thought to be spread by contagion through touch, breath and even the eyes of a leper as well as common use of water.

There was a major re-assessment towards the end of the 11th

century when many infected crusaders began to return from the endemic areas of the Holy Land. It was even postulated that Christ himself may have been leprous and it was redefined as a holy disease. In the 12th century the Pope charged the Order of St Lazarus, a branch of the Knights of St John of Jerusalem, with the specific duty to found and maintain leper hospitals throughout Christendom, and several thousand residential hospitals sprang up in Europe. A small delegation was sent to England although it had little impact. A number of units had already been established before Norman times and many more were created under the patronage of kings, including Edward the Confessor and King John, and in the larger towns such as London and York they had become the responsibility of the city fathers. Leper houses were a popular source of charity and around 283 were reported to have existed at one time in Britain, although many were only single cottages or names mentioned as a bequest in a will. Only a few were on a large scale; Harbledown, established by Archbishop Lefranc near Canterbury as a leper house around 1077, could house over 100 in-patients.

A network of lazar houses was established as the disease spread insidiously across England and Scotland, but it is impossible to deter-

St Nicholas, Harbledown, Canterbury, early 18th century. Established as a leper hospital by Archbishop Lefranc around 1077.

mine the true incidence of the disease at its peak. Estimates in Europe have ranged as high as 30% in some areas, ravaging the population, but this seems a gross exaggeration. In England there may have been 10,000 cases at its peak, most of whom could not have been accommodated in the houses available. One of the problems in estimating the extent of leprosy was that diagnosis was totally haphazard, made by a monk or priest, or even the watchman at the city gate. The Greek word *lopros* embraced a wide range of unpleasant conditions and in Latin *liber* literally means something scaly that peels off like the bark of a tree. Many labelled as leprous were only suffering from relatively harmless skin conditions such as scabies or impetigo. Others had syphilis, which was on the increase at the time. In practice leprosy was a loose term used by doctors and lay alike, as influenza today, to cover a multitude of diseases, although excavated graveyards at some leper sites have shown a high incidence of the condition.

Overall isolation in England was less strict than elsewhere, and lepers were often granted rights to be given food from the local town market, and endowed with land and income, provided they observed restrictions on their behaviour and contact with the public.

Public sympathy began to wane towards the end of the 13th century. One of their entitlements was the right to beg, which became grossly abused and an increasing source of annoyance to townsfolk, who reacted by bans on their entry. London, with ten suburban leper houses, was particularly afflicted and restricted lepers' access to the city by a succession of by-laws, until in 1327 all those living in London were finally ordered to leave. Other cities followed suit, including Bristol, which banned both lepers and prostitutes. For no evident reason leprosy began to die out during the 14th century and the lazar houses began to empty, with many of the smaller ones closing altogether. Their relative security and charitable endowments had attracted many non-leprous inmates from the beginning and any further vacancies were rapidly filled by vagabonds and beggars. By 1341 a Royal Commission had reported these to be in the majority and many housed no leprous at all. The well-endowed also became attractive take-over targets and were converted by their patrons and local authorities for use as almshouses for their infirm and aged staff. The last six in London were finally closed down in 1549 and their few remaining patients transferred to St Bartholomew's.

Hospital development was greatly influenced by economic circumstances. At least 110 hospitals are known to have been founded during the second half of the 12th and first part of the 13th centuries, at a time of great economic growth and urban development in the boroughs under monastic or royal control. Many were derived from redundant leper hospitals and located on the outskirts of towns to relieve the influx of migrating impoverished farm labourers, and were generally funded by the new wealthy trading and merchant classes.

Of these hospitals fewer than 20 devoted themselves to the care of the sick poor. Many of the rest might include some such patients amongst their other admissions, but all were selective in the cases they would accept. Very few catered for the acute sick or terminally ill, and most had a policy of refusing patients in need of special care and confined themselves to the short-term sick likely to recover. Injured and crippled, including seamen and soldiers, would be rejected, as were the mentally ill and epileptic. Unmarried 'lascivious' pregnant women were refused on moral grounds, probably because the hospital might have to accept responsibility for orphaned or abandoned babies. There were few beds available for victims of epidemics such as smallpox, who would be confined to home. A few hospitals might have specific caring defined in its ordinance, although often restricted to priests. One of these was St Mary's within Cripplegate in London, commonly known as 'Elsing Spital' after the founder, which looked after the blind. Another was St Mary of Bethlehem, founded in 1247 to cater for the insane, which became known as 'Bedlam', infamous for its callous regime. As syphilis was rampant by now, some leper houses were converted to Lock hospitals for venereal disease sufferers, as well as a residence in London that Henry III had established for Jews who had converted to Christianity. An increasing problem in London was pregnancy in unmarried girls who were migrating to the booming towns as servants and prostitutes. In general these were refused admission, but in 1341 St Mary without Bishopsgate and St Bartholomew's were exempted from royal taxation in return for accepting them, and then Lord Mayor of London Dick Whittington founded eight beds at St Thomas's. Inevitably all these units became filled with the servants and mistresses of the wealthy.

Details of day-to-day running and patient care in early English hospitals are totally lacking, but records of the French are intact. Archives of the Hôtel Dieu in Paris show standards of cleanliness and general care that would shame most English hospitals today. Wooden floors were washed and brushed every morning and accounts show 1,300 brooms were used every year. Nursing sisters washed the patients' face and hands every morning, the women's hair was washed weekly, and the men were shaved or had their beard trimmed. Bed linen was changed each week and washed in the local river by 15 permanent laundry staff, whilst the wards were lime-washed every Easter. The hospital had its own bakery and the master chef would visit a local farm weekly to select the animals he wished slaughtered. Diet appears to have been balanced, with added fruit, meat four days a week and fish or cheese on the others. It is thought likely standards in English hospitals were similar initially – with the addition of a gallon of beer daily – although these were to deteriorate badly later.

In Europe, records of medical care date back to the 1200s. Surgeons and physicians were attached to the Hôtel Dieu, and in Milan there is reference to ten general hospitals and others in the surroundings with 28 physicians and 150 surgeons of different specialities attached, some paid by the commune. In English hospitals, references to qualified medical practitioners only appear a century later. They were few and far between, their primary duties related to royalty and their hospital posts were sinecures. Medical attention was non-existent for the ordinary patient, whilst the attendant staff had no nursing background. The first record of a hospital doctor is in 1479, when a surgeon was bequeathed £25 to attend St Thomas's and Bartholomew's over a five-year period.

Many of this generation of hospitals were under strict Augustinian control, regulated by the bishop under whose jurisdiction they fell. The friars largely devoted themselves to their ecclesiastical privileges of burial, bell ringing and the care of souls, whilst any practical aid to the sick was dependent on female communities such as the Sisters of Stow, who established religious communities outside the monastic atmosphere for charitable work at parish level.

As the donations poured in from the towns and villages, the hospitals began to build up substantial land holdings within their precinct, which they rented out. Some, such as All Saints, Cambridge, even became money lenders to the larger landowners, offering a lower interest rate than the Jewish money-lenders who dominated this field at the time. Even villagers were offered short-term mortgages for a levy on their produce. Over time the hospitals would take over ownership of the property with default on interest payment.

With the depression and famine of the early 14th century, charitable contributions and rental income fell sharply. Problems became much worse following the outbreaks of plague between 1348 and 1368, when the Black Death decimated the population. The toll amongst clergy in closed communities such as monasteries was especially high, and hospitals suffered equally. Economic depression and inflation were rampant, and during the second half of the 14th century falling revenues forced the closure of more than 100 smaller hospitals – some 20% of the total stock. Others gave up any charitable work and became merely chantries to say prayers for their founder. The larger units reduced their charitable works as they focused on self-interest and the maintenance of religious devotion. Clerical salaries had increased greatly and many records show how the proportion of hospital income absorbed by the clergy had increased at the expense of patient care, which was even given up altogether. They continued to levy their tolls and raise rents, with inevitable loss of public respect and increasing resentment, which peaked during the Peasants' Revolt of 1381 when several churches and hospitals were attacked and sacked by the mob. Progressively their right to local levies was abolished and a century later the wealthiest hospital, St Leonard's, York, was to lose the right to claim 'Petercorn'.

Their situation was aggravated by the increasingly detached attitude of the Augustine brothers, who in 1387 reverted to an entirely religious role, devoting their time to a study of the scriptures in the cloisters and observing canonical hours, except when saying divine office or engaged on house business. In contrast the sisters would continue to nurse and feed the sick under the supervision of the master.

The high attrition rate of functional hospitals continued, with failure of donations reflecting the loss of care standards, and by the latter part of the medieval period, of the original 112 only 39 still cared for the sick poor, one quarter had closed and 49 converted to other activities. All classes of hospital had suffered from financial maladministration and corruption. Some of the smaller closed or merely became chantries for saying prayers to their founder or his successors, others would have long-term residents, even women, who could afford to pay for their stay. Some became colleges or schools, as St Paul's in London which still exists today. The master of St Leonard's, York, with a single large dormitory dedicated for 206 sick poor, demanded large sums of money for admission, most of which he appropriated. The Bishop of Ely began to house students at St John's, Cambridge, as a charitable experiment and later set up the first Cambridge college, Peterhouse. The hospital itself went on to achieve full university status as St John's College in 1511.

Actual dishonesty was rife, with most hospitals involved in one way or another. Before the dissolution of the monasteries by Henry VIII, it was a common practice for the monks, aware that forfeiture of their goods was imminent, to convert these into cash and transfer the house properties into their own name by bogus sales. In 1403 St Mary's Bethlehem was investigated by a Royal Commission that found the deputy warden and his wife had stolen the entire hospital income for the past four years and part over the previous fourteen, and had sold off many of the hospital's assets, including the chains with which the patients were restrained. At St Mary's without Bishopsgate the patients were deprived of their allowances for food and drink, and even the lamps above their beds were sold. St Thomas's suffered from a succession of larcenous and incompetent masters and a matron who was arrested three times for drunken behaviour. Of the few exceptions St Bartholomew's appears to have been the main one.

In the late 14th and 15th centuries there was a change in hospital pattern at local level and a new generation of independent almshouses was created, restricted to long-term care of the aged and poor, to clear the streets of beggars. Although often called hospitals, many were only a small group of homely cottages. An increasing number were founded by trade guilds under the control of a city company or local authority. A strong link was usually retained with the local clergy through the collegiate system based on parish churches that had replaced monastic influence. Whilst the primary duty of the chaplains remained prayer, they extended their interest to education and opened schools attached to the larger hospitals.

The general decay in monastic standards had spread throughout Europe. As early as AD 1311 the Pope had issued a decree – the Quia Cintingit – ordering reform, with little response in England. At the end of the century John Wycliffe and the Lollards initiated an attack on church and hospital standards, and increasing public concern aroused the attention of the House of Commons. In 1414 it petitioned Henry V for action and he agreed to order the Church Commissioners to investigate the absorption by the clergy of benefits for their own use, as well as an inquiry into the Royal Hospitals of St Thomas's and St Bartholomew's, but no action was taken before the Reformation.

The Victoria History of the Counties of England details the history of each county. It lists some 585 hospitals and almshouses at the start of the Reformation in 1534, although many of the smaller would not be included. Some were wealthy long-established religious foundations,

Palace of the Savoy, 1519.

whilst many were impoverished or had lost any pastoral function and only supported clergy to say individual masses for the dead. Only a few of the larger hospitals remained active in serving their local community as a medical unit. There were three in London – St Bartholomew's, St Thomas's and St Mary's without Bishopsgate – along with St Leonard's, York, but not a single new general hospital had been built. Henry VII had planned three before his death, but only the Savoy was completed some years later in 1519. This was designed on an extravagant scale to house 100 poor vagrants nightly in relative luxury for the time. It proved expensive to run and attracted the least deserving from a wide area and its endowment and assets were eventually transferred to St Thomas's. Henry VIII had no such interests and the wealth of the Church was a natural prey for funds to support his wars and extravagant lifestyle. The monasteries were shown to own 26% of the land in England at the Domesday Book survey of 1086, much acquired from grateful individuals for spiritual support and physical shelter, or when a man would hand over his assets to the black monks of St Benedict's on his deathbed. In France ownership was even higher. The Crown had already claimed rights over the property of the insane and mentally retarded (non compos

16

mentis) in return for a promise to support them properly, and after appointing himself head of the Church in 1534, Henry VIII had church property revalued. He imposed heavy new taxation, known as 'first fruits and tenths', in which hospitals were included. Religious houses with an income under £200 p.a. were closed down in 1536, followed by progressive surrender of the monasteries, completed by 1539. These were converted into cathedrals or collegiate churches, themselves subjected to taxation.

Around the country many of the remaining long-established hospitals tied up with the Church were involved in the dissolution and progressively forced to close. Only the smaller units, including lazar and almshouses which could establish their charitable basis, were spared. Some major towns lost 50% of their hospitals with these closures and their destitute inmates were thrown onto the streets as beggars. Amongst these were St Leonard's, York, and in London, St Mary's without Bishopsgate, as well as St Thomas's and St Bartholomew's.

Henry VIII had promised Parliament that the 'sick and poor would not suffer if the religious houses were transferred into his safe hands' and the funds would be redirected into poor relief and education,

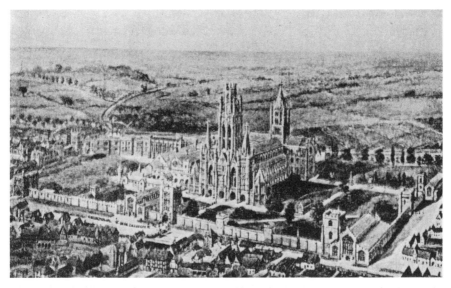

St Edmundsbury. This reconstruction shows how one of the eight hundred hospitals and shrines suppressed by Henry VIII would have looked before its destruction.

along with hospital reform. These reassuring words reflected the views of both Catholic and Protestant reformers of the time, who considered that misused monastic and associated hospital funds should be confiscated and redirected to the establishment in every town and local district for houses to lodge the infirm poor, with salaried doctors and nurses. His receipts from the take-over of monasteries and associated hospitals were enormous and would match any 'windfall' tax today. Annual rental income then was £37,000, equal to £14 million now, with a capital acquisition of over half a billion pounds. However, only one fifth of the value may have gone to the clergy of the time as Henry gave away a great deal as goodwill to his cronies. Records suggest nearly half this money was spent on his wars against France and another quarter on personal activities. Little, if any, was directed towards hospital reform.

Chapter 2

St. Thomas's & St. Bartholomew's, Guy's

Only two of the hospitals were to be revived after the holocaust of Henry VIII's dissolution of the monasteries, St Bartholomew's and St Thomas's. Each was started on a small scale in the 12th century as an annexe to an Augustinian monastery and was destined to mature into a centre of medical excellence with an international reputation and a major medical school.

Their early medical role is not documented apart from references to the 'sick poor' and, although labelled 'hospitals', would initially have mainly offered overnight stay to pilgrims and travellers who could not afford an inn. St Bartholomew's was located alongside the main route of entry into London from the north, St Thomas's on the road from the south. Travellers would have slept on the floor with the clergy, who would match them in number, and there was no room for any acute or long-term sick occupancy in the earlier years.

Medical care for patients was minimal, with any nursing supplied by the nuns, probably with some support from lay workers. Certainly the priests played little active part and confined their contribution to the patients' souls, dedicating themselves to prayers in which the inmates would be compelled to join. A patient's confession would be heard before admission, followed by prayers and attendance at lengthy services two or three times a day. The first reference to outside medical attention is the employment of a surgeon paid £25 in 1499 to attend the two hospitals for five years, but his services may have been more for the benefit of staff and household than any in-patients.

St Bartholomew's was founded in 1123 by Rahere, reputedly a court jester who entered the court of Henry I and became a minor canon at St Paul's Cathedral. On a pilgrimage to Rome he fell seriously ill and vowed that if he recovered he would devote his life to helping the sick poor. On his way home he had a vision of St Bartholomew telling him that he should found his centre in Smithfield and he successfully petitioned Henry I for permission to build a priory and hospital on an area of marshland between the city wall and the River Fleet. The site was described as 'foul, abounded with filth and muddy water, part

19

used as a market and horse fair in the summer as well as the site of the local gallows and a former Roman burial ground'. The hospital was built close to the priory as a single-storey white-washed building.

The earlier years of St Thomas's are less clearly defined. Its foundation probably dated back to around 1173 as an infirmary attached to the Priory of St Mary Overie, later to become Southwark Cathedral. It would have had travellers and pilgrims entering London over the ancient Roman bridge, the only route in from the south, and the district was thick marsh surrounded by deep ditches. The name was changed to St Thomas Spital in 1173 after the canonisation of Thomas à Becket, the Archbishop of Canterbury murdered by order of Henry II, and a separate hospital was built on a site in Borough High Street in 1215 when the priory was burnt down. This was a two-storey wooden structure with a thatched roof that formed one side of a court-yard. The hospital was initially staffed by four brethren, three sisters and a master, who slept on the ground floor. Up to 40 patients slept on the upper floor, initially on straw pallets until wooden beds were introduced by the end of the 13th century, each shared by two or three patients who slept naked. A church was built on the facing side, which was also used as the first hospital ward.

The newly built hospital enjoyed independence when the priory was rebuilt, but at St Bartholomew's there was increasing dispute between the priory and hospital managements after Rahere's death over their financial relationship. The hospital obtained partial freedom in 1147 to 'tend the needy, orphans, sick and homeless wanderers' in return for a vow of obedience to the priory, but was only to achieve full independence in 1420.

Both hospitals initially co-operated in fund-raising with their monastic attachments, but with time financial relationships became an increasing source of friction as they became increasingly competitive for the charity sources on which both were dependent. The hospitals would send out their own proctors to sell indulgences and absolutions on commission, emphasising the benefit of these for the 'sick poor'. St Bartholomew's would open up chantries, and there is a record of one staffed by two paid priests to say mass daily for the souls of one James of Thame and his extensive family, friends and their successors. St Thomas's would take in long-stay residents, and in one surviving gift of deed a widow left her lands and goods to the master and brethren in return for beds and bed linen for herself and her maid within the court of the hospital during her lifetime.

Bart's and St Thomas's were to extend their premises, with extra space set aside for patients, but this was only to a limited extent and details of this aspect during the medieval period are not available. By 1338 Bart's could accommodate up to 90 sick men and women and St Thomas's 40, but the sick and travellers continued to occupy accommodation side by side and the numbers of nuns and brethren concerned with the hospital had not changed since foundation. At the time of their closure by Henry VIII patient numbers were only 32 and 40 respectively, insignificant for a town with a population of over 50,000, and several hospitals throughout England had far more beds, including St Mary's without Bishopsgate, also in London, with over 100.

In contrast both hospitals expanded commercially and built up extensive land and property holdings throughout London and the Home Counties from charitable donations. Most of the records that survive from before the dissolution of the monasteries relate solely to property transactions, numbering over 2,000 for each hospital. There are no proper accounts for the period for the charitable and rental receipts, but it is evident that for the monks charity began at home and they came progressively to enjoy a comfortable lifestyle.

St Bartholomew's was given extra land by Henry II, steadily extended its boundaries through donations locally and was the site of extensive property development. From the records, little of this was for the benefit of patients, who were confined to a few scattered small wooden huts and a central hall with beds, a fireplace and an altar positioned to be visible to all. Benefactors who had given money to maintain a lamp in front of the altar had their good deed commemorated daily. The sisters responsible for patient care were given a loaf of bread and a half a gallon of beer a day. There was little reference to medical care apart from exceptional miraculous cures, but patients would include stray children from the streets as well as infants from Newgate prison. By the 15th century the sisters were looking after so many children that they were granted a royal licence to acquire additional lands and rents to support this work, and a school was started with a Latin master.

The first hospital plan on record is dated 1617 and shows a complex of houses and shops around the borders of the site. Built to rent, a roll of the tenants recorded would have graced *Who's Who* today, as Smithfield became a fashionable wealthy area. There were two cloisters with extensive gardens, three chapels and two cemeteries – one for the

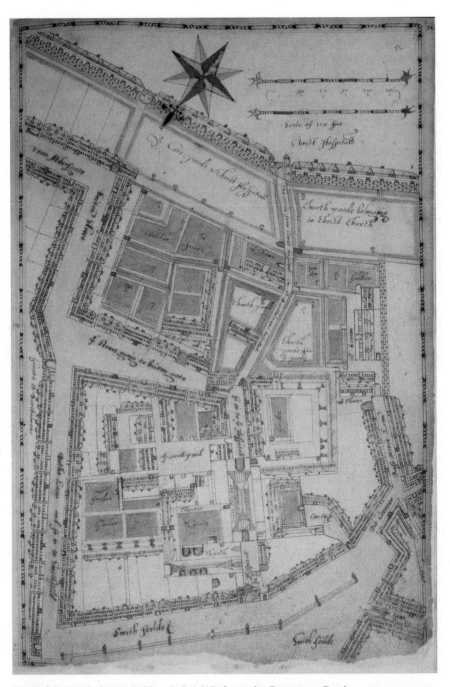

Plan of St Bartholomew's Hospital, 1617, from the Repertory Book.

staff and a larger one, established for patients, which became a popular burial place for the local population.

Outside its boundaries St Bartholomew's acquired a large property holding in the surrounding city, which extended through more than 60 parishes in London and the Home Counties. Many of the gifts were shops, along with some land which would be rented out in return for produce. Discipline remained firm and the brethren were given specific administrative duties alongside their religious ones; presumably this would involve management of all these property holdings.

The rebuilding of St Thomas's was funded by contributions helped by the Bishop of Winchester, Peter de Rupibus, who granted a remittance of 20 days' penance to anyone who contributed to the fund. With the benefit from the sales of this indulgence and donations from local traders and landowners, the hospital, although never as wealthy as St Bartholomew's, would also build up a major land holding throughout London and the Home Counties over the next two centuries. Besides small-holdings and shops, some land gifts were large, one over 200 acres. Often this land would be of poor-quality marshland, but the hospital developed a technique of leasing a site on a peppercorn rent, initially giving the tenant the right to build property. At the end of the lease, or on the death of the lessee, the land and property would revert to the hospital.

No records of further developments survive before 1507, when the hospital was in a very dilapidated state. Six new gabled buildings were built on the site of the skittle alley of the nearby Falcon Tavern, probably forming a second cloistered square leading from the existing one. However, the bed space for patients remained around the 40 level.

In contrast to Smithfield, Southwark degenerated and became a centre for prostitution and infamous 'stew-houses'. The hospital reflected its immediate surroundings and became known as the 'bawdy hospital' as internal discipline was lost. During the 14th century complaints about the standards of patient care and staff behaviour began to build up, and the friars were accused of running the local brothels. This reputation and the immense wealth of property made St Thomas's an easy and attractive target for Henry VIII. An inspection by commissioners in 1535 reported that services were not held and the conduct of the master was filthy and indecent: he kept a concubine in the hospital and was selling off church plate, saying it had been stolen.

Although monasteries and religious houses may have been the main victims of Henry VIII's asset stripping, the associated hospital

23

St Thomas's new six-gabled hospital, 1507.

property holdings were significant. St Bartholomew's annual rental income was assessed at £371 13s 2d and St Thomas's at £266 17s 6d, worth over £250,000 today, whilst that of hospitals such as St Leonards, York, with local levies was far more. The Lord Mayor and Aldermen of the City petitioned the King and Thomas Cromwell in 1538 to spare London hospitals 'to clear away the offensive sight and smell of the poor sick who offended the senses of the clean', but to no effect. St Thomas's and St Mary's without Bishopsgate surrendered in 1540 and were closed down, the latter permanently and the former to lie derelict for 11 years.

The priory of St Bartholomew's had been suppressed in 1539, but the hospital and its premises were left untouched as the master in charge had had the foresight to accept Henry VIII as Supreme Head of the Church of England four years earlier. In 1543 it was reconstituted with all its possessions restored by the King, who appointed a new master and four chaplains with the power to run their own affairs. In 1547, a fortnight before he died, Henry VIII signed a second document formally handing the hospital over to the City of London, returning much of its former property with an income value of £336 6s 8d and defining its constitution and obligations, which would remain the basis of its control until absorbed into the NHS in 1948. In return the City was to match the income the hospital would receive from this returned property. At the time the London streets were unsafe, crowded with beggars from the countryside and discharged ex-servicemen, many disabled, from the Irish wars. It was planned for Bart's to house 100 of these. Eight beadles were employed, uniformed and armed with staves, to patrol the streets and arrest any homeless, sending genuine cases into hospital for treatment or the 'night-layers' ward, and beggars into Bridewell or prison cells. In fact few of the 100 beds allocated were filled at first, and at one time only three were occupied. The initial restored religious management proved totally negligent and was replaced by a Court of Governors appointed by the City, at first presided over by the Lord Mayor himself.

The general situation in London remained out of control and eventually in 1551 the City persuaded the child King Edward VI to sell them St Thomas's, along with Bridewell and Christ's hospitals, 'in view of the sick and infirm lying begging in the streets and places of London and its suburbs to the infection and annoyance of the King's subjects'. The hospital was re-opened with a target of 300 in-patients and had out-patient facilities, but could only achieve a fraction of this number as the granting patent restored less than half its former estate. This could only support 20 beds until the Savoy was closed and its assets transferred to the hospital.

Initially each hospital was under the direct control of the City of London, which appointed aldermen and administrators. As more and more independent governors were appointed, the influence of the City was reduced progressively. At Bart's there were 12 at first, 46 by 1601 and 278 at the end of the century. This was to swell further during the 18th century when money was needed for rebuilding, as anyone who made a substantial contribution would become a governor, with his name emblazoned in the Great Hall. There was an equal increase in the numbers at St Thomas's.

During the 17th century 'ad hoc' committees began to be formed and multiplied, as do quangos today, with only a few performing any important function such as the building planning committee. Patient numbers also increased, although the hospitals only became of significant size when they underwent major building developments at the end of the 17th and first half of the 18th centuries. By 1550 Bart's had built two extra wards with 100 patients and in 1588 numbers peaked at 180 from the intake of service casualties after the Armada – only to fall back to 100 patients later. By 1636 St Thomas's had 20 wards with 280 beds, but 50 years later their audit committee reduced this number to 160 for financial reasons. Both were compelled to accept injured servicemen from the succession of wars throughout this period at the expense of any civilian sick. During the second Dutch war Bart's was ordered to prepare six wards with 91 individual beds for service casualties. Both hospitals had treated over 3,000 such cases by the end of the century. The failure of successive governments to pay their allowance of 4d daily per soldier compounded the financial crises the hospitals faced through the loss of rents that followed the Plague of 1665 and the Great Fire of London a year later.

The 1673 Test Act debarred anyone from holding office who did not take an oath of allegiance and sacrament according to the rites of the Church of England. Nine staff at Catholic Bart's were sacked and later the cook for refusing to give up their faith.

Both hospitals became deeply involved in the politics of the time over the succession to the throne and the vicious struggle for power between the emergent Whig and Tory parties. St Thomas's was predominantly Nonconformist and a Whig supporter, whilst Bart's was a stronghold of Anglican royalism. As each had extensive property holdings and revenues, they were able to influence the local electors. In 1683 the City of London's Charter was dissolved and the City placed under the control of Royal Commissioners during Charles II's reign. Both hospitals were purged of Whig governors and staff, and St Thomas's, seen as the local source of London Whiggery, was most affected, losing the physician, a surgeon and six sisters – even the porters and the beadle.

The pendulum was to swing the other way under James II and William and Mary towards the end of the century. St Thomas's reversed to remain a bastion of London Whiggery, with Bart's firmly committed to Tories. It is doubtful if politics affected patient care as both were packed with injured soldiers and sailors from the war with France.

On their re-establishment after the dissolution, the atmosphere at the hospitals remained monastic, with strict discipline imposed on both staff and patients. Alongside nurses, resident priests were appointed who would conduct three lengthy church services daily which patients were obliged to attend. One would be the hospitaller in control of the hospital administration and finances. His position was no sinecure; he would collect any levies from the patients and rents from tenants, as well as being responsible for the patients' food supplies and assets. At St Thomas's he interviewed all new admissions and was on duty night and day in a foul atmosphere for a salary of £10 per annum, with an allowance of four pints of beer daily, later increased to eight. In Elizabethan times five died within four years from contracting the plague. They were chronically in debt and dishonesty was common, such as charging patients for admission or selling off their clothes and other goods when they died. One appointed his wife in charge of the ale buttery which supplied patients with their allowance of daily beer, two pints in winter and three pints in summer, making a 12d profit on each barrel.

Hospital regulations were hung on the ward walls and read out weekly. There were severe penalties for any infringement, which included the stocks and whipping post. Even the sisters were not exempt and at St Thomas's one is recorded as receiving '12 stripes well laid on'. For a time all patients with venereal disease spent a time in the stocks before discharge as a warning to others. A second infringement earned discharge from the hospital. Any contact between sexes was strictly banned, as was strong drink, although drunkenness was common amongst patients and staff. Gambling and smoking were forbidden, except at St Thomas's, where men were allowed to smoke in an area of one of the courtyards next to the foul wards and the dead-house. Patients were expected to contribute towards their keep, either by money or service according to their trade, at a rate that varied from time to time. Early on, St Thomas's would charge patients 12d a week food money and 20d if suffering from venereal disease and on the 'foule' ward. In 1731 there was a hospital entrance fee of 2s 6d to the 'cleane' ward and 5s to the 'foule' ward. A final charge of 6d a week for washing sheets was only removed in 1821.

St Bartholomew's was free of fees initially, but introduced a returnable burial fee of 19s 6d on admission, which was spread between the staff if the patient died. Even after admission patients had to tip the ward sister a shilling, the beadle and his assistant 6d for being carried to the ward and 2s 6d to the sister if admitted to the salvation ward.

The cost of surgery was 2s 6d to the theatre sister and a shilling to her assistant. These fees were only ended much later when nurses' salaries were increased in compensation.

Overall, the patients appear to have been well cared for, with adequate beds and bed linen. Food appears to have been reasonable and checked regularly by the governors, although unbalanced by present day standards, consisting entirely of bread, meat and cheese with 2 oz of butter daily and a generous allowance of beer. Fruit and vegetables were only added late in the 18th century. Heating stoves appeared in the wards around 1587 and lighting was by candles made from melted meat fat until oil lamps were introduced around 1800.

The main problem in the staffing of the re-established hospitals was to achieve nursing care to replace the dedicated nuns of the monastic era who had devoted their lives to this purpose. Nurses had to be recruited from the uneducated labour poor available and although the title 'sister' was retained, their work was menial and poorly paid and conditions harsh, so that morale and standards were low. The pay was initially £1 a year with an allowance of 12d per day for food and beer, and they had to eat and sleep in the female ward. They were not allowed out after 7 p.m. in the winter or 9 p.m. in the summer and were sacked if they married or even became engaged. There was one sister on average to each ward of 20 patients, and their work was largely domestic. They were responsible for all the cleaning and washing the laundry, which had to be done with wood ash until soap was supplied late in the 17th century. At Bart's they were given flax to spin into yarn that could be made into bedding and it was here the traditional blue uniform was introduced in place of the grey of monastic times. They were under the supervision of a 'matron' who would have her own house and servant, a higher salary and board allowance and often additional perks, ranging from a fee for each patient admitted to a monopoly to sell beer in the hospital, which she would keep in the cellar under her house. With such a background dishonesty and corruption were inevitable and there were many complaints of theft from the patients and drunkenness amongst the staff, which often extended to the level of the matron. At St Thomas's, around 1620, the matron was arrested three times for drunkenness and ended up in prison for debt at the same time as the hospitaller was there for dishonesty. They were both bailed out by the hospital authorities.

The number of sisters employed at any one time would vary with the total of patients. There was usually one to each ward, and they would be hired and fired as wards were opened and closed due to the hospital's financial circumstances. Their total would have averaged 10 to 20 at each hospital, with St Thomas's peaking at 25 in the mid 1600s. The numbers rose dramatically after the hospitals were rebuilt and within a century the matrons of both hospitals were in charge of over 100 nurses – compared with over 1,000 today.

Both pay and conditions were to improve slowly over the next two centuries. By 1580 basic salary had doubled to £2 p.a. with 16d a week living allowance, whilst by 1730 the sister of a foul fluxing ward would receive a salary of £40 p.a. The sisters on the clean wards were being paid £25 p.a., out of which they had to provide each new patient with crockery, soap and cleansing materials, as well as a first pair of sheets! The sisters were given separate accommodation from the patients and by the end of the 18th century would have their own bed-sitter at the end of the ward. 'Night-watchers' were hired at 4d a night, which was later raised to 6d. A laundress was brought in to do the washing and a lower grade of 'nurse' as an aid to the sister. These changes gradually improved the level of applicant until a Commission in 1821 stated sisters 'have received some education and lived a respectable rank of life', and ward sisters had to serve a time at nurse level before they would be appointed.

The first medical appointments at each hospital after their reconstitution were three surgeons, all members of the Company of Barber-Surgeons, at a fee of £15 per annum. They would attend at 7 a.m. and divide the patients amongst themselves. Initially they treated the medical cases as well as the surgical, visiting the wards daily. Most of their work would have been minor, lancing boils, dressing ulcers, pulling teeth and blood-letting. The main surgical procedure was amputation and in 1562 an observer noted that of some 300 cases with infected limbs 120 would require amputation; records show payments for the provision of wooden legs and crutches. The other major surgical procedure was removal of bladder stones which appear to have been a common problem at the time, and for a while a specialist lithotomist was appointed jointly to St Thomas's and Bart's at a salary of £30 p.a. He also had to treat 'the rupture or falling down of the guts into the cods by cutting', which carried a high mortality. The surgeon's fees increased steadily over the years, reaching £40 p.a. by the end of the 17th century. There was an additional payment for each amputation. At St Thomas's this amounted to 3s 4d for an arm or a leg and

1s 8d for a finger or toe. Later, surgeons would be paid separately for the removal of a breast or testicle, and even 3s 4d on tapping for dropsy. Apart from private practice, an important source of income for the surgeons was the fees paid by their quota of apprentices, as much as £50 p.a.; posts were eagerly sought in the hope the student would inherit their chief's position when he retired.

The first physician to each hospital was appointed around 1566. They were of a different social class to the surgeons, who were rated as tradesmen. Physicians were university graduates, and although they lacked any clinical experience, surgeons could only prescribe medication under their direction. They would not deign to visit the wards, but would sit in the reception area and have the patients brought to them. There they would feel the pulse, inspect the tongue and write out a complex prescription. Early physician appointments were unfortunate. The first at Bart's was a Dr Lopez, who served the hospital for 20 years and was physician to Elizabeth I, only to be hung, drawn and quartered for his implication in a plot to poison the Queen. The first physician at St Thomas's to visit the wards had a phobia about spitting, which was a common practice at the time, and he carried out his round wearing a large white wig with a sword at his side, preceded by two patients with brooms sweeping the floor in front of him.

Probably the most important addition to the staff was a resident apothecary appointed at both hospitals at the beginning of the 17th century. Besides dispensing, he was responsible for cupping and bleeding and although theoretically not allowed patients, would be on call night and day to out-patients and accident cases. Initially they would have to provide drugs out of their salary and would often be found supplying out-of-date or inferior medicine. They were to remain resident for the next two centuries at St Thomas's until the move to Westminster in 1871, when they were replaced by house-surgeons.

In addition to the qualified staff, lay people, mostly women, would be called in for specific conditions which the surgeons refused to treat. The commonest of these was 'scalde head', a form of impetigo of the scalp, possibly related to the extent of infection by lice that was universal at the time. It must have been a severe condition as some patients were treated as in-patients until 1660 at both hospitals. Treatment was well paid, probably more rewarding than surgery. At St Thomas's one John Bryce was paid four 'nobles' (26s 8d) for curing six children of 'sore head' and given an extra 6s 8d as a reward. His prescriptions are recorded. The first was to take a pint each of mustard and strong vinegar, a quarter of a pound of verdigris, oil of spikenard, salt and pepper, all boiled together and smeared on the scalp. For those unfortunate enough to suffer a recurrence, a second ointment was used, made from lard, goose and sheep dung, spikenard, honey, pepper and stavesacre. At Bart's a woman was paid 20s for each case cured and in 1635 earned £125. Another lay worker was a Mother Edwin, who in 1563 was paid 13s 4d for curing a boy of hernia and 12d for the materials to make a truss.

All towns faced the problems of public hygiene and sanitation that arose from the influx of population from the countryside, along with industrialisation. Public 'stool-houses' were built on the outskirts and emptied into local streams, contaminating the water. Enteric fever and dysentery were rampant. Men, women and children would drink beer in preference with every meal. Refuse from slaughterhouses, forges and tanneries, along with animal and human waste and sewage, would be emptied into the 'kennel', an open sewer or gutter that ran through the centre of the street. This was shovelled out by the 'nightman' and sold to farmers as manure or dumped into nearby rivers, which often became blocked.

Hospitals, with their concentration of patients within a confined environment, were especially vulnerable to the lack of adequate sanitation. The patients at St Thomas's had the right of way through tenants' gardens to privies built on the bank of ditches and serving a group of houses, but complaints about the noise and smell forced hospital governors to build a great common privy on the site of the original burial ground behind the hospital, and in 1560 there is a record of a £6 payment to clean this out.

St Thomas's initially depended for its water supply on a single well that had been sunk at its foundations, and a second had to be sunk in the 16th century when this became inadequate. One of these became too foul to use and in 1651 water began to be pumped from the Thames into a tank by the back gate for £4 a year, which rose to £20 by 1759. Bart's obtained its water through lead pipes from a head in Islington, shared first with the priory and then with the inhabitants of St Bartholomew the Great parish after the dissolution. There were constant arguments with the new owner of the source, Lord Riche, as to liability for repairs to the piping and in 1661 the hospital switched to Canonbury for its supply. Both hospitals ended up with a large cistern which was filled, through open wooden mains constructed by the New River Water Company, with water brought down from Hertfordshire or pumped from the contaminated River Thames. Supply was restricted to a few hours a week and contracts were expensive.

The first practical reforms in Britain were introduced towards the end of the 18th century when Parliament passed an Act to allow civic authorities to construct new paved streets that could be cleansed and drained. Initially this only affected the wider streets lined by distinguished Georgian houses, whilst the slums continued to fester behind. It was only during the Victorian era that a proper sewerage system was to be constructed.

Both hospitals developed their own burial grounds to collect the funeral fees that they would otherwise have to pay out to monasteries. In 1720 patient burials were 401 at St Thomas's and 250 at Bart's, nearly 10% of their total patient number. The first ground at St Thomas's became full and a second was opened in 1600. The bodies were layered in shrouds and by 1632 it was ordered they should be buried at least two feet deep as the shallowness of the graves allowed putrefaction to show above the ground. A third ground had to be opened in 1696 when the old one overflowed, and in 1700 it was laid down that bodies should be buried in wooden coffins in a plot six feet deep, six feet long and two feet wide, for which the gravedigger was paid a fee of 18d. Bart's had two burial grounds, one for the staff and a larger for the patients, which also became a fashionable site for their wealthier tenants.

Until both St Thomas's and St Bartholomew's underwent major rebuilding programmes at the end of the 17th and first half of the 18th centuries, development at both hospitals was piecemeal. A few wards were added, although these were mainly replacements to adjust to changing medical practices; but overall bed capacity and staffing were not greatly changed and the number of wards ranged from 10 to 20, fluctuating with financial circumstances. The first to go was the 'night-layers' ward, which offered overnight accommodation on straw for the homeless, who were decanted into workhouses. Next were the male and female 'sweat-houses', probably to house patients with diseases such as malaria, which was endemic until it died out in the 17th century, and any cases were transferred to separate pest-houses. These were converted to 'foule' wards for venereal patients as syphilis and soft sores became rampant. At St Thomas's these wards were in the churchyard and their patients were not allowed to leave the wards, to enter the main hospital or chapel, or even sit on the courtyard seats. They were the forerunners of the fluxing or salivation wards for patients undergoing treatment with mercury, which became standard for venereal disease. This was applied by inunction; the mercurial ointment was smeared on the arms and legs and the patient sat wrapped in red flannel in front of a fire. The area was extended daily until the gums were swollen and the teeth fell out. Salivation was so intense the patients were given a pint pot in which to dribble and could not lie on their back for fear of aspiration of their saliva. This was combined with surgical excision of any chancres. The atmosphere was so foul the staff were paid extra, and at St Bart's, as late as 1739, a patient had to pay the ward sister 6s 6d – from which she had to provide flannel to soak up the saliva.

The rebuilding of St Thomas's began in 1693 and continued over the next 16 years as funds were raised. In all these added up to over £37,000, entirely from voluntary sources, with no contribution from the state or royalty. The old monastic buildings were in a dilapidated state and were totally replaced. There had been little rebuilding earlier, apart from a new block of three wards in 1583 and a sweat ward in 1567 in the churchyard which was later used for 'scald head' patients whilst they were still treated as in-patients. Repairs and redecoration had been minimal. In Elizabethan times the timber and daub walls had been replaced by brick, reducing the constant threat of fires revealed by the frequent reference in earlier minutes to the purchase of fire-fighting equipment. Overall standards had fallen steadily and in 1651 the six great wards were described as 'offensive with an unwholesome smell', as it was impossible to clean under the beds due to the settles attached to the bedsteads, whilst later the old tile flooring was replaced by deal.

Credit for the initiation of the rebuild is given to Sir Robert Clayton, who was elected President in 1692. He was a successful businessman who had been a Governor of the Bank of England and Lord Mayor of London. As a Whig MP he had moved a Parliamentary Bill to exclude Catholics from the throne and been a member of the deputation to bring William of Orange over to the throne.

The end result of the reconstruction was a row of four communicating squares, each lined by buildings. The first to be developed was planned for 'clean' male patients and consisted of eight wards with 231 beds along three sides of the square, which was named after Clayton

St Thomas's in 1758, featuring the new four courts. The front shows the Edward VI and Four Cripples frontispiece.

due to his contribution – an existing marble statue was later placed in the centre. The next development was the central Edward Square in place of the old great wards. This was entirely administrative, flanked by a new chapel, church and staff accommodation. At the back, above the entrance to Clayton Court, was a new great hall and staircase for the governors, supported on massive Tuscan pillars, where their names were emblazoned in gold paint. At the time the main road of St Thomas's Street, from which the entrance to the old hospital led, was reconstructed and the hospital was given permission to demolish the almshouses and create a new Fore Court where a column of three wards on either side would house 114 'clean' women patients.

Standards were high; water was pumped up to the wards and the mattresses were made from 'good stuff and sacking' at 38s per bed, and only one patient to each. However, the atmosphere may have been confining when the capacious windows of the wards were boarded up through window tax and remained so for nearly 100 years.

The entrance from the Fore Court to the central one was adorned with the only part of the old hospital to remain, the stone frontispiece

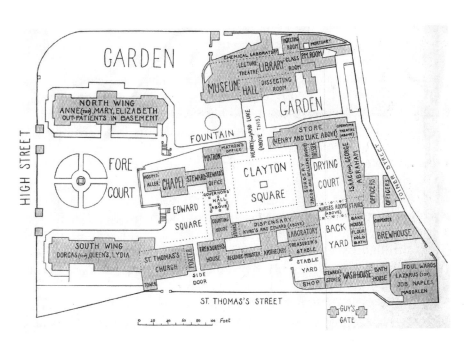

Plan of St Thomas's Hospital, about 1853.

St Thomas's in 1862, showing the new wings added in the 1830s and 1840s.

of King Edward and the Four Cripples surmounted by a large clock. At the very back was a small court with a cluster of outbuildings where facilities were less developed. It included the two salivation wards, each with some 16 beds and a small male cutting ward with 7 beds for lithotomy. It also contained the 'dead-house' and was to develop with a lecture theatre and dissection room for students. A bagnio, or Turkish-type of bath, already existed as hydrotherapy was in vogue, and a cold bath and nurses' accommodation were to be added to the area.

General additions included proper accommodation for the apothecary, with a preparation room and dispensary and a patient reception area. There was a new kitchen and bakery and a hospital brewery near the burial ground. Supplies of beer had been costing £350 yearly through issue to patients and generous allowance for staff. The matron only received 4 pints daily, but the hospitaller and steward were given 10 pints and the treasurer as much as his family needed. His was a new essential appointment because of many financial irregularities. One of the most serious was by the senior surgeon and physician, who had defrauded the Government of £1,382 with false claims for the treatment of injured seamen during the war with France.

36

The next significant development in the life of St Thomas's came when one of their major benefactors, Thomas Guy, funded the establishment of a new hospital to be built on land rented from St Thomas's on the opposite side of St Thomas's Street. Thomas Guy was a bookseller and printer who had made a fortune by buying at half price the bonds that a bankrupt government was issuing to seamen in lieu of their wages. He was able to invest these at full value in the South Sea Company when this was formed to take over the National Debt, and sold his stock at its peak before the 'bubble' burst. Although pilloried as a miser, Guy was one of the most generous benefactors and devoted his fortune to charity. He established almshouses and a training school for apprentices at Tamworth, where he had been born, and a trust to buy out the poor in prison for debt. As a governor of St Thomas's he had funded a block of new wards for the female Fore Court. At the time St. Thomas's refused to accept incurable or insane patients and Guy planned his hospital specifically for these groups, to house up to 435 patients. The cost was £18,793 16s 1d and it was opened with 60 patients admitted in 1725. A month later he died, endowing it with £220,124 2s 7½d in his will. Within seven years the governors had been able to frustrate his primary wish for it to be a hospital for incurables through legal manipulation of the wording in his will and it became a general hospital taking overflow from St Thomas's; but it would be 100 years before they could close a ward confined to 20 mentally ill patients. Standards were high, with the nurses and other staff paid much higher rates of pay than were current, but they were faced with dismissal if they extorted any extra money from patients. By 1733 it was admitting nearly 2,000 patients a year, although over 250 would be buried. Accommodation was expanded, and after an inspection by John Howard in 1788, the new wards were furnished with iron bedsteads, hair beds, ventilation and sanitary arrangements with hot and cold baths. He criticised the ceilings in the older wards as too low and the wooden bedsteads as infested with bugs – a bug-catcher was appointed at £40.

The two hospitals retained a close connection which was consolidated as each established a medical school, and they lived together as the 'United Hospitals' between 1768 and 1825, although the union was to become increasingly unharmonious and they were to part and go their separate ways.

At St Thomas's it is possible dissection by the surgeons was carried out as early as 1670 in the dead-house or mortuary, a room in the

Guy's Hospital for Incurables, 1725.

Guy's Hospital in 1776.

back square above the apothecary's quarters, and by the end of the century Richard Mead, an eminent physician of the time, was carrying out post-mortems and lecturing in anatomy. By 1730 the whole area comprising foul wards, dissecting room, cutting room and brewhouse were condemned and rebuilt with a separate dissecting room and lecture theatre. The dissecting room could just house 12 tables, around each of which sat six to eight students, whilst the oval lecture room was 20 feet high with tiers of seats for 200 around a centre table. There was little ventilation and the atmosphere in the overcrowded rooms, with the bodies only injected with nitre, if at all, was so foul and unhealthy that many students would drop out of practical dissection, and the life expectancy of anatomy demonstrators was low. Until a new glass-domed ventilated theatre was built in 1819, student training was hazardous as well as expensive, and by the end of the sessions, which started in winter, many had fallen ill. At operations the dressers sat in the front row, their role being to hold down the patients and hand over the instruments and dressings, with the more experienced actually assisting.

Guy's developed a similar pattern of apprenticeships and pupils, and the two hospitals worked closely together. By 1768 they were called the United Hospitals, with the students able to attend lectures at both hospitals. Anatomy and surgery were taught at St Thomas's and the school was a great success, at the turn of the century, attracting pupils from all the London hospitals, due to the calibre of the lecturers. One of these was Sir Astley Cooper, who was able to obtain a regular supply of bodies for dissection at four guineas a time from the resurrection men, who could often charge up to £20. If they cut off supplies, it could force the students to leave the school. It is suggested this arrangement was due to his support in helping their families if they were caught and sent to prison.

At Guy's the lectures were on medicine, midwifery and chemistry, and the staff worked out an amicable financial arrangement. Pupils' fees were to be divided between them and no dresser was to pay less than £50 for a year or 30 guineas for six months, or a surgeon to have more than four dressers at a time. In addition to basic fees, students had to pay to attend lectures for dissection facilities, which could easily bring up the cost for a year to £100. The pupils at that time appear to have been very fashion-conscious in their dress and foppish in their personal appearance, especially in relation to their hair. Powder was the current craze and there is reference to the purchase of

'Bagg, Puff, Powder and Pomatum' – the latter a perfumed oil to put on the hair to make it smooth and shiny.

By 1814 a separate new school had been built with a glass-domed circular lecture theatre, a gallery and tiers of seats that could house up to 400 students. There was good ventilation and a revolving demonstration table and chair for the lecturer. There was a separate well-lit ventilated dissecting room that could house up to 200 students, as well as a dissecting room, library and museum.

Inevitably, the interests of the two sides began to clash, with arguments about division of fees between the lecturers and riots between students over admission to lectures. Things reached a climax in 1825 over the appointment of a successor to Sir Astley Cooper, and Guy's set out to create a new, separate school that was an instant success. By 1827 the apothecary there had registered 82 medical pupils, 111 surgical pupils and 41 dressers for the coming year.

One of the bones of contention at the break-up was the fate of the museum, which was privately owned by two of the lecturers who had defected to Guy's, and St Thomas's had to buy them out to retain it. Although the schools were separate the students at Guy's retained the right to attend operations at St Thomas's. At one time they had needed identity tickets to obtain entry, but this system had lapsed. However, it was suddenly re-introduced without notice in 1836, and admission was refused to those not showing their passes, which largely had been lost. This caused a riot and the theatre, already over-crowded, was invaded by a mob. Eventually the police had to be called. Six of the students were arrested, fined £10 and bound over for two years.

Any joint management was ended in 1837 and Guy's medical school continued to flourish, opening many new departments. The Society of Apothecaries Act of 1815 introduced regulations that required medical schools to teach practical chemistry on the premises, which Guy's already did. Dental students had featured from the start and a formal dental school was opened in 1893, enrolling around a hundred dental students every year.

For some years after their separation St Thomas's remained successful, with a full range of lecturers who were well paid. On a basic salary of £40 p.a., physicians were receiving £199 and surgeons £248 from their pupil fees, apart from lecture fees and their apprentices, who paid 500 guineas as a lump sum. Numbers peaked in 1831 with 240 students, and for some ten years the students of Guy's retained cross-rights for pupils to see surgeons practise. From then there was a progressive downhill slide in the school's fortunes for a range of reasons. There was increased competition from the private schools, whilst new medical schools were opened at King's and University College Hospital to which many able lecturers defected. Overall there were more than 40 medical educational establishments in London, many operating from private rooms. St Thomas's lost two of its leading lecturers and the residue were dreary and ineffectual. Those that remained were in open dispute, disparaging one another to the students, and minutes of their meetings showed half the time was taken up with their squabbles and threats of resignation.

In 1842 all the lecturers threatened to resign and the hospital governors took over financial and administrative control, appointed a new team of lecturers, including Richard Grainger, who closed down his private school and transferred his private pupils, with a short-lived increase in numbers. A librarian and a curator to the museum were appointed, but staff quarrels continued and matters went from bad to worse. Numbers continued to fall, to 48 in 1848 and 34 in 1855. In 1845 closure of the medical school was seriously discussed. Examination results were bad, with many students failing and a breakdown in their discipline. Lecturers and surgeons had a bad reputation for unpunctuality and neglecting their duties. The governors tried to introduce a panel of lecturers who were specialists in their own fields, but the medical staff resented and resisted any such scheme. In 1858 the school was transferred to the teachers, each receiving a salary of £60 p.a. and one third of the students' fees.

The dominant role of the apothecary was also reviewed. Since the time of Edward VI he had functioned as resident medical officer, but also acted as secretary and treasurer of the medical school, collecting the students' fees and retaining a percentage of the receipts. He was allowed private apprentices and unlimited powers in purchasing drugs and supplies, with an assistant and staff of four, and held the title of 'Hereditary Grand Apothecary'. In 1855 an inquiry held into hospital expenditure found the cost of drugs and chemicals at St Thomas's was double that at Guy's – the cost of quinine more than ten times as much – whilst analysis of the drugs showed a third were impure or diluted. At the time the apothecary's salary was £600 p.a., but as the only person with knowledge of the details of the working of both hospital and medical school he held the whip hand. He retained his position on adjusted terms of becoming non-resident, with a house and salary of £250 p.a.

Fraud was also commonplace among the hospital staff, particularly the position of 'receiver', the precursor of a present-day hospital secretary, with control of the hospital finances. It was a well-paid post, with a free house and perks that included beer and oil, and the office holder had to supply guarantors as security. In 1843 the receiver had defrauded the hospital of over £6,000, and was eventually prosecuted and transported.

Meanwhile, the hospital itself had started a major rebuilding scheme, but was faced with a problem that resulted from the priority given at the time to railway development over all other social needs. In 1859 after more than 20 years of argument the House of Commons finally passed the Charing Cross Railway Bill authorising the extension of the S.W. Railway Co. line from London Bridge Station across the Thames to Hungerford Market. It rejected complaints that this would cross the north-west corner of the hospital's gardens at a height of 24 feet, within a few feet of the newly built north wing of wards. Proposed compromises such as a 6 m.p.h. speed limit and restrictions on whistle blowing were considered valueless, and it was evident the hospital would have to move. After protracted argument the whole site was sold at a knockdown price as the railway company was in a position to insist on immediate possession to start demolition – it was able later to sell on the surplus land for development at a handsome profit. This left the hospital homeless and an urgent hunt for a new site began. Ultimately the present eight-and-a-half-acre Thames-side location opposite the Houses of Parliament at the foot of Westminster Bridge was chosen. At the time it was far from ideal as the Albert Embankment had not been built and the sandy foreshore to the Thames, which still carried the sewage outflow from London, consisted of shabby boatyards, dark tenements and rotten wharves. Rebuilding would evidently be a lengthy process and temporary accommodation had to be found.

The site chosen was Surrey Gardens, a derelict recreational ground in Kennington, formerly a combined botanical centre and small zoo. The large old music hall was converted into a 200-bed hospital on two floors. The upper floor, with four wards, was reached by a covered outside staircase at one end of the building. Soiled linen was dealt with on the balcony, where the latrines were also located into which the bed vessels had to be emptied. The kitchen doubled as the operating theatre and in the first years the death rate after amputation was 42%. The giraffe house became a cholera ward and the elephant house a

42

St Thomas's Hospital on the Albert Embankment, as opened by Queen Victoria in 1871.

dissecting room. The medical school continued to function in outhouses, although the intake fell to 15 annually, as did the Nightingale School of Nursing, which was already well established at the old hospital.

The hospital remained there for seven years until the building of the new hospital was completed in 1871 at a cost of £500,000 with a provision for 560 beds, but five of the new wards could not be opened for some time due to the heavy rating demands of the local council.

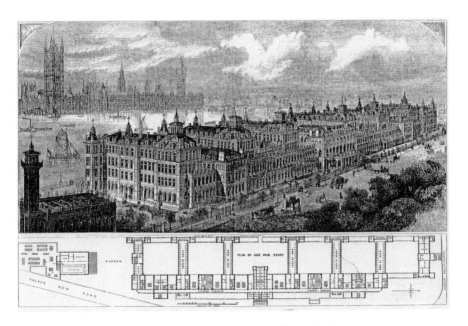

The new St Thomas's Hospital in 1871, including a plan of its layout.

43

St Thomas's was the first large general hospital in Britain to be designed on the pavilion plan advocated strongly by Florence Nightingale, in place of the previous courtyard pattern, which was ruled out because of the long narrow nature of the site. This had been developed in France when the Hôtel Dieu in Paris was rebuilt after it had been destroyed by fire, and copied in England when Blackburn Infirmary and the Royal Marine Barracks Hospital at Woolwich were built. Six ward pavilions side-by-side stretched back from the river, which the twin sanitary towers that housed the ward toilets and washing facilities overlooked. Patient intake was slow, with only ten transferred from Surrey Gardens, but within six years 350 beds were in use.

The governors were faced with a financial crisis as they were entirely dependent on investments and rental income. With no outside support, in 1879 they decided to bring in charges for patients. Two wards were turned private at 8s a day and 12s for a private room, whilst those in general wards were charged 3s. The new Nightingale School of Nursing was soon to flourish but the medical school was slower to recover its status, in spite of the expanded teaching facilities and improved calibre of the staff – although they remained poorly paid and dependent on private coaching fees. In 1892 the number of first year medical students had dropped to 43, in contrast to 1,500 applicants for the 32 vacancies open to probationer nurses. That year the governors lent the staff £16,000 at a low interest rate of 3% to build a new block of extra classrooms and a students' club, and by 1910 the numbers had quadrupled. Two storeys were added to the original Nightingale House and a new residential home with a swimming pool. It would be destroyed with part of the hospital by bombing in 1941.

Although electric lighting was only introduced throughout the hospital in 1900, electrotherapy had been in vogue 90 years earlier and was revived in 1848. The first diagnostic X-rays were started in 1895 in the electrical department within a month of Professor Rontgen's first publication and extended to treatment of cancer. Unfortunately, the dangers were not realised and the doctor concerned was to lose two fingers and later his life from radiation.

Anaesthesia had been introduced and in 1849 St Thomas's could claim the first death in any London hospital from chloroform poisoning, in a patient having a toe nail removed. The number of operations carried out trebled in ten years and early in the 20th century a new block of four operating theatres was built based on

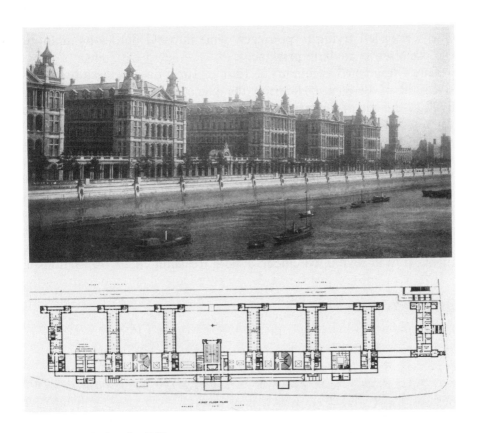

St Thomas's during the 1920s.

latest developments in knowledge. By the same time two children's wards had been built and eleven specialist out-patient departments.

During the First World War 200 wounded troops occupied the first-floor wards and an extra 300 in huts built between the blocks. In the Second World War bombs, unlike lightning, struck more than once as the hospital was a vulnerable target because of its position. It was hit by bombs repeatedly in the early part of the war, fire bombed and hit by flying bombs in the latter part. There were many casualties, mostly staff who had stayed on to cope with air raid casualties in the area, and three of the ward pavilions were totally destroyed. The only consolation for the destruction was that the hospital would be completely rebuilt after the war under the auspices of the NHS, to a pattern comparable with up-to-date medical standards, whilst Guy's and

45

Bart's were left trying to pour new wine into old bottles by adapting old premises to modern medicine.

Guy's flourished through the 19th century, due to the administrative skill of Benjamin Harrison the younger, appointed treasurer in 1797 at the age of 26, who was to earn the nickname 'King Harrison' for his dedication to make Guy's one of the foremost hospitals and medical schools in the world. He was to reign for 50 years and during this time and the next 25 years the hospital underwent extensive redevelopment, with the appointment of resident medical officers and the establishment of a maternity unit. In the last quarter of the century the hospital fell into serious debt due to a fall in income from its agricultural endowments, and wards had to be closed. The hospital became dormant in its old buildings and lost its stimulus to development. It was revitalised under a new treasurer, Sir Cosmo Bonsor,

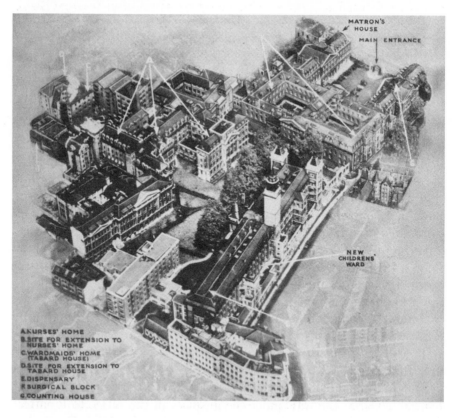

Guy's Hospital, 1936.

46

who raised the funds to modernise the hospital with new operating theatres and lifts and treble the size of the out-patient department. A new residential Nurses' Home was the first fully equipped one to be built; later to include a swimming bath through a donation by Lord Nuffield. The established dental school mushroomed to become a leader in its field.

Under the NHS, policy was to link the larger medical schools with multi-faculty colleges of the University of London and St Thomas's & Guy's became reunited in 1982. The following year Guy's and The Royal Dental Hospital were combined to form the largest dental school in Europe. St Thomas's was joined with the Dreadnought Seamen's Hospital and St John's Hospital for Skin Diseases, Guy's with the Evelina Children's Hospital. The two hospitals became the Guy's & St Thomas's NHS Trust by an arranged marriage in 1996 and then an amalgamation with King's College. Academic research has been focused at Guy's, with many of its medical services transferred to St Thomas's where extensive redevelopment plans have been initiated.

Bart's had only narrowly escaped the Great Fire of 1666 and comprised a disparate group of buildings erected at different times. Even the governors complained 'the whole had hardly so much as the outward appearance of an hospital!'. As a result of the loss of income from the destruction of its City property, five of the fifteen wards had to be closed and the sisters sacked. One ward was converted into nine shops, whilst others were built in the cloisters, churchyard and the Long Walk. As matters improved, haphazard ward building added extra beds to bring the total to 300. A new cutting ward was privately financed in 1691 and in 1702 the Henry VIII Gateway was flanked by rooms to be occupied at first by the beadles and later the first resident house surgeons.

These changes were quite inadequate to deal with the pressure put on the hospital from the great increase in the local population, and a total rebuilding had to take place. The governors commissioned James Gibbs to design a new hospital. The outcome was a practical plan, with four large separate three-storey blocks arranged around the sides of a courtyard, resembling a college court that he had used before for King's College, Cambridge. Due to lack of any immediate major donors, rebuilding was a slow process extending over 30 years. The

Future plans for St Thomas's Hospital.

Future plans for Guy's Hospital.

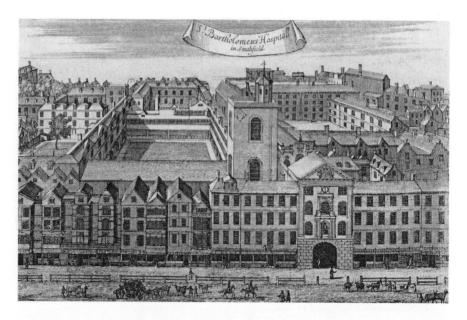

St Bartholomew's Hospital in 1720.

first stage, completed by 1738, was the creation of a North Block to house the administration and a residence for the treasurer, the chief executive on the ground floor, with a grandiose Governors' Hall rising through two storeys occupying most of the first floor, premises appropriate to their eminence. The walls were emblazoned with the panels and shields of the benefactors and the plaster ceiling richly decorated. It was approached by an equally grand staircase lined by two large frescoes painted by Hogarth and was used for their court meetings and banquets.

The three patient blocks were completed by 1740, 1753 and 1769, each of four storeys with a high pitched roof, containing 12 14-bedded wards to give a total of 504 beds. The plan was of up-to-date design, with the main staircase and ward entrances in the centre of blocks, earth closets in an annexe at the far end of the wards and pumps in the centre of the courtyard to bring water to every floor. There was a sister's bed-sitting room at the other end of the wards where she ate and slept, although there was no nurses' sitting room until 1819. The overall Palladian facades gave a uniform appearance to the whole site and it became one of the first London buildings to be faced in Bath stone, although this had to be replaced later with Portland, as it was

St Bartholomew's Hospital in 1752.

unsuitable for London's polluted climate. One of the reasons for the delay in progress was hold-ups in the shipping of the stone, due to the Dutch wars and a treasurer who absconded with £4,000.

The patients were in comfortable surroundings with well-spaced curtained wooden beds and best flock mattresses and bolsters, wheelchairs and warming pans. They were, however, obliged to 'tip' the nursing staff, the steward beadles and box carriers until 1821 when the system was abolished and wages increased in compensation. By 1750 admissions had risen to 2,000 annually and 45 out-patients weekly – as many as in a year before.

One of the problems for the new hospital was that the public right of way through the hospital grounds remained until 1854 and the better class of tenant who rented the houses and shops had been replaced by a lower level, and there were constant complaints from the patients that they were pestered by beggars and tradesmen to buy beer and tobacco. These included the surgeon's personal 'box carriers', who would carry his instruments, clean the theatre and prepare dressings. Each surgeon was entitled to five of these pupils, and their fees were an important addition to their salary. These would only be replaced by 1821 when each surgeon would appoint his own resident house surgeons, initially for food and candles and later a salary of £25 p.a.

Alongside these was an apothecary who was resident until 1867 and as a qualified medical person would treat casualties as well as supervise the dressers.

Rebuilding work continued steadily. By the time the last block was completed, the old houses that had been left in the middle were demolished and the square paved, whilst the apothecary moved to new premises. The old cutting room was replaced by a main operating theatre in 1791 as an annexe to a new Abernethy casualty block beside the administrative block, but post-operative patients had to be trundled across the open square to their ward until separate theatres were built attached to each of the blocks. Sanitation became progressively separated from the wards themselves, with increasing privacy from communal slop bins or privies and relocation to twin towers as an annexe to the wards, as at St Thomas's.

Out-patients were seen in rooms next to the apothecary's shop. As their numbers soared, the old premises were totally inadequate and a new purpose-built block was started in 1841 in the north-east corner of the hospital on the site of the Treasurer's house, stable and garden. The new casualty and out-patients building had a large waiting room and examination rooms and four wards with an operating theatre. Numbers of patients approached 250,000 a year by 1878 and demand had to be restricted by the introduction of an inquiry system into those seeking attendance. A number of extra assistant physicians and surgeons were appointed and casualties were passed along to the house surgeons for treatment, helped out by the student dressers or clinical clerks.

The development of a medical school was a more haphazard affair than at St Thomas's and Guy's. There is no record of its beginning but formal recognition was given to one by the hospital governors in 1822. Students may have been attending the hospital practice in 1662 and there is a reference to a library for these in 1667 and a museum early in the next century. Leave was given to the surgeons by the Barber-Surgeons' Company to lecture on anatomy in the dissecting room in 1734, some 20 years after they had publicly reprimanded a surgeon at St Thomas's for the dissection of 'dead bodies of malefactors' contrary to the company's bye-law in that respect!

The credit for systematic instruction in anatomy and physiology and the initiation of a proper medical school is given to John Abernethy. He was a man of great character who could slouch into the lecture room, whistling with his lower jaw projecting forwards, throw himself into a chair and sling one of his legs over an arm. His character and the quality of his lectures attracted many fee-paying students. A new lecture theatre was built for him in 1791, and a larger dissecting room in 1822. The students were given a signed certificate of attendance. They were predominantly surgical and in 1820 numbered several hundred, against only three studying medicine.

The facilities for a developing medical school were totally inadequate in 1876. The old scattered buildings were pulled down and replaced by a new block containing the library and museum, lecture theatres and dissecting rooms. In 1921 the medical school, which had earlier been a voluntary association of the teachers, was granted a charter of incorporation with a common seal under the title of 'The Medical College of St Bartholomew's Hospital in the City of London'. Full-time professors of medicine and surgery in the University of London, each with a 50-bed unit, were appointed.

A major opportunity for rebuilding came when the adjacent old Christ's Hospital Bluecoat School moved to Horsham in 1902, but

The square and fountain at St Bartholomew's, 1920.

53

because of the cost involved it could only afford a fraction of the site – the rest was snapped up by the Post Office – and restricted development to extension of the out-patients' department and a new pathology block. The redevelopment of the out-patients' department was long overdue. The large main room and side rooms accommodated the casualty surgeon, an assistant surgeon and physician, 5 assistant house physicians and 10 house surgeons, 40 surgical dressers, a dental surgeon with dressers and an ophthalmic house surgeon, apart from nurses and porters. In the morning there would be up to 600 patients queuing up on the hospital steps for admission, whilst in the afternoon there would be consultations for patients referred by practitioners.

The development of specialist departments was slow and subject to considerable criticism by the press and the medical school. Although

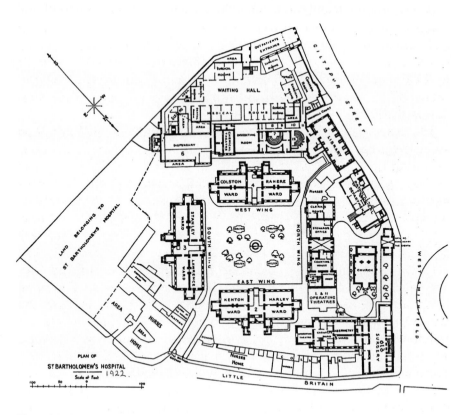

Plan of St Bartholomew's, 1922.

many of the staff expressed interest, their efforts were frustrated. The only excepts were in ophthalmology, dentistry and a few beds for gynaecology patients. 'Lying-in' patients were only accepted in 1910, and beds made available for specialist surgery. By 1895 specific beds for venereal disease patients, which had been as many as 75, were finally abolished.

Although a department for children's diseases was opened in 1904, a separate ward for children was only available in 1924. One area where the hospital was to establish a leading role was in cancer treatment, and a deep X-ray unit was opened in 1936. The new out-patients' and casualty department was opened in 1907, followed by a new pathology block, by which time electric light and telephone system had been introduced. A new surgical block with 250 beds and five operating theatres was completed by 1930 on part of Christ's Hospital land and seven years later an adjoining medical block was added.

During the second half of the 19th century the nursing staff was completely reorganised. 'Scrubbers' were appointed for the cleaning and menial work and each sister was given three day nurses and a night nurse. A training scheme for probationers was introduced which by 1906 required four years' service. They had to continue sleeping in rooms off the wards until Queen Mary's Home for Nurses was built during the 1920s.

The hospital escaped serious damage during the Second World War and a great deal of rebuilding took place during the initial years after its absorption into the National Health Service, including a new nurses' home with 130 rooms, a swimming bath and a large entertainment room. One of the most important measures was a new radiotherapy department equipped with the first 15 million volt linear accelerator in the country and a new cobalt unit. All the funding was provided from the governors' endowment funds.

In 1974 it became the teaching hospital for the newly formed City and Hackney Health District, but plans to set up a self-governing Hospital Trust within the NHS, as proposed by the Government in the late 1980s, were frustrated when the Report of a 1992 inquiry into the London Health Service, under Sir Bernard Tomlinson, could not see any future for the hospital. It recommended its total closure and a new single hospital to be built on a site in Whitechapel that would incorporate it with the Royal London and London Chest Hospitals. This threat provoked a public uproar and a petition signed by over one million people to save the hospital on its Smithfield site. This led the

Government to review the policy and Bart's obtained a stay of execution. It would surrender any general hospital services, but remain open to provide specialist cardiac and cancer care.

Chapter 3

The Age of Hospitals:
Voluntary Hospital System 18th Century;
London and Provinces

The 18th century, designated as 'The Age of Hospitals', saw the development of a hospital system that was to be extended throughout the country. Starved of any central finance, no new hospitals had been established since the ravages of Henry VIII, although trade and commerce were booming. The great majority of working people existed on the breadline with little access to any medical care. The Poor Law Act of 1601 passed by Elizabeth I had laid down that parishes should provide relief for the 'lame, blind, elderly and others unable to look after themselves', but this was confined to paupers, and the great majority of parishes lacked the resources or motivation to fulfil any such obligation. A few London boroughs would pay for treatment at the two chartered hospitals, but these had to restrict their services to those born within the parish to avoid a flood of vagrants from outside. The only free facility was a dispensary opened for the 'sick poor' in 1697 by the Royal College of Physicians in the City of London, copying a project started in Edinburgh in 1682. This had been initiated as a direct challenge to the Society of Apothecaries, with whom the doctors were in dispute over their respective status, and within a short time was treating 20,000 patients a year, although it would be closed down in 1725 due to the costs involved.

The wealthy would have their own physician visit them at home. The standard fee was a guinea for the select few who were registered doctors and 10s for the unregistered majority. The fashionable doctor could earn £5,000 in a year, long before a Harley Street address would carry a premium.

The poor majority had to rely on home remedies, or resort to the unqualified therapists who flourished then as now. Labelled as 'quacks' by the medical profession, some were more knowledgeable in their trade than the doctors, with skills handed down over generations. Amongst these were unlicensed apothecaries versed in herbal medicine and skilled manipulators of both sexes, such as the 'back walkers'. Most were simply charlatans peddling bottles of coloured water containing 'magic' ingredients in the markets. At least most of these would have been harmless, which is more than could be claimed for orthodox medicine, which was going through one of its worst dogmatic and arrogant periods at that time. Treatment was still based on the galenic concept of humoral imbalance and had failed to absorb the advances in science and physiology that were being made by such eminent men as William Harvey, the physician at Bart's. Their empirical approach comprised bleeding, cupping and catharsis with restriction of food and water, along with toxic doses of chemicals such as mercury, arsenic and antimony alongside opium, which were more likely to be harmful than of any value, and could often prove fatal.

At the turn of the century there was an increasing number of educated people with a maturing social conscience who began to group together and consider how to develop hospitals in the absence of any central funding, and this gave birth to the voluntary hospital system that was to be dominant for the next 200 years until a comprehensive state system would be introduced. Five were to be opened in London between 1720 and 1745, each serving a different district. The first tentative step was taken in Westminster, which had become one of the most blighted parts of London although in the previous two centuries it had been a fashionable area where nobility had built their mansions on the bank of the Thames. There were no roads and the whole site had become an isolated swamp, threatened with constant flooding by the Thames, which had no embankment and was the only means of access to the City. Whole families were packed in a single room of the old houses or a network of hovels in alleys alongside the wharves. There was no sanitation and enteric fevers and malaria were endemic. It was within this background that a group of four well-intentioned people met in 1716 to discuss the foundation of a hospital, but their ambitions were frustrated as they could only raise £10 between them, which was ultimately spent on food for the sick prisoners in the local jail.

A reformed group met three years later to establish a residential infirmary that would exemplify the problems that many of the future hospitals would face in their turn. Lacking any wealthy patrons or official support, they rented a small private house in Petty France, formerly occupied by a tallow chandler. There was considerable resistance from neighbours who were afraid it would become a centre for the spread of infectious diseases and a focus for undesirable vagrants. A Dr Lovell who lived opposite this house feared it would interfere with his monopoly of private practice locally and challenged the use legally, but on April 27th 1720 a sign was put up outside: 'Infirmary for the Sick and Needy', and the Westminster Infirmary opened. A resident matron was appointed at £6 p.a. with a staff of a nurse, housemaid and messenger, and one of the founding group was a doctor who gave his services free. Their first patient was a lad to be cured of 'evil in his joints and scurvy', and in the first two months 15 in-patients and 15 out-patients had been treated and labelled 'cured', with only one death. The nature of their illnesses were noted in the minutes, with two incurables with 'asthma and dropsy' and 'consumption', six cases of 'ague' and two 'obstructions' discharged as cured. One had been discharged for insulting and drunken behaviour.

To attract support they established a pattern that would be developed to fund the voluntary hospital system throughout its career. Subscribers of one guinea a year would become a hospital governor with the right to vote on all decisions and appointments, as well as an entitlement to recommend patients for admission.

The initial premises were insanitary and unsuitable but as support increased, the infirmary moved to another house after five years. Even here the owner and his wife retained the front parlour and room behind with two cellars for their own use, and could share the use of the kitchen. Sanitation at the time was almost non-existent. Water was pumped direct from rivers into vats, whilst human and industrial waste was collected in cesspools that emptied into open gutters which ran through the streets and ended in the self-same rivers.

An equal problem of the time was staffing as there were no trained nurses. Pay was a pittance and they had to live, eat and sleep on the ward. Only the lowest type of woman would serve and many had to be sacked for drunkenness or theft from patients. The matron would have her own accommodation with control of the patients' beer and food supplies and was often equally a problem. The Westminster was lucky with their first choice, but the second had to be sacked for dishonesty and the next five died from fevers contracted from patients, a common fate for all staff.

At first medical care was in the hands of a dedicated few, whose support was opposed by an establishment afraid of the intrusion on their private practice. As the hospitals became established, professional attitudes changed and appointments to the staff were keenly canvassed as a source of income from private patients and their entitlement to appoint students.

The commonest admissions were for infectious diseases such as malaria or typhoid which would be self-limiting in course, and the main benefit for patients was rest and regular meals in hospital in contrast to their appalling conditions at home. At the time professional treatment played little part, with limited knowledge of anatomy and almost total ignorance of physiology. Surgery before anaesthesia and antisepsis was largely restricted to first-aid level, apart from amputation and removal of bladder stones. An early Westminster surgeon, William Cheseldon, achieved fame for devising a new technique for extracting stones that would become standard, as well as for being the first to operate on cataract. There were no follow-up records and if discharged, the patient would be labelled as cured.

In turn the second location became increasingly inadequate, and the search for new premises would highlight the division between the medical staff and ruling authorities that had been festering for some years. The doctors regarded the board as inefficient and suffocating, whilst the governors regarded the doctors as their inferiors and would inaugurate changes without consultation.

Records of the closing stages of the dispute are muted, but this must have been deep-rooted as the five medical staff resigned along with the President, the Bishop of Winchester, and many of the subscribers, to found a new hospital at Hyde Park Corner, St George's. The hospital governors were to exemplify the social and moral prejudices of the time in addition to their anti-Papist attitude, in spite of their claim to help the 'sick and needy'. Venereal disease sufferers were refused admission and if admitted by mistake would be instantly discharged. This general attitude led to the foundation of the Lock Hospital in 1746, although some were admitted for a while to the new building in Westminster. Although women subscribers were accepted as Trustees, they were forbidden to attend meetings and only in 1754 allowed to exercise their vote through a male proxy, against intense opposition. As with the chartered hospitals, patients labelled incurable were rejected or discharged after two months, but after an anonymous donation of £400 in 1734 for this specific purpose the board agreed to accept one solitary incurable and the public response was sufficient to fund the first ward for this purpose.

The major overt issue in their disagreements was the choice of a site to which the Westminster should be relocated. One of the board

60

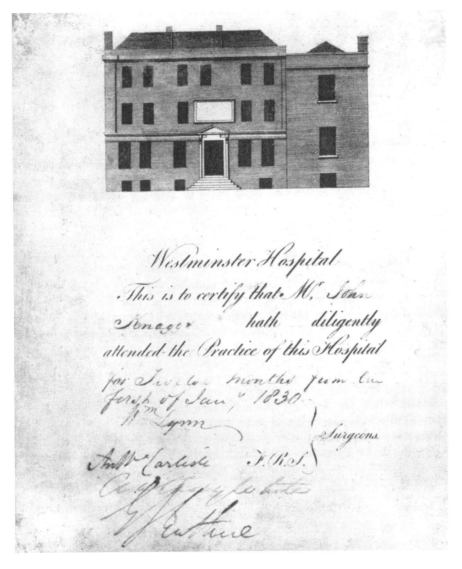

Westminster Hospital, Petty France, 1735–1834, as it appeared on a student's certificate of 1830.

owned a block of five houses nearby in Petty France and offered these at a reasonable rent. This proposal had passed inspection by a committee which had actually included the doctors involved, who then put forward an alternative at Hyde Park. Another bone of contention may have been the strong religious prejudices of its founders. From the start patients were obliged to appear before the board to thank God and the society for their cure and to give public thanks in the parish church. In the new premises there was a prayer desk in each ward, on which was placed the Bible and Book of Common Prayer, together with depressing tracts on penitence and death. Roman Catholics were excluded altogether by 1741 and discharged if found out after admission, whilst in the following year the cook and best nurse were sacked as 'Papists'.

The Westminster Infirmary appointed new medical staff and moved to its new chosen site near Petty France, where it would remain for the next hundred years. It expanded rapidly by conversions and acquiring neighbouring houses. With bed numbers increased from 31 to 98, it was renamed the Westminster Hospital for the Sick and Infirm. The great increase in numbers of benefactors raised a problem that would face all voluntary hospitals in turn: the board of governors became increasingly unwieldy as their numbers increased, with several hundred entitled to vote, creating chaos at board meetings. In 1760 it was decided to appoint an official administrator, a 'hospital master' whose duties would range from daily prayers and burials to supervising the staff and disciplining the patients, as well as keeping accounts and preparing the board meetings; all for £25 per annum. The only applicant was a publican, who was rejected, and it was 1826 before the first medical committee would meet monthly to regulate treatment and check the drug bill, and another seven years before the first hospital secretary was appointed.

The hospital wards were long and narrow, heated only by a fireplace at one end and lit by candles, with an oil-lamp over the entrance. Conditions were dirty and verminous; a bug-catcher was employed at a shilling per bed, until the old wooden bedsteads – which were liable to collapse – were replaced by metal ones.

Conditions deteriorated steadily and eventually it became evident a new hospital had to be built. Suggestions of a merger with Charing Cross were rejected and eventually the Broad Sanctuary site opposite the west doors of Westminster Abbey was bought from the Treasury in 1831 with funds from a series of legacies. A new hospital was built within three years and continued for another 110 years.

Although the initial plan was of advanced design with a wide corridor running the length of the building with spurs at each end leading to three wards, the new hospital would remain plagued by plumbing problems. Each ward was fitted with a water closet separated

Westminster Hospital, The Sanctuary, Westminster, 1834.

by a thin matchboard partition. They were so unpleasant that a rising airshaft from floor to floor was introduced. This was designed to remove the offensive smell up to the outside air, but only produced an opposite effect and spread this downwards. There were only two baths in the basement for over 100 patients and drainage was into a cesspool, leading to repeated complaints about the insanitary conditions and outbreaks of erysipelas. In 1875 a proposal to rebuild the hospital at Millbank was seriously considered. Major improvements ranged from new teak floors which could be polished in place of the old boards which had to be sluiced down, new sanitary towers with water closets and a bathroom for each ward, although it would be another 20 years before the governors eventually accepted the need for main drainage.

Lack of funds would lead again to deterioration of conditions, and failure to provide beds for midwifery and the specialities, such as ear, nose and throat and eye surgery, threatened the hospital with loss of university recognition as a training centre for higher degrees. An appeal raised sufficient funds for major refurbishment, during which the hospital had to be closed for over a year before it could be re-opened in 1924.

Westminster Hospital in the 1930s, after renovations 1923-4.

Major improvements had been carried out, ranging from new specialist and out-patients departments to accommodation for nurses and residents, lifts and a hot water system, but it was recognised these could only give temporary relief. As there was no room for a large

Westminster Hospital in 1965.

The atrium of the Chelsea and Westminster Hospital

modern hospital on the Sanctuary site, it would have to be relocated. A new site was obtained at St John's Gardens, Westminster, which the new buildings would straddle. The hospital opened in 1939 on one side of the gardens and the nursing home and medical school on the other. It was relocated to the present site in Fulham Road in 1993 as the Chelsea & Westminster Hospital.

The background to the Westminster Hospital as a medical school was precarious. Initially any training would be obtained by serving as an apprentice attached to a surgeon or physician on the hospital staff and paying his fee of £21. This would entitle the 'cub' to accompany his master on hospital rounds, but he would be dependent for any formal lectures or training at one of the private medical schools that were being established both by the hospital staff and frustrated doctors unable to obtain an official appointment. It was possible to practise medicine without any examination until the Apothecaries Act of 1815 and another ten years before the College of Surgeons would insist on certificates of proficiency in surgery from surgeons attached to recognised London hospitals. In turn hospitals initiated their own medical schools, but the Westminster would be the last to do this as the earlier efforts of the staff were thwarted by the refusal of the governors to support or finance a scheme. As early as 1833 five of the hospital team opened a 'Westminster School of Medicine' unsuccessfully and the next year another group committed £3,000 to purchase another building in Dean Street. This was refused any official support initially, but later the board accepted that the hospital should be associated with a medical school and students were given the hospital porters' day room in the basement as a museum and reading room, whilst the school itself remained in Dean Street.

The governors bought the school freehold, on which they would later make a profit, and assumed control, but refused any further financial help. The lecturers had to pay for the privilege of their appointment in the unrealised hope that they would be reimbursed from student fees. In other medical schools the management committee was composed of the lecturers themselves and the school would meet the running costs and apportion the fees. The Westminster school was initially successful, but student numbers fell sharply as part of a general trend, leading to the exodus of several leading staff, including the anatomy lecturer, who removed his anatomical specimens with him, so the students had to be transferred to King's College for their lectures.

Although the new medical school was designed with a lecture theatre that could hold 100 students, at times numbers were in single figures, in 1909 only four, and never enough to make it an economic proposition. In 1905 pre-clinical teaching was transferred to King's College, along with St George's and Charing Cross students, and during the First World War it was taken over as a laboratory. When it re-opened there were only nine students and it was threatened with closure, but the new Dean, Sir Stanley Woodwark, canvassed a scholarship system around the leading public schools and raised numbers to 130 before he retired 14 years later, and the Westminster had become an established school when it moved into St John's Gardens. Adjacent to the new hospital, it was to merge with Charing Cross Medical School in 1984 and both moved to the new Chelsea and Westminster hospital premises. The school became part of Imperial College of Medicine in 1997.

The development of St George's, the new hospital founded by the breakaway group, was to be a very different pattern from its parent Westminster. They had leased Lanesborough House, a mansion built in 1719 on land at Hyde Park reserved to the Abbey, at a rental of £60 p.a. Grosvenor Square had become established as a fashionable area, but Piccadilly was still open ground on which a 'May Fair' continued to be held for many years, whilst Chelsea and Kensington were fields dotted with small villages. Lanesborough House was a splendid building outside the western gates of London and the turnpike at Hyde Park Corner, on the edge of the wealthy Westminster area and with convenient access for the governors and staff, who claimed that the healthy country air would benefit the patients from overcrowded slums in Westminster 'more than physick'. But there was much public controversy and accusation of self-interest.

St George's was opened in 1734 with 30 beds in two wards on the first floor and staff quarters above, approached by a grand staircase with a boot scrape at its foot. It was an immediate success and even attracted royal support. Subscribers poured in, with more than 150 prepared to pay the minimum of £5 p.a. required to become a governor with a vote on the hospital board. Initially six physicians and three surgeons were appointed on a voluntary basis, each required to visit the hospital one morning a week on a rota basis, and to attend the weekly board of governors meeting at 9 a.m. each Friday, when patients were admitted or discharged. The couple who had previously served as caretakers at Lanesborough House were appointed porter and matron. The matron was paid £10 p.a. and was responsible for day-to-day hospital administration, patient discipline and control of the 'inferior servants' – who included one nurse for each ward paid £6 p.a. and a cook paid £7 p.a. The patients were well fed with meat, cheese and bread, but no fish or vegetables, and three pints of beer daily. Those on a salivating diet had no solids, but a pint of warm beer hourly during the day, and a half pint hourly at night.

The hospital expanded rapidly by buying its freehold and the adjoining houses remaining on its original site. The number of beds available had increased to 250 by 1747, although the number actually

Turnpike at Hyde Park Corner, 1786.

occupied was restricted as the maintenance cost of each had risen to
£30 p.a. The number of wards had increased to 15, with surgical and
medical cases side by side. A separate room was opened for operations, which had previously been carried out in the wards. The number
of untrained nurses had been increased to more than 20 and there were
a resident apothecary and surgeon's apprentice. The hospital underwent complete rebuilding between 1827 and 1834.

St George's Hospital near Hyde Park, 1736.

The East Front of St George's Hospital draped for the Coronation of King George V, June 1911.

St George's Hospital decorated for the Coronation of Queen Elizabeth II, 1953.

Pupils were accepted from early days and were attached to the physicians and surgeons, but as usual they only enjoyed ward rounds and had to rely on private schools for their basic education. Anatomy would be studied at the famous school headed by William Hunter and its successor founded by Samuel Lane in Grosvenor Place, until St George's staff set up their own rival school, which moved in 1868 to buildings attached to the hospital and became the official medical school. It remained as a small unit, transferring pre-clinical studies to King's College in 1901, along with Charing Cross.

Efficient overall administration as a hospital was established by the appointment in 1875 of a resident medical superintendent, F.S. Marshall, responsible for the welfare of the medical and nursing staff as well as the patients. He held his position for the next 30 years, setting up committees in place of the mass meeting of governors to control hospital activities. This eliminated the extensive canvassing for appointments which was commonplace. Out-patient numbers were restricted to 15 at each sitting and the time of treatment restricted to 4 months. Beer was discontinued as a standard article of diet and the cost of medicines sold to patients by the porters because of lack of a nearby pharmacy was limited to 2d.

St George's, 1933–83.

Aerial view of Springfield Hospital (A) and
Site of new hospital residences & Medical School halls of residence

Site of New Hospital (formerly Fountain & Grove Hospitals)
A. New Boiler House   B. New laundry   C. Clinical Research block
D. Staff & students social centres   E. Ingleby House residential block
F. S.W. Thames RHA Blood Transfusion Centre   G. Former Fountain Hospital
H. Former Grove Hospital.

The new St George's Hospital at Tooting, 1983.

71

Modernisation was slow both in the development of specialist departments and structurally. It would be 1935 before the old lift worked by a porter with a rope was replaced by an electric one; and although it was close to Harley Street, the only specialist services were eyes, ENT, dermatology and a small children's ward with convalescence beds at the Atkinson-Morley Hospital in Wimbledon.

The need to rebuild a hospital and medical school elsewhere had already been realised and by 1946 the search had been directed south of the river. This had been planned as one of the first major hospital redevelopment schemes, but Government indecision and financial crises would lead to a 20-year postponement with escalating costs. The site selected was the run-down Grove Fever and Fountain Mental hospitals in Tooting and plans were prepared for a phased development of the hospital and medical school at an estimated cost of £10 million. In fact this was spent on the medical school component for 80 students, the first unit to be built, which was completed by 1977. As much again was spent to create the first hospital ward block two years later. The piecemeal creation was the result of a decision by the Department of Health to change the policy for hospital construction from large contracts over a five-year period to smaller three-year components. Initially it had been planned to combine a medical and dental school, but the University of London decided to merge the Royal Dental Hospital School of Dentistry with Guy's. It would be 1984 before the medical school was completed to house 150 students, and become one of the largest in Europe, and phase two of the hospital development began.

An artist's impression of the new St George's, 1983.

Alongside the medical school has been the development of large schools in nursing, physiotherapy and radiography, whilst the hospital has over 1,000 beds and recently absorbed the Atkinson-Morley Hospital, which had been transformed into a neuro-surgical unit of the highest repute during the Second World War.

The next major voluntary hospital to be established was also in London, near the Tower, and the pattern was very similar to the early days of the Westminster. In 1740 London had been subjected to one of its worst winters and conditions for the poor were appalling. A group of seven men, including a surgeon, apothecary and lawyer, met in a tavern and voted to found a hospital. The surgeon, John Harrison, then 21, was one of the last members of the old Barber Surgeons company and had been apprenticed to a surgeon at St Thomas's at the age of 14. Between them they raised 100 guineas and rented an old house backing onto a burial ground, outside Moor Gate. A couple were appointed as staff, and The London Hospital opened the same year with only one shilling in the bank. They sent out 2,000 letters to canvass subscriptions and the Duke of Richmond became a patron, encouraging support. Patient demand was so great that they had to move within a matter of months to larger premises. These were just outside the City limits, in an area notorious for brothels, gin palaces and entertainment centres that had been banned from the City. It consisted of four dilapidated houses, labelled 'The London Infirmary', in Prescott Street, but by 1754 it had 130 beds. Unlike other voluntary hospitals, it accepted patients without sponsorship by a subscriber on payment of 1d and introduced 'means testing' for patients. Those who could afford it paid 10s 6d a week subsistence charge, along with a similar returnable deposit for good behaviour.

The premises became increasingly dilapidated and insanitary. The floors were covered with sand, which was coming through the ceiling into the kitchen and rooms underneath, the roof was leaking and the cold bath overflowing into the apothecary's laboratory, and the woodwork was infested with bugs; but the major problem was the lack of any sanitation. There were no sinks in the wards and waste water was thrown out of the windows into the street. Sewage was collected in buckets and slopped out by a night-man into an overloaded cesspit, and the stench led to legal action by the neighbours.

It was evident a new hospital would have to be built and in 1744 a

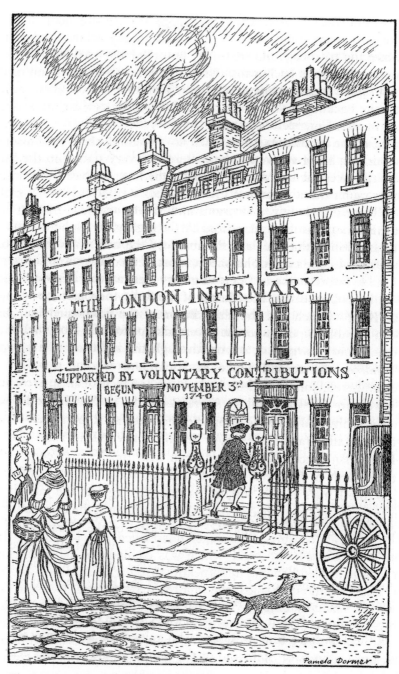

The London Infirmary in Prescott Street.

special fund was started and the search began for a site. After lengthy negotiations a green-field location, White Chapel Mount, was bought for £800 and a ground rent of £15 p.a., near the river. It included a fort long since demolished that had been built in 1642 at the outbreak of the Civil War and subsequently used as a dump for rubble from the Great Fire of London. By 1752 the old hospital was a dangerous structure with the flooring and party walls in a state of collapse and it was decided to build and equip the central block of the new hospital, although this was a gamble due to lack of funds. It comprised six wards on three floors with a nurses' room attached to each, an operating room in the roof, a bleeding room and cold bath on the ground floor and a fully equipped apothecary's quarters. There was a separate luxuriously furnished room for the physicians as they would not have condescended to share accommodation with the surgeons. Water from the New River Water Company was pumped up for the sink, but sewage was still collected in privies or 'close-stools' in each ward which had to be emptied into buckets by the night-man and flung into the sewer running down the Mile End Road. Thirty beds were opened in 1757, rapidly increasing to 160, whilst the remainder of the old hospital's seven-year lease was sold to Magdalen Hospital as a home for 98 'penitent prostitutes'.

Over the next 20 years money poured in from subscriptions and letting surplus agricultural land, and in 1775 and 1798 the east and west wings, each with six wards were built, to give a 300-bedded hospital. Then a combination of circumstances began to lead to a progressive financial crisis and steady decline. Rampant inflation due to wars with the American colonies, France and Spain led to a massive increase in costings, and governors were overloading the number of patients for admission. It was the only hospital not charging and a fee of one guinea towards maintenance was inflicted on parish officers. New expensive electrical treatment was coming into fashion and administrative discipline began to break down with high levels of waste. Resident staff were even keeping dogs on the premises at a time when hydrophobia was not uncommon. The governors responded initially by restricting admissions to 20 a week and cutting back on patients' food, especially for the most sick, but then panicked, closed the east and west wings, reducing the bed number to 89, and sacked many staff. It was derided as a big modern empty building with a chapel that could hold 500.

But standards of maintenance and service continued to degenerate

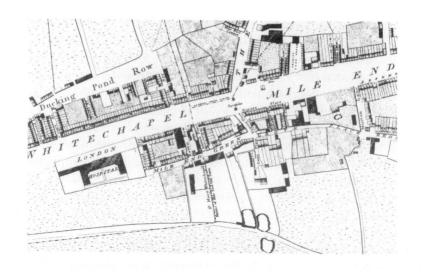

The New London Hospital in Whitechapel Road, 1780.

and by the turn of the century the state of the hospital was almost as bad as the old one. The walls of the wards were damp, the plumbing blocked and the beds were verminous, with no proper bed linen. The mortality rate had risen to 20% and the burial ground was overloaded. The situation led to a series of inquiries by the governors into the financial and general state of the hospital. They found overall the administration was bad and the running costs well above average. Their solution was to appoint a hospital superintendent and raise a new appeal for funds, whilst they were able to sell off some surplus land for council road development schemes. As a result matters were turned round. New sanitation was installed and beds and both wings were re-opened. By 1840 there were 300 beds treating 4,000 in-patients and 15,000 out-patients annually. The nature of the patients had changed greatly; two thirds were industrial accidents and emergencies, leaving less than a third available to the governors, who found many of their patients recommended by them for admission had to be refused, and against intense opposition by the medical staff and students they introduced resident medical officers to help out.

The hospital had been built on a green-field site which over the next 100 years underwent totally unregulated building development to create a vast slum area of tenements where four or five families lived, slept, bred and died in a single room. These were interspersed with heavy industry, polluting the atmosphere, and extensive docks. Sewage was either discharged into overloaded brick-lined sewers in the streets, infested with rats and often blocked, or collected under the houses, and the situation was ripe for the cholera epidemics which occurred in rapid succession. The hospital refused to accept cholera patients during 1832, but did subsequently and was at the centre of the fourth and last, and most severe, epidemic in 1866, when a third of the hospital beds were given over to cholera patients. A thousand were accepted, of whom nearly half died, and the hospital had to make a public appeal for medical and nursing help.

Expansion continued and when Queen Victoria opened a new wing endowed by the Grocers' Company in 1876, it became the largest hospital in the United Kingdom. It had over 900 beds and a flourishing medical school which was to dominate the future marriage with Bart's. Pupils had been accepted from the start, either as dressers or 'walking the wards', and a small school was opened in 1785 through the initiative of a newly appointed surgeon, Dr Blizard. He held control for some time, but as he aged discipline collapsed, with the staff arguing about student fees and who should give lectures. There was no constitution or governing body and even minutes of the staff meetings or proper accounts were not kept. The school appears to have been originally in the possession of Dr Blizard and then passed on to some of the medical staff. An inquiry was held by the governors in 1834, but although the school was recognised and retained its independence, it had to remain self-financing, despite the students being an integral part of the hospital service. A new school was built in 1854 with a bequest by Dr Powell, a GP in Tottenham, and it was only in 1876 that a joint college board was formed to run the school, which flourished from then on.

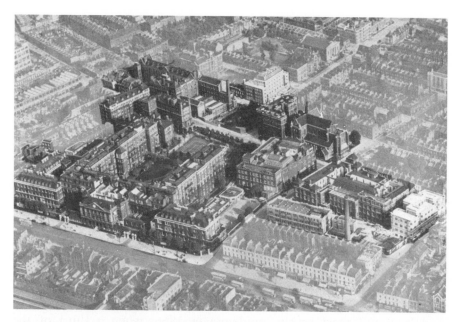

Aerial view of The London Hospital, 1940.

The Middlesex Infirmary opened in 1745 to serve the 'sick and lame' of Soho, a particularly blighted area of London at the time, in two small houses rented from a Mr Goodge for £30 p.a. in Windmill Street. The site had been a home for 40 lepers, founded by the wife of Henry I in 1101 and closed down by Henry VIII. The hospital was founded by 20 benefactors with 15 beds initially. At the time St Giles and Soho was a thickly populated area where the inhabitants lived in poverty. Four in five were scarred by smallpox, then endemic. When medical advice was needed the apothecary was sent to see a doctor in practice in the city, where he described the symptoms and for a fee received a prescription in Latin and advice on treatment. Only in the severest cases would the patient be seen by a doctor.

The hospital was able to attract subscribers who paid 3 guineas a year, or 21 guineas for a life membership, in return for a share in the management. It had a troubled start and within a year had to sack the paid staff, including the matron and apothecary, for 'indecencies and irregularities', the apothecary's actions being described as 'vile and enormous'. Uniquely it accepted maternity cases, but one of the two doctors appointed plotted to make the hospital purely maternity and was himself dismissed. It survived several financial crises and in 1757 moved to new purpose-built premises with 64 beds and a separate maternity unit.

The site chosen is still occupied by the present-day hospital. At the time it was on the extreme edge of London, separated from Tottenham Court Road by ponds and marshland, 'a good place for snipe-shooting', and adjacent to Farthing Pie House, the last inn before taking off into the country. New wings were built in 1766 and 1780, but the latter remained unoccupied for lack of funds and the successful maternity ward had shrunk from 34 to 2 beds. In 1791 Samuel Whitbread, the brewer, left £3,000 to endow a ward for cancer patients.

The first paying patients were French clergy in 1786, refugees from the Revolution, who filled two wards and were charged 8s a week, exclusive of burial fees, nurses' wages and bedding. In one year 430 were admitted, of whom 109 died. The Napoleonic Wars precipitated another financial crisis, and a nurses' strike was threatened when their food and beer allowances were reduced. It was resolved by adding rice to their diet.

The hospital expanded rapidly and by 1832 the number of beds had

The hospital site near 'Farthing Pie House'.

79

The first Middlesex Hospital, Windmill Street, 1840.

increased to 240. Extensive alterations were made until the present hospital with 712 beds opened in 1935. As elsewhere, surgeon pupils were taken on for a fee of 15 guineas a year, and banned from the women's wards and the apothecary's shop. Physician pupils were admitted in 1766, and a Medical Society founded in 1774 allowed them to meet in the physician's room twice a week for a fee of three guineas a quarter; they had to pay for their own candles. In 1812 Charles Bell took over the private Hunter School of Anatomy and two years later was appointed as a surgeon to the Middlesex. Over the next 14 years there was a successful collaboration with students learning anatomy at the Hunter School and clinical studies at the Middlesex.

In 1828 University College, the beginning of London University, was opened and proposed that the Middlesex should join up to establish a combined medical school. The Middlesex decided to have no truck with the 'godless institution in Gower Street' and formed its own medical school in 1836. University College was to establish a separate North London hospital and medical school which were an on-going success, whilst the Middlesex was to fall into serious decline as it lost the leading staff, including Charles Bell, who returned to Edinburgh as

The Middlesex Hospital in 1757, 1829 and 1848.

The Middlesex Hospital during rebuilding works in 1925.

The rebuilt Middlesex Hospital, 1935.

Professor of Surgery. For a year the medical school was threatened with closure, but new funding and support from the hospital governors rejuvenated it, and the school recovered its earlier reputation.

These hospitals were the trend setters for the development of the voluntary hospital system that spread across the country. By the end of the century 38 had been established and many more were to follow later. The underlying basis for success was the formula that had been worked out to raise the necessary funding in the absence of any state or local authority aid. The target was the new middle class of industrialists and tradesmen, many of whom were disturbed by the general poverty and lack of care for the sick. Direct charitable handouts were largely diverted to individuals, rather than reaching the roots of the problem, with the professional beggars and the workshy more likely to benefit than the genuine needy.

The first requirement for a successful launch was to raise the initial capital, and in the absence of benefactors this would necessitate an origin in rented and often unsuitable dilapidated premises, especially in overcrowded London. In the provinces only a single hospital would be needed for each town, and initial support was more easily obtained from flourishing tradesmen. The clergy and doctors would also often play a leading part in the establishment of a local hospital. The first to be founded was Winchester in 1736, and in their promotional material the governors laid out 16 benefits for all categories of the population to encourage support for such a charity. In 1776 Addenbrooke's Hospital, Cambridge, and in 1770 the Radcliffe Infirmary, Oxford, were named after the doctors who founded them. Isaac Maddox, Bishop of Worcester, led the campaign to open an infirmary there in 1746. The local response often allowed the original hospital to be transferred to new purpose-built premises within a few years, as at Manchester. Ten of the 28 provincial English voluntary hospitals and all five Scottish opened by the end of the 18th century were to be awarded royal patronage and the right to include the designation 'Royal' in their title, the first being Manchester Royal Infirmary in 1830.

Once the decision to go ahead and initiate a hospital had been reached, it was important to attract the support of dignitaries who would allow their names to appear at the head of the note-paper, to attract the attention of prospective subscribers. Royalty were not generally supportive initially and it would be a bishop, local nobility or important local citizens. Compared with the Catholic Church in Europe, the Church of England had not played a conspicuous role in social reform and was facing a crisis with migration of the workforce into the industrial centres. The country 'rent-a-pew' system, which placed the local establishment in their correct social order and ensured their peasants were regular attenders, was breaking up and in the new city slums the working classes were not interested in a church which showed little concern for their plight. There was, however, a strong Quaker and Nonconformist movement with considerable financial resources which was responsive. The new hospitals retained a strong religious background and the established clergy welcomed a new captive audience. Prayers remained more regular daily events than a doctor's visit! The general impression of the working classes was that they were immoral and profligate, with one in eight adult deaths attributed to drinking spirits, and venereal disease rampant. Both clergy and employers hoped that public gratitude for the hospitals would extend to reform after their discharge.

The picture painted in the promotional literature was often idyllic, with the proposed hospital presented as a place where the worthy sick would receive good care and treatment and early recovery of fitness to return to work. Families would be relieved of the burden of caring for their sick, parishes would be freed of their support, and money released to improve provision for the aged, and single parents, who were as big a problem then as today.

There was considerable antagonism to overcome. As always, doctors were apprehensive of any change and feared the new hospitals and dispensaries would draw patients from their private practice. The ongoing antagonism between physicians, surgeons and apothecaries was also a major problem. With time they came to appreciate the benefits to themselves financially and in professional status and would offer their services freely. There was public concern that the beds would become blocked with people whose proper place was the workhouse, whilst eligible patients feared they would carry this stigma. In the provinces there was concern that the hospital would attract an influx of vagrants and Irish immigrants who would breach the barriers that had been established and become dependants on the local rates. This was overcome by the requirement for patients to have sponsorship before admission, whilst the advantage of treatment locally, in place of a journey that could take several days, was overwhelming.

The immediate need was to attract regular annual subscribers and a number of appeals were devised. Each sponsor would have the right to take part in their hospital management, equivalent to the position of a member of a board of governors today. He could vote at meetings on policy, including staff appointments and patient admissions, and serve as a house visitor to inspect the hospital. Most important was his right to nominate patients, who could only be accepted through a Trustee's nomination. This entitlement was related to the amount of their subscription. In general one guinea purchased the right to one out-patient nominee, two guineas one in-patient. The wealthier establishments could raise this to £5, and 25 guineas for a life-long subscription. Until it became over-used, sponsors could take advantage of this privilege for their servants, a badly treated class. Their masters were responsible legally for their board, but had no liability for medical care and welcomed the opportunity to off-load this. Any casual labourer who was sick had to appeal to a subscriber's charity, until working men's guilds were established and would take out a block subscription for their members. Patients were not charged, in contrast to the chartered hospitals, but sponsors might have to pay one shilling a day for their servants and apprentices, as would officers responsible for soldiers. They would also have to make a deposit against burial charges or returning a patient home.

Another important inducement was the uplift in social status and the opportunity for the new middle class to mingle with the nobility and men of position in the local community. Even a small subscriber could reach a high position on the board of management and attend all the social functions and fund-raising events, which were often important ceremonies.

Charity fund-raising was an important source of income and many leading artists of the time gave their support. Handel's concerts at Westminster Cathedral supported the London hospitals for many years and he also sponsored the Foundling Hospital. The clergy held special services, preaching the spiritual benefits of charity, and later were to start 'hospital Sunday funds'. From 1850 onwards 'hospital Saturday funds' were launched to raise small weekly subscriptions from the lower paid, to give each group the rights of an individual subscriber. In time many future wealthy industrialists would donate large sums to an individual hospital to found a ward or establish a new specialist wing, and some of these remain today, still bearing the name of their benefactor.

The strict rule that prospective patients had to be sponsored by a subscriber at first excluded the great majority of people, although there were exceptions. Accident and emergencies were admitted, and assumed significant numbers in sea-ports or where the railways were being built. Scottish hospitals were less restrictive, and at the London admission could be petitioned by payment of 1d. There were also formidable limitations to the nature of cases accepted, imaging the chartered hospitals. These included children under six and pregnant women, although the Middlesex opened a lying-in ward and the London accepted maternity cases. Chronic cases that would block beds or place a demand on nursing were generally excluded, as were the terminally ill. Venereal conditions raised a moral dilemma with many of the patrons, although in 1775 Leeds General Infirmary opened up to 'married persons of good character' and later several hospitals opened special wards. Infectious diseases such as smallpox were a contentious problem and the attitude varied from hospital to hospital, and time to time. Most would reject them to a pest house, but the background to their contagious nature was not understood at the time and many hospitals continued to accept them – with medical support – until separate wards or buildings were established.

Most hospitals would publish annual reports recording the diagnoses of the patients admitted, and the terminology reflects the limitation of medical knowledge at the time. Of over 40 categories, most would be purely symptomatic, with labels such as 'dropsies, colics, palsy and bloody flux'. The report would be an essential part of the hospital public relations campaign locally and patients who were discharged were largely classified as 'cured' and were expected to pay tribute to the governors and at their local church.

Admissions had to be clean and free from vermin, with clothes and cutlery, and a deposit to cover bed linen and washing. There might be charitable funds available for the destitute, or else this was the matron's responsibility. Both nursing and medical staff were equally defective. The matron was a housekeeper responsible for maintenance of the premises and discipline of the nurses and patients. The status of the nurses was of the lowest. The choice would be middle-aged women without family who were otherwise unemployable, at a salary of £12 p.a., at best, with a ration of beer. Most would be sacked at the end of their working life and enter the workhouse.

The medical profession had an established pecking order, with the apothecary, the only paid professional, at the bottom. He would be resident and supply all prescriptions from his salary. He was responsible for bleeding, cupping and leeching, which were the standard treatments of the time, and could only leave the hospital with authorisation. He, along with the matron and hospitaller, was poorly paid, and dishonesty amongst apothecaries was common. The physicians were in the chair and it was accepted their weekly visits would depend on their private commitments. Surgeons were still second-class citizens, professionally, and could only prescribe under physicians' jurisdiction. Surgeons were not to acquire respectability until they developed their own faculty at the end of the 18th century. Hospital appointments became increasingly sought as a route to successful private practice and applicants would canvass the governors for their vote with all the fervour applied to a parliamentary election campaign, even persuading their friends to become subscribers and offering the governors bribes.

At the time Oxford and Cambridge universities held a total monopoly in the training of physicians, and their courses were more concerned with the humanities than medical topics. The best-trained had studied on the Continent, particularly Leiden University. The first faculty of medicine in Britain was established at Edinburgh in 1726, and although graduates of Scottish universities were not legally allowed to practise in England until the Medical Act of 1858, they increasingly began to fill the hospital posts. At Leeds General Infirmary four of the first five physicians were Edinburgh graduates. In England any training had to be obtained through a seven-year apprenticeship as a surgeon's dresser or physician's pupil, and pupils paid increasing fees to their chief for the privilege. In 1771 Radcliffe Infirmary began to accept medical students from Oxford University, but London lagged behind and it was the next century before the chartered and leading voluntary hospitals began systematic lecture courses and went on to found medical schools. As a result private medical schools were established by some of the leading surgeons of the time; the most famous was that of William Hunter in Great Windmill Street.

The founders of the earlier hospitals were naive and totally inexperienced and there would be a long period of floundering before a sound doctrine of hospital practice, administration and discipline would be established. Those offering voluntary services often proved the most difficult to deal with, and as the number of voting subscribers mounted there were inevitably clashes of opinion on policy. They also had to deal with a jealous and contentious medical profession. The governors had the right to dictate admission policy, but on their weekly inspection of the wards they would often find the doctors had accepted patients without approval, or were negligent in their duties. Overall, the system flourished throughout the country and by the end of the 18th century 32 voluntary hospitals had been established in England and five in Scotland. In addition a large number of out-patient dispensaries opened, many of which would become hospitals later.

Openings accelerated during the first half of the 19th century and in 1861 England and Wales had 23 teaching hospitals and 123 general hospitals providing free medical aid. Beds had increased from 4,000 to 12,000, treating 30,000 in-patients yearly. In Ireland the first voluntary hospital was opened in Dublin in 1718 and there were a further six by 1773. By 1804 there was at least one general infirmary in each county, some partly state funded, but most entirely dependent on charity.

The provincial towns had been quick to respond and develop their own hospitals, often with more beds and staff. The first to be established was at Winchester in 1736, followed by Bristol the next year. Salisbury was a town that had enjoyed a monastic hospital but it had been closed down by Henry VIII in 1540 and not replaced. Some 10% of the population died from smallpox in the first half of the 18th century and in 1763 a subscription list was opened to provide a smallpox hospital. Five years later Lord Feversham bequeathed £500 to start a general hospital, initially in a row of cottages but soon to be replaced by a purpose-built building with around 100 beds. A feature for the governors was the annual Infirmary Walk through the town to a cathedral service, with precedence for the major donors, followed by a dinner at the Assembly Rooms.

Bristol Royal Infirmary, 1742.

Bristol Royal Infirmary, 1923.

Salisbury Infirmary, 1766. Its first site was a row of cottages in Fisherton Street.

Salisbury Infirmary, 1866.

Salisbury Infirmary, 1966 (now a block of flats).

During the first half of the 18th century Liverpool expanded into a major port and became the centre of the slave trade, attracting a vast influx of labour from the surrounding countryside, Wales and Ireland, into overcrowded slums with no sanitation. There were no hospital

Worcester Royal Infirmary, 1825.

Worcester Royal Infirmary, 1947.

The General Kent and Canterbury Hospital, 1793.

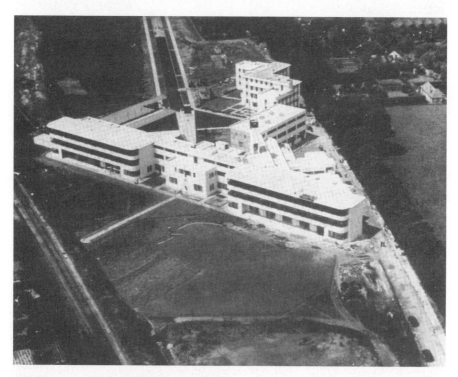

The Kent and Canterbury Hospital in 1936.

facilities, and although the building of an infirmary was started, it was interrupted when the town raised the Liverpool Blues in defence of George II during the Jacobite rebellion and was only completed in 1749, at a total cost of £2,618 3s 6d. It was a three-storey building with

The Royal Infirmary, Sheffield.

Leicester Royal Infirmary, 19th century.

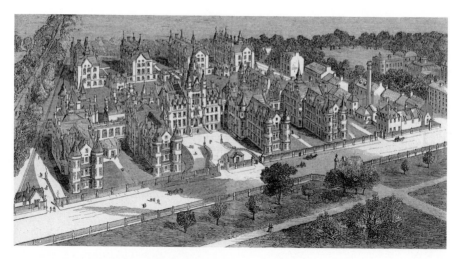

The New Royal Infirmary, Edinburgh, 1879.

two 18-bed wards on the first floor, two smaller surgical wards and a theatre, with a salivating ward on the second floor and staff accommodation in the attics. Three years later two large blocks were built as wings to the infirmary, but completely independent in management. Called the Seaman's Hospital, these were really almshouses for aged

The Fever Hospital and Royal Infirmary, Glasgow, 1832.

The Surgeons' Hall, Edinburgh, built in 1697.

seamen, their families and orphans, and it was largely supported by a levy of 6d a month which was deducted by Act of Parliament from the pay of all seamen sailing in ships registered at the Port of Liverpool. As a result it was often known as the 'Sixpenny Hospital'!

Bristol Royal Infirmary was opened in 1737 with 34 beds, after 78 local dignitaries committed themselves to an annual subscription of 2

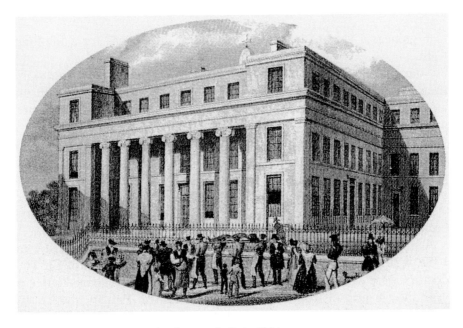

The second Liverpool Royal Infirmary, built in 1824.

Artist's impression of the New Royal Infirmary, Liverpool, 1887.

to 6 guineas a year to become a Trustee or 20 guineas for a life-long right.

Four physicians and two surgeons were appointed on a voluntary basis. Also, an apothecary was paid £30 per annum, along with an assistant. A matron was appointed at £15 per annum, with a 5 guinea gratuity, who was to slave for 33 years.

Standards of behaviour were laid down for the patients, which, in turn, became generally adopted. Patients were forbidden to swear, gamble or play cards or dice and, also, to lie on their beds in clothes or shoes. They were allowed out to church at first, but this privilege was withdrawn, as, on return, they clearly showed signs of having been to an alehouse, rather than a church.

A public infirmary with twelve beds was initiated in Manchester in 1752, with a matron paid £6 per annum and her maid-servant £3. The doctors were voluntary, but a paid apothecary was engaged after a year and surgical instruments were also purchased. Patient restrictions were severe and cases with venereal disease refused. A new infirmary with 50 beds was built in 1755 and extra wings soon had to be added.

96

The Liverpool Royal Infirmary today.

New Manchester Infirmary, 1755.

The Lunatic Hospital, Infirmary and Public Baths in Manchester, 1790.

An adjoining lunatic asylum was built in 1766, along with an adjacent set of cold, warm and vapour public baths, which the trustees could use at a reduced price.

There were major developments over the next century, but overall deteriorating conditions led to severe press criticism of the medical

The new building of the Royal Infirmary, Manchester, fronting Oxford Road, 1908.

Manchester Infirmary from the air in 1925.

care, with some surgical staff not attending for weeks and patients dying as a result. A final decision was made to build a new hospital fronting onto Oxford Road which opened in 1908.

Two voluntary hospitals were established in Birmingham. The first in 1770 was the General Hospital to house 100 patients. Four nurses

Birmingham's first General Hospital, 1791.

The second Birmingham General Hospital, 1897.

were appointed at a salary of four guineas per annum, with the promise of 'an additional guinea if they behaved well', along with a barber paid two guineas a year to shave the patients twice a week. As the population expanded patient demand grew and a new up-to-date

The Queen's Hospital, Birmingham, 1841.

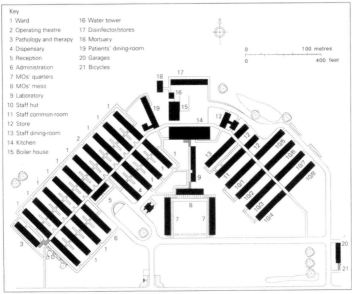

The Birmingham Hospitals Centre in 1934. The main hospital is in the centre, with the nurses' home at the rear and medical faculty in front.

General Hospital was built in Steelhouse Lane near the centre of Birmingham.

By 1826 a Medical School had been established at Queen's College, but the medical facilities at The General were inadequate for the number of students and a second voluntary hospital, Queen's Hospital, was built. A municipal Poor Law Infirmary was opened in the latter part of the 19th century to house the chronic sick and elderly, and was taken over by the military for casualties during the 1914-1918 war. Afterwards the City Municipal Health Committee began to develop the infirmary into a general acute hospital and the building of a new hospital at Selly Oak. Lack of funds restricted the independence of the General & Queens which amalgamated in 1933 to form the 'United Hospital' which was built adjacent to a new University on land donated by Messrs. Cadbury, and is now known as the Queen Elizabeth Hospital.

The Voluntary Hospitals of the 18th Century

London

	Date of Opening
Westminster Hospital	1720
Guy's Hospital	1724
St George's Hospital	1733
London Hospital	1740
Middlesex Hospital	1745
St Bartholomew's Hospital	1123 (refounded 1546)
St Thomas's Hospital	1213 (refounded 1551)

Provinces

	Date of Opening		Date of Opening
Winchester County Hospital	1736	Salisbury County Hospital	1766
Bristol Royal Infirmary	1737	Staffordshire County Hospital	1766
York County Hospital	1740	General Infirmary at Leeds	1767
Royal Devon & Exeter Hospital	1741	Lincoln County Hospital	1769
Bath General Hospital	1742	Radcliffe Infirmary, Oxford	1770
Northampton General Hospital	1743	Norfolk and Norwich Hospital	1771
Worcester Royal Infirmary	1746	Leicester Royal Infirmary	1771
Royal Salop Infirmary	1747	Hereford General Infirmary	1776
Liverpool Royal Infirmary	1749	Birmingham General Hospital	1779
Royal Victoria Infirmary, Newcastle	1751	Nottingham General Hospital	1782
Manchester Royal Infirmary	1752	Hull Royal Infirmary	1782

Gloucester Royal Infirmary	1755	Bath City Infirmary	1792
Chester Infirmary	1755	Kent and Canterbury Hospital	1793
Addenbrooke's Hospital, Cambridge	1766	Sheffield Royal Infirmary	1797

Scottish Hospitals

Edinburgh Royal Infirmary	1729	Glasgow Royal Infirmary	1792
Aberdeen Royal Infirmary	1742	Dundee Royal Infirmary	1798
Dumfries & Galloway Royal Infirmary	1778		

Chapter 4

19th Century London Voluntary Hospitals

The development of the voluntary hospital system would intensify during the next century. Two of the more famous London hospitals were initiated through the dedication and perseverance of a Holborn GP, William Marsden. It is recorded that he found a dying, destitute girl on the church steps and personally took her to Bart's, Thomas's and Guy's hospital in turn, but she was refused admission in the absence of a governor's letter, although he offered her burial deposit and entrance money. He was a Freeman of the Cordwainers' Company and within two months had raised enough funds to rent a house for £20 12s 6d a quarter, hire a resident apothecary for £30 p.a. and open a dispensary in a single room on the first floor, approached by a narrow staircase, called initially the London General Institution for the Gratuitous Care of Malignant Disease. Opened in 1818, it was to treat more than 1,000 patients in the first year, many of them from the most desperate and destitute groups in the slums, where up to 30 people would sleep on the floor of one room in a lodging house for 1d a night. At the time many survived as scavengers of the streets, river bed and sewers on droppings from the tables of the rich. 'Street-finders' collected rags and bones, and 'pure-finders' buckets of dog manure to sell for leather tanning.

Marsden was subjected to intense professional and establishmentary antagonism in going against hospitals' cardinal principles by treating patients free and without any need for an introductory letter, although subscribers would be registered as governors. Within three years it was treating over 2,000 patients and was known locally as the 'Free Hospital', although financially unable to consider in-patients. In 1832 there was a severe outbreak of cholera, and whilst most of the established hospitals refused to accept cases, the Free opened two wards on the top floor with 50 beds. Most of the early intake died, but Marsden revolutionised the standard treatment of calomel and opiates. He recognised that the intense dehydration from vomiting and diarrhoea led to circulatory collapse, and forced fluid, including saline, which would even be given intravenously in isotonic strength,

105

and 580 of the next 700 patients recovered with the help of only a handful of staff.

Finances were exhausted and the beds could not be kept open after the epidemic finished, although two years later it was possible to rent the house next door and open two small wards. Unfortunately, around this time the first of the two public scandals developed. It emerged that the apothecary and one of the surgeons were advertising and selling a quack remedy for venereal disease, called Frank's Specific Solution, which was claimed to be better than the authentic treatments. Marsden was only able to obtain their dismissal by the governors after considerable public controversy and publicity in *The Times* and the *Lancet*.

One of the first acts of the young Queen Victoria on her accession to the throne in 1837 was to become a patron and grant the title Royal Free Hospital, as she did for the Society for the Prevention of Cruelty to Animals.

A new hospital was built in Gray's Inn Road and completed by 1843. It uniquely contained two wards specifically for patients with venereal disease and this created another public scandal. Two young sisters who claimed to be 'respectable' had to be refused admission as the only beds available were in the venereal ward, and they died in the workhouse. An anonymous long letter to *The Times*, signed 'HUMANITAS', accused the officers of the Royal Free Hospital of cruelty and neglect, and a second letter claimed the hospital would welcome 'strumpets off the streets' from the City of London Union – a refuge for destitute prostitutes – in preference to respectable women. The hospital was exonerated at a coroner's inquest, but the identity of 'Humanitas' was never revealed.

The next major challenge to the hospital occurred on its 21st anniversary during the great cholera epidemic in 1849, when it had to accept 157 children from the 'infant pauper asylum' in the village of Lower Tooting. Attention had been drawn to this Dickensian location when 150 children had died from cholera, to be buried four to a coffin in the local cemetery. Surrey Hall, as the institution was called, had been a dumping site for orphan children from a wide area by the Poor Law Commissioners, with over 1,500 boys and girls packed into accommodation for 900. The manager, Peter Drovet, had been paid 4s 6d a week to clothe and feed each child but appropriated much of this, and when the children were removed they were emaciated and in rags. Living conditions were appalling, with up to 20 beds packed in

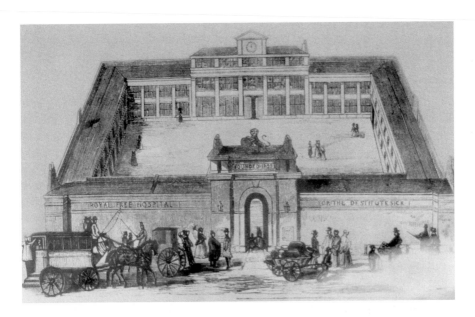

The Royal Free Hospital, Gray's Inn Road, 1844.

The men's waiting room at the Royal Free Hospital, 1843.

The women's ward at the Royal Free, 1843.

one room and up to five children sleeping in one bed. Sewage and waste were emptied into a ditch that ran through the playground and would become blocked. It had been emptied by some of the older boys at the time of the cholera outbreak and the manure piled on the banks for a local farmer to collect as manure for his land.

In 1851 William Marsden was to initiate the second hospital associated with him. His specific area of interest had always been cancer, and a Free Cancer Hospital was opened for out-patients in a single house in Cannon Row, Westminster. Unlike the Royal Free, there was no controversy, and great pressure on demand. Within a year it had moved to larger premises with in-patient beds and in 1861 to a purpose-built hospital of 80 beds, funded by Baroness Burdett-Coutts, on a site in the Fulham Road which was to mature into one of the foremost centres for cancer treatment. When granted a Royal Charter by George V in 1910 and finally the designation 'Royal' in 1936 by Edward VIII, William Marsden became the only person to have initiated two Royal Hospitals.

In 1853 a medical school was started at the Royal Free and in 1877 it made history by becoming the first hospital in England to offer the

The Royal Free Hospital, c. 1890.

The Royal Free in the 1920s.

The Royal Free today.

London School of Medicine for Women students ward facilities for clinical studies. Later it was to become single-sex as the London Royal School of Medicine for Women, until in 1947 it was compelled to return to co-educational status.

The first new general hospital to be established in London after the Middlesex was the Charing Cross. It was started by a 21-year-old medical student, Benjamin Golding, as a dispensary from his digs at a rented house in Leicester Square. At the time this was a fashionable oasis in one of the worst slum areas in London. Trafalgar Square did not exist and the site was largely occupied by the Royal Mews, stabling the King's horses and coaches. The surrounding areas of Covent Garden and Soho were a network of narrow alleys lined with decaying buildings where families lived in squalor in a single room, with little or no sanitation. Worst of all was the area known as the Bermuda, centred on the Strand, now the Aldwych, a nest of doss-

The King's Mews at Charing Cross, c.1800, the site for the proposed hospital.

houses where men, women and children huddled together lodging on a straw covered floor for 2d a night.

As there were no facilities in London for a medical degree, Golding had begun his training in 1811 at the age of 18 in Edinburgh, and two years later moved down to St Thomas's as a 'surgery-man dresser'.

The Suffolk Street Institute, 1818.

Within a year he was beginning to treat patients free at his lodgings in the morning before attending his studies – at the time anyone could set up practice as a doctor without any form of qualification. He treated 20,000 patients over the next three years, before renting a house in Suffolk Street, by the back door of the Haymarket Theatre, when he teamed up with a couple of medical friends to start the West London Infirmary and Dispensary. By then he had passed his MRCS, but only returned to Edinburgh in 1823 to complete a medical degree.

From the beginning they had ambitious plans to start a comprehensive hospital offering general medical and specialist facilities and a medical school, and set up a committee to raise funds. By January 1823 they were able to move to a four-storey house in Villiers Street, rented for seven years. On the ground floor was a 12-bedded ward where patients would be cared for by a housekeeper resident in the basement and paid five shillings a week with full board. The top-floor attics housed medical baths, and later an electro-therapy unit offering electrical muscle stimulation and continuous galvanic spasm, which had become established as a therapy in France. It was the first such unit to be established in Britain and put Charing Cross in the forefront of medical development. They also appointed an Anatomical Machinist to set up a department for the treatment of deformities such as club foot. A porter had to be employed to carry the patients upstairs for their treatment. Another venture was the employment of midwives at 3s 6d a delivery to carry out domiciliary confinements, although several had to be sacked for fraud, conniving with the patients. Four apprentices were taken on at the dispensary for training, each paying two guineas for a six-year course and required to help with bleeding and cupping, tooth extraction and gum lancing. Two early famous students were Thomas Huxley and David Livingstone. In 1827 the name was changed to Charing Cross Hospital. It had already established itself as 'our hospital' locally.

Demand soon exceeded capacity and a building fund was set up to develop a larger hospital. During the search for a new site there was a temporary panic when the Westminster threatened to rebuild locally, but in a major redevelopment of the whole area their governors were offered a lease by the Government on a site that was to become the hospital's home until its removal to Fulham 150 years later. There were two main problems. The ground rent of £400 p.a. was beyond their means and forced the hospital to sublet a third of the site, developed into shops, a theatre to be called Toole's and the Westminster

Eye Hospital. Building work was started to develop part of the remaining area, but the planning authorities of the time – the Commissioners of Woods and Forests – forced completion of the entire frontage of the site. The end result was a long narrow building only two houses deep and three storeys high. Only the ground floor and first two storeys could be made inhabitable, with the upper part to be left as an empty shell for the next 20 years.

The hospital opened in 1834 with four wards containing 60 beds and a medical school of 22 students, with a large lecture theatre in the basement next to the morgue and chapel. The standard limitations on patient admissions were imposed, with incurables, chronic cases such as ulcers and tuberculosis, infectious diseases or syphilis, pregnant women and the insane excluded. By now there were seven unpaid medical staff, and a resident dispenser and two principal nurses were hired at £36 p.a., supported by two under nurses, a cook/housekeeper, beadle, porter and housemaid, all on a salary of £30 p.a.

Discipline was strict for both patients and staff, with instant discharge for any infringement of the rules. There were 'audible' morning prayers in all the wards that all had to attend. The wards were well furnished, but the patient diet was strictly regulated, with meat only to be boiled, to save the broth for future use, with no pork, fish or vegetables other than potatoes or rice. Beer or tea with sugar

An 1840 print of Charing Cross Hospital by Thos Shepherd.

were the only drinks. In contrast there was only a small out-of-date operating theatre, with a portable table which was liable to collapse if the patient weighed more than 12 stone, until a new surgical block with six wards and two new operating theatres was created during the major rebuilding that started in 1877.

In 1866 the hospital contracted out the nursing and domestic services to St John's House, a Protestant sisterhood that trained nurses, in place of their directly employed staff. This had comprised a matron, 3 sisters, 10 nurses and 6 scrubbers, all of whom cooked their food in the wards, for a total cost of £250 p.a. St John's insisted 13 nurses were employed, along with a night nurse for each of the five wards, and meals were cooked in the kitchen. The annual cost of £1,000 p.a. was heavily criticised by some subscribers, but this arrangement was to continue for 22 years until the hospital appointed its own matron and nursing staff and built a nursing home with 66 bedrooms and separate dining and sitting rooms for probationers, nurses and sisters in 1902.

In 1832 Charing Cross was approached by King's College, which had started a medical faculty, with the proposal the two should co-ordinate their faculties and Charing Cross be the clinical base. After lengthy discussions this offer was rejected and King's were to open their own hospital in 1839. The number of students at Charing Cross increased to 81 and in 1839 it was recognised by the Senate of London University as one of the institutions from which it would accept a certificate of graduation, although pre-clinical teaching was transferred to King's in 1912.

The number of students steadily increased, attracting many pupils from the Commonwealth. One of the hospital surgeons initiated the Volunteer Medical Staff Corps, which was to become the Royal Army Medical Corps. A new medical school completed in 1881 was built on the opposite side of the road, connected to the hospital mortuary by a tunnel which could only be three feet wide as it had to run between the gas and water pipes. Bodies would be trundled along this tunnel to a lift in the medical school and taken up to the dissecting and post-mortem room, a welcome improvement from the old site, where there had been complaints for years of the smell due to the lack of refrigeration. In 1916 women medical students were admitted for the first time, but they were banned again from the end of the war until 1948.

The hospital was to suffer recurrent financial crises along with other voluntary hospitals and competition between them for funds was cut-

The Charing Cross Hospital medical school at Chandos Place, next to the hospital.

throat. Charing Cross brought fund-raising to a fine art form from its beginning, using all the methods in general use and devising new ones. Ten guineas bought a subscriber life membership as a governor and the right to nominate a patient and vote on all appointments, whilst 500 guineas bought the title of vice-president. Later new grades were introduced and 50 guineas gave the lifetime right to send an unlimited number of patients to the infirmary, whilst for 100 guineas this became hereditary. Outdoor salesmen would sell stationery and even soup, whilst the old 'monastic system' was revised, with collectors employed on a commission basis. Fund-raising exercises were organised through the local churches, and subscription books opened at banks and business houses. Funds would pour in, allowing phases of development. The first of these was in 1877 when a fourth floor was built, a lift installed and an obstetric and a children's ward added. The hospital was able gradually to start buying back the leases let at its origin and finally acquired the entire site. Rebuilding started in 1902 to create a hospital with 298 beds and including nine specialist depart-

Charing Cross Hospital in 1967.

ments. A large bank loan had been raised and the interest charges proved crippling. Threatened with foreclosure, half the beds had to be closed in 1914 as running costs were to double, whilst in 1919 patients were invited to contribute.

The hospital survived with some windfall donations until in 1921 a

young man, John Inman, was appointed as Secretary and Superintendent, and set about fund-raising on an ambitious scale. He began to
write a weekly column, 'in Sunshine Ward', for *John Bull* magazine
and newspapers about the hospital's work. This made the hospital
famous and subscriptions poured in. As it was at the centre of the
theatre district, many of the leading stars and comedians of the day
gave charity concerts. Inman even visited America for a successful
fund-raising trip. By 1928 the lady almoner was active, raising contributions from the patients, and she was even accused of refusing
patients who could not pay, or charging too much.

It was always too small for a major teaching hospital and plans were
made for removal to a new site. By 1930 it had bought up a great deal
of surrounding property at The Adelphi on the Thames. This plan was
rejected by The King's Fund, which although it had no statutory or
mandatory powers, carried great influence as a source of funds and
would evaluate major schemes, issuing a salutary or damning report.

The Ministry of Health insisted it would have to move out to the
suburbs, but their chosen site at Northwick Park was rejected by the
University Grants Committee as outside their administrative area.
Rebuilding was proposed at the site of a Poor Law infirmary, Fulham
Hospital in West London. There was intense local opposition, but
eventually a new hospital with 896 beds, 632 in a tower block, was
built. There were separate paediatric and geriatric blocks, a swimming
pool and accommodation for staff and students.

In 1947 Charing Cross integrated into the University of London.
Until then only Bart's and the Royal Free, of the 12 London teaching

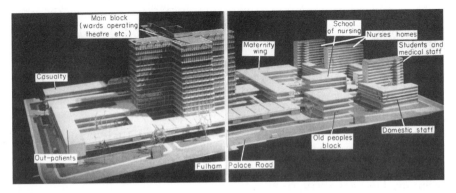

Model of the new Charing Cross Hospital, Fulham Palace Road.

The new Charing Cross Hospital at Fulham Palace Road, 1974.

hospitals, had been chartered, but now all were brought under the supervision and control of the University of London.

The last major voluntary hospital to be developed in London was St Mary's, Praed Street, Paddington. By 1800 Marylebone development, which included Harley Street, then purely a wealthy residential area before its development as a medical quarter, extended to the Edgware Road. In 1795 the Grand Junction Canal was extended through Paddington and a basin constructed with wharves and road access. Later the Great Western Railway developed Paddington Station, leading to extensive local property development, and an increased population for which there was no hospital provision locally. An initial dispensary failed, and a fund was set up to build a hospital which was calculated should provide 376 beds to meet a population now estimated at 150,000; but it was a long time before it was to reach this size. The first stage, to give 150 beds, was started, but progress was slow as the first building contractor died and the second went bankrupt, and the building was only completed in 1851, six years after Queen Victoria laid the foundation stone.

The choice of staff was contentious as they could not be obtained from the other voluntary hospitals, and the *Lancet* was highly critical of the methods by which they were selected by the governors. Appointments were decided by a small committee. Choice was limited but ten senior highly rated medical members of the staff were appointed, although subsequently replacements were made through the old system where applicants would solicit the votes of the governors, who numbered 1,500. Doctors who only attended out-patients held the inferior grade of assistant surgeon or physician, but in 1857 St Mary's became the first hospital to raise them to the full consultant's status.

It had also been planned for the hospital to have a medical school and in 1852 it was recognised by the Royal College of Surgeons for surgical teaching, but was turned down by the Society of Apothecaries as a school of medicine on the grounds there was no resident apothecary or separate medical school. One of the resident medical officers was the official apothecary. A building fund for a medical school was raised by the issue of 'thirty-two presentation cards' at £80

St Mary's Hospital Medical School, 1854-1933.

St Mary's Hospital Medical School, 1933.

with a full value of £100, a form of redeemable debenture. These entitled the purchaser to use all the medical facilities of the hospital, or a student a full training course. Building was completed within four months and amongst the staff appointed was Samuel Lane, who had run a successful private school for 20 years and donated his museum. He gave specialist lectures in military surgery during the Crimean War

The site in Praed Street in 1892 before the building of St Mary's Clarence Wing.

The Clarence Memorial Wing, St Mary's Hospital, 1896.

and taught medical jurisprudence. The school opened in 1854 with 20 students and was immediately recognised by the University of London.

The first extension to the hospital was built after 15 years, but the original building was closed in 1875 to remove the toilets from the wards and build a sanitary tower, and again ten years later, when the old drains were leaking. Further development was slow, and only the ground floor of a proposed new Clarence Wing was opened as an out-patient department in 1898 until funds could be raised and the building completed in 1904. Surrounding buildings were gradually bought, but a proper operating suite was only built in 1926. A major rebuild was completed by 1933, a nurses' home three years later and a large separate private Lindo Wing the following year at the site of the former medical school. Within the NHS it would become part of a teaching hospital group that would absorb the Samaritan Free Hospital for Women, the Western Ophthalmic, Paddington Green Children's Hospital and Paddington General which was later closed.

The hospital was to become a centre for the development of vaccine

The Queen Elizabeth the Queen Mother Wing, 1988, St. Mary's Hospital.

therapy under the direction of Dr Almroth Wright, appointed as lecturer in Pathology and Bacteriology in 1902. An Inoculation Department with a separate committee from the board of the hospital was developed and played a big part in the development of typhoid and tetanus prophylactic vaccinations during the First World War. It extended its work into the allergy fields, especially hay fever and asthma, with less long-term success, although preparation and sale of private vaccines was financially supported. It was in these laboratories that Sir Alexander Fleming was to make the first observations that led to the discovery of penicillin.

At the start of the 19th century only 100 of the 300 physicians licensed by the Royal College had been educated at Oxford or Cambridge, and most in practice had not even applied for a licence and along with the 6,000 members of the College of Surgeons had trained at a University in Europe such as Leiden or in Edinburgh. The two English Universities excluded many potential candidates through a stringent Christian religious screening, and the cost of a lengthy course with high College residence charges and expensive student habits. As a result very few members of the learned profession, especially medicine, received any general University education.

In the early 1820s a group of reformists began to form a 'Deed of Settlement' that would legally establish a 'Council of the University of London'. Those concerned included a Jewish financier, Sir Isaac Lyn Goldsmith, some Protestant dissenters, Charles Bell and leading anatomical surgeon and his lawyer brother George. They bought an eight acre freehold site, then a dumping site for refuse and by 1828 had raised enough money to build a College as a non-resident University. This is still the present location of University College Hospital and the University of London.

A medical school was opened with Charles Bell Professor in Anatomy & Surgery, and John Conolly a medical colleague who was also a founder member of the first Council of London University as Professor in the Nature & Treatment of Disease. Their lectures were an immediate success and over 50 students enrolled. Clinical studies were held at a dispensary opened at a house locally, with a resident apothecary who could also visit patients at home. Pupils could attend the Middlesex where Charles Bell also worked, but the hospital rejected any proposal for a closer relationship.

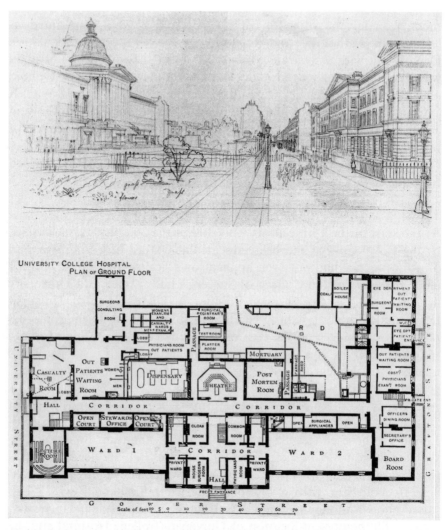

University College Hospital, 1840. Engraving by G Scharf. With plan of the ground floor of the original University College Hospital.

In the critical outline of the objectives of the Council of London University shares were sold at £100 each to 'Proprietors' who were entitled to nominate a student for each share they held, who was entitled to attend a medical course of lectures and a year's attendance at The Middlesex Hospital for £50.

There would be increasing conflicts of interest between the professorial staff, apothecary and Council members, in which the students

UCH: The old hospital, c.1880.

University College Hospital, rebuilt 1897–1906.

Patients waiting in the new out-patients room at University College Hospital, 1872.

An operation in progress at UCH, 1898.

became involved that would lead to the resignations of Bell and Conolly amongst others and for a time the future of the University was in doubt.

It became evident that a hospital was essential and a public appeal raised sufficient funds to initiate building, and a central block with 130 beds called the 'North London Hospital' was opened in 1834. A south wing was added in 1841 and a north wing in 1846. Subscribers were offered the usual entitlement to submit patients for an annual fee of 3 guineas.

The new hospital would attract some leading medical men of the times. Amongst these was Robert Liston who came from Edinburgh with a reputation for his surgical skills and speed in operating. In 1846 at the North London he carried out his first major operation under ether anaesthesia in Europe. An early student who went on to achieve fame was Joseph Lister who established the antiseptic treatment of wounds with carbolic spray in Glasgow. He had applied for a vacancy at the College in 1866 but was not appointed and would finally settle in London at King's College in 1897.

The medical school became popular, at times with over 350 students, and there were disputes over the allocation of their fees with the teaching staff, which were finally resolved when the lecturers agreed to waive their fees. Recurrent financial crises would cause bed closures and lead to fund raising ventures, one of which was a dinner sponsored by Charles Dickens that raised £1600. Another problem would be hospital infection related to poor sanitation, and it became evident that rebuilding was essential.

Two donations would lead to major advances, Sir John Maple, owner of the neighbouring furniture store in Tottenham Court Road, would donate £100,000 and fund a rebuilding of the hospital with 300 beds that was completed in 1906, and a nurses' home.

In 1920 the Rockefeller Foundation awarded a million pounds to the hospital, part of which would be used towards the development of Medical and Surgical Units by the University Grants Committee of the Board of Education. These would lead on to research in the development of many areas of medical and surgical advance over the next generations in which UCH would be one of the leaders. It also funded an Institute of Obstetrics building. Previously midwifery training had been negligible, and in the early 1920s consisted of a routine lecture on labour with a visit to a home delivery by a midwife or 'handy woman'. One student at the time said forceps and caesarean sections were

127

The new University College Hospital in 1906.

A horse ambulance at the Casualty entrance to University College Hospital.

The future of London's healthcare.

unknown, whilst at the single weekly antenatal clinic blood pressure readings were not taken or urine examined until an obstetric unit was opened in 1927. Extensions were opened in 1937 by when 2,000 patients were seen yearly.

The Hospital and Medical School would be separated in 1905, becoming University College instead of the North London Hospital when Sir Donald Currie would give £100,000 to build a new medical school and nurses' home. St Pancras Hospital for Tropical Diseases and the National Temperance Hospital would become joined in 1968 and the old Board of Governors dissolved in 1974.

The medical schools of University College and the Middlesex were finally brought together at the Gower Street site along with the Royal Free.

Equally motivated by the religious bigotry of Oxford and Cambridge with their prohibitive cost for study, was the development of King's College and the allied hospital. During the 1820s leading reformers supported the concept of a University to provide a broad education to the middle class students who could live at home, but felt some religious education should be included in contrast to University College. It was established in The Strand, next to Somerset House, and would become one of the two oldest and largest colleges of the

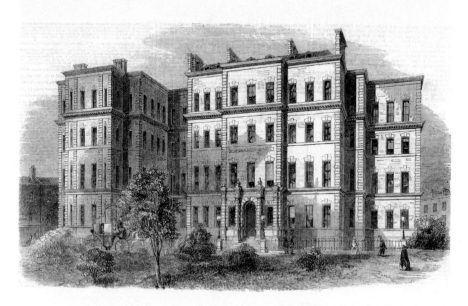

King's College Hospital, Portugal Street, Lincoln's Inn, 1861.

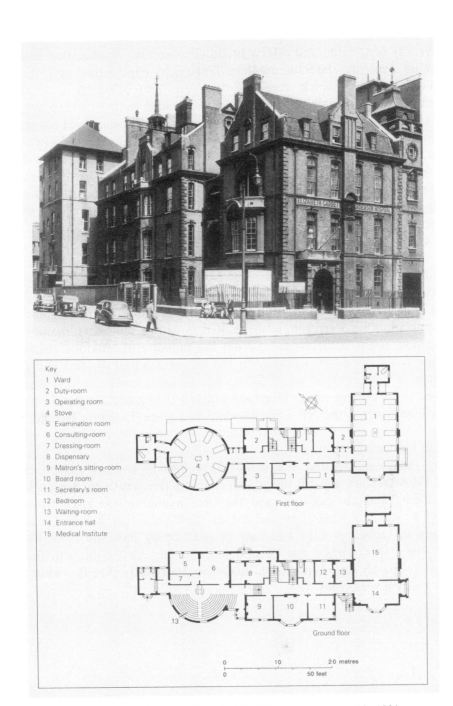

Key
1 Ward
2 Duty-room
3 Operating room
4 Stove
5 Examination room
6 Consulting-room
7 Dressing-room
8 Dispensary
9 Matron's sitting-room
10 Board room
11 Secretary's room
12 Bedroom
13 Waiting-room
14 Entrance hall
15 Medical Institute

First floor

Ground floor

0   10   20 metres
0   50 feet

The Elizabeth Garrett Anderson Hospital for Women was opened in 1891.

131

University of London and offer a broad cross-section of education and teaching covering the law, modern languages, engineering and the sciences amongst which medicine featured, and achieved a legal charter in 1829. Initially medical students attended lectures and dissections in the Strand buildings but clinical work had to be carried out in neighbouring hospitals such as Charing Cross. Discipline initially was poor, with students skipping chapel attendance and some of the staff in trouble with the law, but discipline became tightened with a new Professor of Physiology in 1836, Robert Bentley Todd, and the examination requirements of the Society of Apothecaries and College of Surgeons.

As with UCH the need for clinical facilities increased, but an approach to Charing Cross for cooperation was rejected and it was decided to develop its own hospital. In 1839 a workhouse in nearby Portugal Street was converted into a teaching hospital with 120 beds. This was located in one of the worst slum districts in London and patients multiplied tenfold to over 30,000 within ten years making relocation essential, accentuated from the pressure of 'noxious gases' issuing from the corpses rotting in the adjacent burial ground. As a solution a new hospital was built on site in 1861, but in 1913 it was moved to its present site at Denmark Hill. In 1923 a dental school was added, and within the NHS, the hospital was given Teaching Hospital status. Under the 1974 reorganisation it became the centre for all health service management in its area.

By 1861 England and Wales had 23 voluntary teaching hospitals and 130 voluntary general hospitals providing free treatment for both in-patients and out-patients, and the beds available had risen from 4,000 in 1800 to 12,000. In Ireland the first voluntary hospital was opened in Dublin in 1718 and was followed by six more by 1773. By 1804 there was at least one general infirmary in every county in the country – partly state funded, but mainly supported by charity – along with many dispensaries.

Chapter 5

Succour for the Sick Poor
or Gateways of Death

In spite of the euphemistic claims made by their developers, the voluntary hospitals were to acquire an increasingly bad reputation during their first 150 years of existence – even to be labelled 'gateways of death'. In an article published in *Population Studies* (1956) two leading medical historians, McKeown and Brown, writing about hospital work in the 18th century, stated that any patient admitted was likely to contract a fatal infection and it was only much later that they could be reasonably certain of dying from the disease with which they were admitted. Such comment might not have allowed for the appalling social conditions at that time and the ignorance about the causes of infection, or the dangers of overcrowding, lack of sanitation and personal hygiene. These problems were pointed out by a number of people during the 18th century, although only slowly absorbed generally. Among the first was a Quaker cloth merchant, John Bellers (1654–1725), who wrote on public hygiene and the need for street cleaning, refuse collection and the regulation of obnoxious trades, such as abattoirs – public health measures that would only gradually become statutory over the next 200 years.

Two medical officers serving in the Army compared hospital and prison conditions. James Lind was Physician General to the British Army between 1742 and 1758 and had previously complained of the foul conditions of naval life, carrying out experiments to show citrus fruits cured scurvy, although unaware of the reason. He observed that armies 'lost more of their men by sickness than the sword' and attributed fevers to material generated by dirt and overcrowding. Working at Newgate prison, he described 'gaol fever' – typhus – and said that this was best prevented by personal hygiene and clean clothes. He recommended prisoners' old clothes should be burnt and replaced at public expense.

Another army surgeon of the time, James Pringle, in his *Observations on the Nature and Causes of Hospital Fevers*, described prisons as unclean and infectious places, where the seeds of infection seemed impossible to eliminate by scouring and vinegar, once they had been sown. The main killers of the time were the infectious diseases. Smallpox and typhoid were endemic, and there were frequent epidemics of typhus and cholera, from which people were as likely to die at home as in hospital. During the Plague the rich, along with the doctors, fled the city, whilst the poor had to remain. Their dead were collected in carts to be buried in communal pits. Any pest-houses, as in Finsbury and Westminster, were provided by the parishioners themselves.

The attitude of the general hospitals towards infectious diseases would vary from hospital to hospital and even change year by year. In general overt cases of smallpox, for example, were refused, but the disease might only develop after admission. This could lead to an epidemic and enforce the closure of wards or the entire hospital before separate isolation units or fever hospitals were created. Scottish hospitals were an exception to the rule, and during its first five years 14% of admissions to Glasgow Infirmary were fever cases.

Gradually hospitals came to accept a social responsibility towards patients with infectious diseases and were under increasing pressure to accept them during epidemics. They began to isolate them initially in separate wards and, as demand increased, in detached buildings. Chester General Infirmary was one of the first to admit such cases into two fever wards as a deliberate policy, under strict regulations. The patients and nurses were not allowed into other parts of the hospital and any visitors had to be accompanied by an apothecary. Manchester Infirmary created an isolation unit for patients who developed a fever after admission, located at first in wards above a newly built out-patient department, then in 1796 in a separate 'house of recovery' where fever patients for two miles around could be accepted.

The industrial towns were breeding grounds for a whole range of contagious diseases that included measles and diphtheria along with epidemics of typhus and cholera, and the success of the Manchester experiment led other hospitals to follow suit and open 'wards of prevention' or take over separate premises. Faced with typhus epidemics in 1817, Aberdeen Infirmaries took over unoccupied army barracks where the matron and several nurses contracted typhus themselves and died, and in 1822 Salisbury Hospital purchased the old county jail. The local authorities opened some fever hospitals, but their facilities were totally inadequate to cope with epidemics and the

134

voluntary area was under constant pressure to open up new facilities. The resources would again be overwhelmed during the cholera epidemics during the first half of the 19th century, with most London hospitals refusing to accept cases in the earlier outbreaks. With each a Cholera Board was established to apply pressure, and St Thomas's and Bart's set up a separate building, while the London Hospital bore the brunt of the last epidemic. Unfortunately, the board would be abolished between each outbreak and no facilities were left in hand to meet the next. The first separate fever hospital – the Institution for the Care and Prevention of Contagious Fever in the Metropolis – was opened in 1802, but it was 1866 before a Sanitary Act empowered the local sewer authority to provide and maintain hospitals if they wished. Only London responded then, and it was not until the 1875 Public Health Act that local authorities generally began to provide adequate facilities.

There was no attempt to separate the different categories of fever cases and they were all herded together in a single unit. During the first few decades of the 19th century it became standard practice to isolate fever patients in separate units, but towards the middle of the century opinion began to swing back to admitting a small proportion of such cases into the general wards, especially in the larger London hospitals. This was partly because these were considered essential teaching material and partly because the main fever was now enteric and with improved sanitation did not spread as virulently as smallpox and typhus. A survey in 1842 showed strong support for this both in London and the provinces, provided the proportion was kept low. A later survey in 1860 recorded that 8 out of 11 London hospitals maintained this policy, but only 5 of 20 provincial ones. This was in spite of the fact that the mortality rate amongst fever patients was more than double the general rate. In the first six months of 1861 272 cases of typhus and scarletina were admitted to the general wards of six London hospitals. They communicated their infection to 71 persons, of whom 21 died, and for the same year the death rate at the London Fever Hospital was 18.2%.

Outbreaks of the epidemic diseases were gradually brought under control by their isolation and the introduction of adequate sanitation, but besides these the hospitals were creating their own internal diseases. Before 1800 surgical operations were restricted to a minimum due to the risks of shock and infection. In Glasgow in its first three years there were only three operations in 960 admissions, and 41 of

135

803 in-patients in 1800. The scope of these was largely restricted to amputations, cutting for stone, opening abscesses and cataract. Another factor was the limitation of surgical training and knowledge of anatomy due to the lack of bodies available for dissection. Even at that time wound infection was a major problem and part of hospital life. A healthy discharge of pus from the wound was 'laudable', but often it would enter the circulation to cause pyaemia or septicaemia. In the latter part of the 18th century a Scottish surgeon, John Bell, wrote that 'no operation dare be performed, every cure stands still, every wound becomes a sore and every sore is apt to run into gangrene'. At the time the hospital mortality of surgical cases was three to five times as high as patients treated privately at home. These hospital infections were the classical ones, identified with specific organisms today – streptococcal erysipelas, staphylococcal pyaemia and gangrene – while the term phagadaemia covered sloughing sores. It was recognised early on that their incidence related to standards of hospital crowding and cleanliness, and surgical results were much better at Leeds, Northampton and Glasgow than in the overcrowded, dirty conditions in Newcastle and the large London hospitals.

The most famous of commentators on hospital conditions at this time was John Howard, better known for his work on prison reform. As High Sheriff of Bedford he would visit the prisons, and a part from the appalling conditions, found the gaolers were unpaid and dependent for their living on payments levied from the prisoners. As a result prisoners admitted on remand and found not guilty were often kept in prison for months until they could pay their 'gaol delivery' fees, so he persuaded Parliament to legislate that these should be paid from the rates. He then turned his attention to hospital standards, comparing individually those in London and the provinces. He placed Leeds top of his list and commented that 'their ideal conditions ensured many compound fractures were cured that would have resulted in amputation in the unventilated and offensive wards elsewhere'. He suggested the money spent on de-bugging would be better spent on beating and washing the beds, and also recommended the separation of medical and surgical patients.

His comments were often resented, but gradually the general principles were accepted and applied. He was especially critical of conditions in the London hospitals as compared with many in the provinces, although in fairness many of these had been purpose-built and were under less pressure at the time. He noted the old wards at Guy's still

An early nineteenth century hospital scene, depicted by Rowlandson.

had wooden beds which were infested with bugs – at the time it still retained a bug-catcher on the permanent staff, at a salary equal to the doctors'. St George's and the Westminster had sanded floors and their walls needed white-washing, and at the London the beds were old and crowded against the walls.

As the number of surgical cases rose during the early part of the 19th century as a result of the population expansion and industrial injuries, the incidence of these hospital diseases rose dramatically and continued to rise throughout the century until the introduction of antiseptic techniques. At times they reached epidemic proportions and forced the closure of wards or even entire hospitals for cleansing or rebuilding. The problem extended from the London hospitals out to even the smallest provincial ones and in the early 1820s Leeds had to undergo a complete rebuilding programme due to the number of cases of gangrene. At Sheffield General Infirmary 6 of 14 amputation cases died from sloughing sores and erysipelas in spite of reconstructing its drains, and the surgeons were afraid to operate because of the 'black fever'. The major London and Scottish hospitals were especially affected and a survey of 117 hospitals in 1863 showed an operative death rate of 8.43%, which rose to 15.3% if minor operations such as cataract were excluded, with little difference between the provinces and London. The average death rate for all amputations was 20–25%, ranging from under 10% at the level of the foot or hand to over 50% at the thigh or upper arm. The lithotomy rate ranged from 10% to 20% according to the age of the patient and size of the stone. In Birmingham there was a great reduction in erysipelas cases when bed numbers were reduced, separate wards added for infected cases and a new drainage system installed. Even the staff were not without their risks. In 1813 Sir George Blake, a physician at St Thomas's, said that when he was appointed in 1783 infection prevailed so much that his two immediate predecessors and one surgeon had died the previous year of fever caught in the hospital, but since the number of beds was reduced and new methods of ventilation and cleanliness were adopted no medical attendant had died during his 30 years' service.

This was not a problem unique to voluntary hospitals here. Results were reputedly worse at the Hôtel Dieu in Paris and in the United States. Dr George Dock, a lecturer at the University of Michigan, in 1904 told his students that 'in my undergraduate years every surgical case got erysipelas – it was considered part of hospital life'.

The advent of anaesthesia in 1846 extended the scope of surgeons but did not improve results, and hernia and other abdominal operations carried a high mortality. Such figures only related to open surgery; the bulk of surgical cases admitted were superficial and carried little risk, with an overall death rate half that of medical beds, where many of the patients suffered serious organic disease.

Slowly basic standards were introduced throughout the hospital system, walls were white-washed regularly and the floors scrubbed. Iron beds replaced wooden and testers were removed. Ceilings were raised, and there was proper ward ventilation. Fresh bed linen and night clothes were supplied for each patient and stoves for heating the wards. Old cesspools and privies were replaced and surgical and medical cases separated. Initially there appears to have been some improvement. Overall very little had changed in the picture over the past 100 years. Lawson-Tait, a leading Guy's surgeon, pointed out in an 'Essay on Hospital Mortality' that the figures for Guy's had only fallen by 1% from 1780 and suggested standards of hygiene had not advanced as far as they should.

Mortality figures peaked in the third quarter of the 19th century and there was a flood of literature on the ability of hospitals to carry out their function properly. This focused on construction and siting of hospitals, their ventilation and sanitation, although some emphasised that overcrowding and dirtiness could be equally to blame. Florence Nightingale advocated separate pavilion-like structures in the countryside in place of the high-rise blocks in the city centres and support for her views stimulated a government inquiry which Dr J.S. Bristowe and Mr T. Holmes were appointed to carry out. They were the two leading advocates of hospital reform of their day, studying both state and voluntary systems, and their report, *The Hospitals of the United Kingdom, 6th Report of the Medical Officer of the Privy Council 1863*, opted against the pavilion system on the grounds of cost and inaccessibility, whilst acknowledging that in some of the older hospitals the wards were small and close with long narrow ill-ventilated corridors, and these conditions could pre-dispose to the production of hospital disease. Amongst the hundreds of papers about the subject, there were few that paid any attention to medical or nursing standards, and staff personal hygiene in particular, which was non-existent before bacteria had been identified.

From earliest days surgery was a theatrical performance, with the leading surgeons amongst the stars of their day. A surgeon would invite his colleagues, students and even the public to watch his weekly operating session. The usual pattern was for him to enter the adjacent operating theatre from the dissecting room, where he had been demonstrating, at the head of his students, and don his old frock coat, kept hanging on the back of the door especially for use at operations and matted with blood and filth from previous use. One surgeon was especially proud that he had inherited the coat used by a famous predecessor throughout his career. Threaded through the lapel were the silk ligatures ready for stitching the wound. The patient was strapped onto a wooden operating table, with sawdust on the floor to soak up the blood. The surgery itself was a cut and thrust affair; his reputation rested on his speed and dexterity more than the final outcome. One could amputate a leg through the hip joint in 90 seconds, and many would continue this pattern, even when anaesthetics had been introduced. Sydney Jones, a senior surgeon at St Thomas's during the latter half of the 19th century, would turn up the collar of his old frock coat, pick up a knife which he had dropped on the floor and after cutting two long flaps, reach behind him without turning for an assistant to place a saw in his hand. He would cut

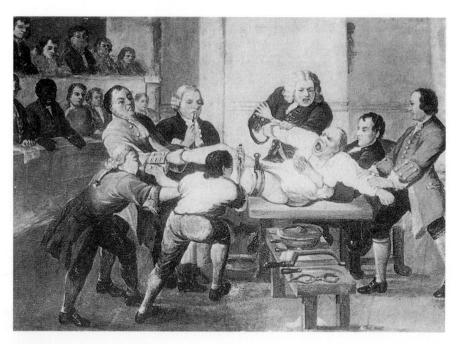
Surgery before anaesthesia.

through the bone, leaving the limb in the hands of a dresser, whilst he walked away to wash his hands. A nurse would help him off with his coat, to display an immaculate white waistcoat and the large diamond tie-pin with his initials S.J. which he always wore.

Things only began to change when Lister introduced antiseptics into surgery in 1867 at Glasgow Infirmary by the use of carbolic acid. In the previous three years 16 out of 34 amputation cases died from infection, whilst in the next three years only 6 out of 40. He based his theory on the experimental researches of Louis Pasteur, who had shown the presence of living cells in fermentation, and concluded wound infection could be the result of contamination by organisms in the air, in water and on the instruments, patient's skin and surgeon's hands. He would use carbolic acid as a general disinfectant, but he found stronger concentrations of carbolic damaging to the patient's tissues and the surgeon's hands. His ultimate technique was to envelop the operation site in a towel soaked in 5% carbolic acid for two hours pre-operatively; and after the patient was anaesthetised and the limb raised to drain it of blood before applying a tourniquet, towels soaked in carbolic were placed under the limb. The instruments were sterilised

140

Antiseptic surgery with a carbolic spray, introduced in 1865.

and the surgeon and assistant would scrub up using carbolic – although Lister operated in his outdoor clothes – and the operation was performed under a cloud of carbonised vapour from a steam spray. The wound was stitched with a rubber drain inserted and covered by a gauze dressing over oiled silk overlain with a thin mackintosh cloth to retain the carbolic acid, but allow drainage.

Lister was appointed Professor of Clinical Surgery at King's College Hospital in 1877 and the technique was adopted by most major London and several provincial hospitals within a couple of years, although the belief that sepsis and infectious diseases were due to atmospheric impurities generated by decomposing animal and vegetable material, damp and filth persisted! Following a lecture by Lister to the BMA in 1871, an article in the *Lancet* sneered that 'disbelievers in the marvellous efficiency of carbolic acid could not fail to notice that with every public appearance professor Lister's solutions become weaker and weaker, whilst his faith appears to grow more and more'. A famous surgeon of the time, Robert Lawson Tait, claimed he achieved equal success without the use of carbolic, but he would wash

141

his hands before operating, against the pattern of the time. Alternative disinfectants were tried as carbolic acid was too irritant to the tissues for internal surgery, but gradually it was realised that the key feature was a strict aseptic technique, and Lister himself gave up using carbolic towards the end of the century.

In the 17th century polypharmacy was at its height, and a summary of the meddlesome medicine of the time is an account of the treatment of Charles II after a stroke in 1685. He was bled twice in succession, followed by cupping-glasses applied to his shoulders and deep scarification. He was given an antimony emetic of which he could only swallow part, followed by zinc sulphate, purgatives and enemas. His hair was shorn and blistering agents applied to the head, along with a red-hot cautery. The 12 doctors concerned said that 'nothing was left untried' and Charles is said to have apologised for 'taking so long to die under their care'.

Numerous pharmacopoeias based on plant and animal ingredients were published throughout Europe during the 17th and 18th centuries, and it was only in the *5th London Pharmacopoeia* of 1746 that such delicacies as human fat, spider webs, moss from human skulls and unicorn's horn were excluded. Most remaining animal material was removed in the 6th 1786 edition, and more active ingredients were introduced, especially cathartics and opium derivatives as well as a new range of mineral and metallic drugs that the pharmacists of the day were producing. Herbal remedies such as willow bark, with an action similar to aspirin, and foxglove containing digitalis would prove to be beneficial, but most of the others were more likely to do harm than any good. Calomel purges, based on mercurous chloride (which was also an ingredient of the popular 'blue pills' which were in every physician's bag), and lead- or mercury-based medicines, would cause violent purgation with severe colic, for which belladonna and other antispasmodics would be given, causing further poisoning. This was similar to the pattern today when many of the powerful drugs given for an anticipated beneficial response cause side effects that lead to a chain reaction of remedies to neutralise these. The *British National Formulary* of today, updated every six months by the Joint Formulary Committee, which promotes safe and effective use of medicines and is used by doctors as their 'bible' for treatment, contains sections on cautions and the side effects of drugs that are often far larger than the

Cornerstones of eighteenth century medicine: bleeding, dosing and enemas.

sections on indications and dosage. More than 10% of hospital admissions today are due to the effects of the drugs rather than the illness for which they have been used.

In 1784 a writer of the time stated that 'indisputable facts' convinced him 'that the established practise of physic in England was infinitely destructive of the lives of His Majesty's subjects' and he preferred the practice of old women unacquainted with the powerful articles of the *Materia Medica*.

The other great vogue in medicine was the extraction of blood by one means or another, and overall few patients left hospital with as much as on entry. There were three main techniques for bleeding the patient. Direct venesection goes back to Hippocratic times and was continued by Celsus during the days of the Roman Empire. It is mentioned in Islamic teaching and the Talmud – the Jewish book written in AD 500. During the monastic era it fell into disrepute and monks were forbidden to draw blood, although during the 16th century exotic anatomical charts were published that showed the sites to be chosen for letting blood. It was popular in Italy and expensive Venetian bleeding-cups became family heirlooms. It was used with discretion by Thomas Sydenham during the last half of the 17th century, but then became indiscriminate and a universal practice as the main remedy in most hospitals. Often a special room was set aside for the purpose when hospitals were developed during the 18th century, as at Bristol, where the out-patients were seated on a bench whilst the apothecary tied a ligature around an arm and opened a vein. The patient was given a basin and left to catch his own blood. Up to 30 patients a day would be bled, and one surgeon is reputed to have taken 47 gallons of blood over seven months, a level that would match a Red Cross blood bank today. The fervour persisted through the next century and peaked with a French physician who bled his patients repeatedly, removing up to three litres from those suffering from pneumonia. Rush, the 'founding father' of American medicine, introduced the practice there with equal enthusiasm when he returned home after studying in Edinburgh. Bleeding a patient until he fainted from the loss of blood was also used as a means of anaesthesia before reducing a hernia or dislocation.

Another popular and safer means of extracting blood was by cupping, using either a wet technique involving scarification of the

144

skin, or a dry method drawing blood to the surface using a heated cupping glass to create a vacuum and draw blood to the surface. At St Thomas's up to a third of medical cases were treated by cupping, over a thousand a year, peaking at over 1,700 in 1840 at a fee of 2s a time. During the first part of the 19th century an increasingly popular approach was the use of leeches. A large leech could extract two drachms of blood; at St Thomas's the number used increased to over 50,000 in 1822, costing 8% of the total expenditure on all medical and surgical supplies, from 10,000 four years earlier. At Bart's use peaked at 100,000 in 1837, an average of 17 for each individual in-patient.

Views on the overall results of hospital care during the 18th and 19th centuries are very variable, but it is clear that death rates worsened during the second and third quarters of the latter, as surgery increased and became more intrusive with the introduction of anaesthesia. The statistics in relation to the medical reasons for admission and the outcome of treatment are hard to interpret, as earlier annual reports only recorded admissions and deaths. The chartered hospitals would report to the Lord Mayor and Court of Aldermen of the City of London annually on Easter Monday at the 'Spittal Sermons preached at St Bridget's Church'; during the first decades of the 18th century each hospital admitted some 5,000 patients annually, with a death rate around 6–8%. Figures for the London and larger provincial hospitals were similar and although in their earlier years the rates in the smaller provincial hospitals were much lower, they tended to catch up as pressure increased.

The diseases treated were either not published or referred to, or labelled under vague headings that were purely symptomatic or based on external appearance: 'lowness of spirits or extreme weakness, colicky flux or pain in the limbs, dropsy or scorbutical fistulous ulcers'. Any type of abscess was labelled an 'impostumation'. Diagnostic aids were non-existent at the time. Laennec did not introduce the stethoscope until 1819, when he was called on to examine a stout young lady with suspected heart trouble and found it embarrassing to place his ear to her chest. He remembered that sound was conducted along a wooden beam, and used a tightly rolled sheath of paper to conduct the sound of the heartbeat. There was no knowledge of bacteriology, and infection was thought to be carried by putrid miasma.

As hospitals became established and the number of patients increased, details of their management lessened and it became increasingly difficult to compare results. The administrators would wish to present subscribers with the most favourable picture of turnover and outcome, and inevitably this could lead to practices that would make comparisons invalid. One was to label all discharges as 'cured'. Another important factor was the admissions policy and the cases included in published figures. In general the London and larger provincial hospitals would include those dead on arrival or dying within 24 hours, and this could add 1% to the overall death rate – at St Bartholomew's these accounted for one sixth of recorded deaths. Many county hospitals would refuse such cases admission; the Radcliffe in Oxford was even accused of discharging terminally ill patients before they died. Positive massaging of admission totals could be achieved by adding the number of patients in the wards to the year's admissions or by issuing a re-admission ticket to in-patients every six or eight weeks, which could inflate the total by as much as 25%. Overall these measures could reduce the death rate by 1%. Each patient would occupy a bed on average from 32 to 35 days, and it was often evident that the total number of admissions contradicted this figure.

It was thus impossible to compare hospital with hospital, or even year by year results. In London and the provinces a greater proportion of admissions were to the surgical wards, and due to the superficial nature of most of these cases, the death rate was only half that of the medical wards, where admissions were more urgent or patients were suffering from serious organic disease. At Guy's and the Sheffield Royal Infirmary during 1862, the medical figures were around 14.5%, compared with just over 6% on the surgical side. Such results were to influence admission policy towards medical cases.

The terminally ill, or those with incurable diseases such as cancer or Bright's disease of the kidneys, would be refused admission, along with those suffering from tuberculosis of the lungs, which carried a mortality rate around 40%. The preference was for acute cases which would show a relatively higher rate of spontaneous recovery and enable a rapid turnover.

Gradually comprehensive returns began to be published and a report on 27 hospitals for 1830 gave an average mortality rate of 4.5%, ranging from under 2% at Winchester County to a peak of 9.5% at Bristol Infirmary, whilst in 1835 it was noted that St Bartholomew's had not risen above 8.3% during the previous 45 years, although the average in the other London hospitals had risen to over 11%. It was not until 1834 that the Government held an inquiry into the nature of hospital admissions, but this only requested division of the patients into acute and chronic, without any specific details. Altogether 117 hospitals completed a questionnaire in 1863 with an overall mortality rate of 7.69%, and over 9% in London – but Manchester had peaked to 13.6%, although over half of the deaths were dying on admission. Bristowe and Holmes, in their report to the Privy Council on the hospitals of the United Kingdom in 1863, pointed out that the wide variation in death rates between different hospitals, especially town and rural hospitals, was due to the nature of the cases admitted rather than hospital conditions or standards of treatment.

One of the more important factors that led to higher rates in London and the larger provincial cities was the steady increase in serious accident cases following industrialisation and the building of the railways and expansion of the docks. The London Hospital in the East End of London treated over 12,000 accident cases in that year, of whom 2,180 were admitted, and in Sheffield 30 of 1,206 in-patients were accidents. Annual turnover in hospital beds ranged from 13 at Liverpool General to under 6 in Colchester. The lower death rate in the smaller provincial hospitals could be attributed at least partly to their strict observation of the admission rules and selecting cases with a minimal mortality. The Royal Devon and Exeter, with a rate of 1 in 35, selected skin patients, for whom their physicians had acquired a reputation.

In the mid 19th century William Farr was appointed as the first Registrar-General and introduced a standard classification of diseases. By then selective control and knowledge made a higher standard of diagnosis possible, and hospitals used this increasingly during the 1860s, although it was not compulsory. Unfortunately he made a major statistical error in his calculations by relating the total patient deaths for an entire year to the number of hospital patients on a single day, to give a mortality percentage of 90.4% for the London hospitals! This particular statistical aberration was demolished by Drs Bristowe and Holmes, and the overall death rate in the third quarter of the 19th century in the larger hospitals probably peaked around 10%, whilst in the smaller hospitals such as Salisbury General it rose to 5.8% from 2.2% in 1840. These results matched any in Europe and the United States, and the voluntary hospitals continued to attract sufficient charitable donations to ensure their development during the 19th and 20th centuries into the respected institutions which form the framework of the National Health Service today.

The dependence on charity for hospital provision was personal to Britain and its limitations were emphasised by the *British Journal of Homeopathy* in 1856. The purpose of the article was to compare our hospital system with the alternatives practised in Europe, not in relation to treatment, which was much the same everywhere, but to see if there were any useful features regarding administration and financing.

In practice the Poor Law did little to meet the needs of the sick poor, and the voluntary hospitals also did little to help them. Subscribers, who had the power to recommend admissions, would be bribed by those with influence to favour their own sick servants or poor relatives.

In France there was a free state-funded system with all the advantages and drawbacks of the NHS today. Hospitals and asylums could only be opened with Government authorisation and were under the direct control of the Ministry of the Interior. Altogether there were 1,270 institutions under 123 governing bodies – *administrations hospitallers* – each averaging five members including three lawyers and the mayor as ex-officio president, who would give their services free, with one member retiring annually.

In total it was calculated 31,500 people were involved in the management of the state system, 6,000 in administration, 2,000 nuns, 2,000 nurses, 1,500 physicians, 800 surgeons and 200 apothecaries. The asylums housed the elderly, incurable, insane and orphans. In Paris the hospitals were regulated by a council of 20, including a Government-nominated Director General and the police chief. Admissions were controlled by a central bureau of 18 paid doctors who were on the hospital staff, directly appointed for a number of years by the Minister of the Interior. Eligible sick poor seeking admission would present themselves to the bureau, who would allocate admission tickets related to a daily statement of bed vacancies according to medical need. Emergencies were admitted at once. The bureau could also arrange state welfare benefit for the blind and paralysed as well as sanitary and support equipment ranging from urinals to dressings, crutches and even wooden legs.

Each doctor looked after 80–100 patients and carried out daily rounds with his pupils. External students were taken on by examination and interns chosen from amongst them. A surgeon and an apothecary were on duty night and day for every 300 patients. Nursing was by Sisters of Charity or matrons assisted by unskilled aides, one for each eight patients. Overall there were 7,000 hospital beds, one for every 150 of the dependent population. Each bed cost £25 a year to maintain and was occupied by 12–13 patients each in a year, on average for 24 days at a cost of £1 17s 4¾d per head. In London by contrast, there were only 4,200 beds, one for each 300 of the population, costing £41 per annum to maintain, to house 8–9 patients in a year for an average of 34 days each at a cost of £4 9s 9½d per head. The funding for the French hospitals and asylums was primarily from the Government and there was even a special levy on all theatre and concert tickets.

In Austria the hospital system was self-financing through a levy imposed directly on the patients, or those responsible for their support. This pattern would be adopted by the English voluntary hospital system, with assessment by lady almoners. At Vienna there was one vast complex comprising up to 4,000 beds, one for each 1,000 of the population. Donations or endowments for any other new hospitals were forbidden. There was an annual intake of 38,000 a year, each at a cost of £1 4s a year. Patients were divided into three classes, paying 2s 8d, 1s 8¼d and (for Viennese citizens) 6¾d daily. Guilds would make an annual contract to cover their members and an employer had to pay for his servant's fees. The destitute would be quizzed as to any family who could pay, whilst if not Viennese the bill would be sent to their parish, or the embassy if from abroad. There was one doctor employed for every 70 beds, which were open to all medical cases except the chronic sick and children under four.

The *British Journal of Homeopathy* report compared the voluntary hospital system with the Poor Law situation, which offered hospital accommodation to over half of those who required it, 'unostentatiously, and maybe shabbily and inefficiently, but does it after a fashion, and if this failed the voluntary system could not cope with a moiety of the sick poor who would besiege their doors'.

In 1848 there were 38 London workhouses with 3,172 single and 217 double hospital beds. In 22 there were no paid regular nurses and nursing was mainly by pauper inmates glad to work for the addition of an ounce or two of meat, a glass of beer and an ounce of tobacco.

149

On average there was only one visiting medical officer to each 84 beds, at Whitechapel only one to the 134 beds. With a few exceptions, they were paid a pittance as low as £110 p.a., from which they had to provide medicines. The workhouses were often poorly located, with 23 of those in London in the immediate vicinity of a cesspool or open sewer, burial ground, slaughterhouse or tallow melter. Ward conditions were deplorable with overcrowding and lack of ventilation. Space averaged 400/500 cubic feet per patient, but was as low as 132 cubic feet at Christchurch. As a result workhouses were in poor odium with the working classes and deterred all but the most desperate.

The voluntary hospital contrasted in every way. They were noble buildings in a salubrious background with clean, lofty wards giving up to 2,000 cubic feet of space to every patient, with separate beds, clean linen and baths. There were skilled visiting medical staff, resident doctors and dressers, along with well-trained nurses. Food was good, with plenty of beer and even wine or port. The 16 general hospitals listed 4,068 beds with 82 consultant surgeons and physicians – one to every 50 beds – a resident apothecary and 50 visiting medical officers, ophthalmic and aural surgeons and dentists.

At the endowed hospitals the medical staff were relatively well paid. At St Thomas's by 1853 the salaries of the physicians and surgeons had risen to £300 p.a. and the apothecary was paid £600, whilst the matron only received £160 and the sister £50 p.a. Apart from private practice, most of the visiting doctors' income came from lecturing and pupils, who could pay over £1,000 for a training course.

The report went on to criticise the fund-raising activities and proliferating expenditure of the voluntary hospitals. The prominence of their appeals for money through the media of the time, newspaper advertisements, junk mail and private solicitations, 'made the words "hospital" and "charity" synonymous' and 'makes us forget the Poor Law system professes to relieve our sick and infirm poor as well as the unemployed and offers hospital accommodation to fully half of those who require it'. The term 'public hospitals' was as big a misnomer as 'public schools', with no student instructions or articles to describe doctors' practices, no annual reports, and nothing known about their patients.

The only London hospitals anyone heard about were the endowed and charitable ones. 'Who thinks of workhouse hospitals – where do students go, or renowned surgeons, and fashionable physicians work? To which hospitals is it an honour to be appointed and vacant posts arduously canvassed? Which do medical journals write about and show to overseas colleagues?'

The range of costing for the specialist units was even greater, from £12 p.a. for a fever or child centre to £116 p.a. at the Soho Square Hospital for Women at the top, followed by the Orthopaedic Hospital. Overall it was considered many of the voluntary hospitals' managements were lavish, without any proper checks on their expenditure, and could serve twice as many patients with proper financial control.

The article concludes with wide-ranging proposals for total reform of the hospital system in the United Kingdom, which was negligible in many parts, and there was a need for a parliamentary investigation to give all the facts, with details of the number of beds, costs, mortality and list of employees. Recommendations included a special Board of Commissioners to superintend all general hospitals, covering the Poor Law, endowed and charitable, with separate workhouses to serve any hospital function with a minimum of 164 cubic feet per patient. Doctors should be paid as in France and Vienna, not appointed by the governors, and not contracted to supply medicines, which encouraged them to short-change patients. Funding should be a state responsibility, with a special hospital tax levied by the Home Secretary. Those who could afford should pay a contribution to their expenses and, as in France, there should be mutual benefit societies for workers. The number of beds in London should be doubled and at a cost of £30 each should only total half a million pounds. Beds should be available for admission before any illness became severe.

Chapter 6

First State Hospitals: Workhouses, Metropolitan Asylums Board, Municipal Hospitals

The State role in the English hospital system was initially totally destructive and then wholly negative until the middle of the 19th century. The existing limited monastic network was closed down by Henry VIII with a few minor exceptions and, apart from the rehabilitation of St Bartholomew's and St Thomas's in London as small units, there was no replacement until the voluntary hospital development. In the feudal era there had been a sense of social responsibility by the landowning clergy and nobility towards their local poor and handicapped, but this was not inherited by the new rich class.

The first part of the 15th century was relatively secure as the feudal system was gradually replaced by small farmers with their own land. Labour was scarce, due to recurrent plagues and the freedom to move to small towns in search of higher wages in the new industries such as wool and shipping. The seasonally employed farm labourers could reinforce their wages by cultivating strips of land, hunting, fishing and poaching.

All this was to alter in the second half of the century with the change in farming techniques. Land that had been open to all, even including village commons, was enclosed by hedges to improve efficiency and converted from arable land to pasture for sheep. 'Where 40 persons had their living now one shepherd and his dog hath all.' Whole villages were closed down and many landless labourers, displaced and reinforced by discharged soldiers after the French wars and the Wars of the Roses, formed bands of 'sturdy beggars roaming the country and threatening towns and farms'.

During the Tudor period strong central government was imposed and the Privy Council introduced a network of draconian legislation to restore law and order when an economic crisis resulted from the rampant inflation which doubled the cost of living. Enforcement was by newly appointed local authorities composed of Justices of the

Peace. A new form of state serfdom was introduced by an Act passed in 1563 that was to remain in force until the restoration of Charles II in 1660. Any able-bodied man between the ages of 12 and 60 not apprenticed or in employment was compelled to serve in bondage to a landowner for a year, even being branded alongside the cattle with the letter 'R' on his shoulder. To control inflation the maximum wages of artisans and labourers were fixed, to be reviewed annually in relation to the price of bread.

There was no relief for the sick or aged until a few workhouses were opened after a Poor Law Act was passed in 1601 by Elizabeth I, two years before she died. This Act compelled the local parish JPs to provide necessary relief for the 'blind, lame, impotent, old and such others unable to work', to be funded by a 'poor-rate tax' imposed on property owners. They could also set up cottage industries for the able-bodied, pay the rent and apothecary fees of paupers and bring up orphan children, before selling them on into apprenticeship.

These two Acts established the 'poor' as a class legally entitled to claim relief through parish rates imposed on the 'landed gentry', with statutory wage control topped up by supplementary benefit during their working life and in old age. It was an experiment in state regulation on a vast scale that had been tried before in Rome and was to be repeated in modern times with disastrous results, due to misuse and loss of initiative. One of the problems was the traffic of labour around the country and into the towns in search of the most favourable terms, so an Act of Settlement was introduced in 1662, under which a labourer could lose his rights of relief and be returned to the parish where he was registered.

The cost of poor relief to the ratepayer rose from £1 million in 1700 to over £7 million by the end of the century as the population doubled. By then over a fifth of the whole nation was on relief, as the parish dole could be as much as three times the wages of a labourer and, once in receipt, the person would be reluctant to work again. In 1795 the county magistrates met at Speenhamland, a village in Berkshire, to discuss a proposal to enforce an increased minimal wage to ease the cost of supplementation from the rates. Instead, under pressure from the farmers' lobby, the basic wage for farm labourers was left unaltered, but they drew up a scale for every 'poor and industrious person' to receive a weekly supplement from the rates related to the size of his family and the price of bread, a system that spread throughout the country. As a result the large employing farmers paid miserly rates, often forcing the labourer to accept part in bad corn and beer, whilst the unemployment caused by land enclosure and conversion from arable to pasture farming was aggravated by increasing mechanisation, with increasing numbers displaced from their tied cottages. Many were to become 'pauperised', quite distinct in contemporary terms from being merely 'poor', and 28% of the population was on permanent or occasional relief by 1802. Rioting became widespread, burning down haystacks, destroying the new machinery and, in one case, killing 20,000 sheep. This climaxed in 1830 when a widespread Labourers' Revolt demanded a wage of 2s 6d a day, which was brutally suppressed. Several participants were hanged and many transported to the new colonies in Australia.

By now the smallholder and independent property-owning parishioners were forced to pay the massive increase in rates to support the cost of the system, and many were facing bankruptcy. In 1834 a Poor Law Amendment Act was passed by Parliament with the primary objective of reducing the burden on the ratepayer, who considered many of those on poor relief were merely unwilling to work.

Birmingham Union Workhouse.

The Act was devised by Edwin Chadwick, Secretary to a new central government authority of three Commissioners to enforce the rules. They divided the country into 21 districts, each under the oversight of an assistant commissioner, with some 600 unions of parishes, each under the control of a new elected board of guardians in place of the former paternalistic Justices of the Peace. Any form of outdoor relief was to be confined to a few sick poor, and a chain of work-houses would be created around the country, into which the unemployed would be compulsorily decanted. Families were broken up, with women and children sent to different workhouses. Conditions in these workhouses would be made as intolerable as possible to deter the workshy. All rights of citizenship were forfeited, discipline was harsh, food meagre and all were compelled to menial labour as if in prison.

In the early years the policy seemed to work. The number of paupers plummeted, allowing the poor rate to be reduced by 20%, but this was probably due mainly to a period of general prosperity. When Victoria came to the throne in 1837 a severe depression set in through crop and industrial failures, leading to the 'hungry forties'. Unemploy-ment rose above a million and as the workhouses filled to capacity conditions became increasingly worse. The situation was aggravated by the Irish potato famine and an outbreak of 'Irish Fever', when over a million died from typhus, dysentery and relapsing fever, and there was a mass migration to England.

Chadwick himself was carefully monitoring the progress of the workhouse system and soon realised many of those entering were sick or aged rather than idle and able-bodied. He advocated separate quarters for orphans and the elderly and infirmaries for the sick, all at public expense, but this was largely ignored and little effective action was taken before the Metropolitan Poor Act of 1867. Workhouse conditions continued to deteriorate as the boards of guardians were primarily concerned with saving ratepayers' money and one institution was as much as they were prepared to support. A distinguished lawyer of the time noted in 1852 that he had visited many prisons and hospi-tals in France and Germany, and the existing workhouses were a disgrace to England, with nothing comparable in Europe. In France medical cases were separated into *hospitaux*, aged and infirm into *hospices*, with separate, appropriate establishments for the blind, lunatics and idiots, bastard children and vagrants. Here there was a common *Malebolge* for all; it was shocking to every principle of reason and feeling of humanity that all these forms of wretchedness should be crowded together into one common abode.

Increasingly public attention was drawn to the appalling state of affairs of the average workhouse. In the lead were the efforts of John Walter in the Houses of Parliament, and articles ran in *The Times*, of which he was the owner. His crusade was highlighted by the exposure of a series of scandals which his special correspondents unravelled. One of these involved Eton Workhouse, which had a succession of masters, one discharged for incest and the next for gross incompetence. The replacement was a bullying retired sergeant major. He refused to allow a married woman to treat her young daughter, who was suffering from chilblains, and when she objected threw her down some stairs into the workhouse punishment cage, known as the Black Hole, a cell with an unglazed barred window, in solitary confinement for 24 hours. It was on Christmas Day, the temperature 20°F, and she had no bedding, food, water or even a chamber pot, so she had soiled the cell. He ordered her to clean it, and when she could not because she was frozen stiff, locked her up again. Sacked after the publicity, he was found to have scalded a small boy to death in his previous post by pouring a bucket of boiling water over him, claiming it was an accident.

Overall the death rate amongst the sick in a workhouse was one in four or five, double that of voluntary hospitals. The general attitude was reflected by a cynical article in *Blackwood's Magazine* after a severe winter in 1858, suggesting how ratepayer's money could be saved by using the bodies of those who had died in the workhouses. Instead of an expensive burial when a parish coffin cost 8s 6d, their skins should be flayed and tanned for leather, their bones carved into spoons and forks and their flesh made into a nourishing soup for the starving loved ones left behind.

The ultimate scandal related to Andover Union Workhouse in Hampshire, again mastered by a former sergeant major and his wife, who ran the place as a concentration camp. The daily work for the paupers was to grind animal bones to dust that was used as fertiliser, a common task at workhouses throughout the country approved by the Poor Law Commissioners. The starved paupers would fight for any scraps of meat, however rancid, adhering to the bones, some of which were found to be of human origin from a local graveyard that had been dug up to build a new church. The outcome of the publicity was that the existing Poor Law Commission, which had survived many earlier scandals, was replaced in 1847 by a board with a Minister of

State answerable to Parliament. There was still little response and the only action was to appoint a Select Committee of the House of Commons in 1861 to study poor relief in the country. After three years' labour it reported the system as basically satisfactory. The only recommendation was that cod liver oil and quinine, with some other expensive medicines, should be provided at the expense of the guardians instead of their medical officers.

In spite of the furore, workhouse conditions continued to deteriorate and public pressure mounted from several directions for improvement. On the medical front this was led by the *Lancet*, a rebel medical journal founded in 1823 where radical views targeted reform of the entire medical and hospital systems. It published fortnightly accounts of conditions in individual workhouses from information leaked by nurses who had worked on site and the findings of a team of three doctors formed in 1865 to inspect and report on the metropolitan ones. They highlighted the insanitary conditions and lack of equipment, with a single bedpan to a ward, lack of waterproof sheets and bed linen unchanged for weeks, flock beds crawling with maggots, and verminous inmates. Although standards varied from one union to another, according to the financial state of the board of guardians and the quality of officials employed, most workhouses were overcrowded, insanitary and badly ventilated. Altogether 39 out of 40 metropolitan workhouses agreed to be inspected by the doctors and overall 13 were rated as totally unfit for use as hospitals. Only one was up to standard, but the rest could be converted if the number of sick beds was halved and enough money provided.

Where any form of medical or nursing aid existed, the quality of care was far below standards in the voluntary hospitals. Workhouse medical officers were mostly part-time, often combining the post with that of district medical officer responsible for outdoor relief (i.e. outside the workhouse) and having to provide any medicines out of their meagre salaries. Although in theory outdoor relief should have been available for the sick and aged poor, it was often easier to decant these cases into the workhouse. Some unions rejected any form of outdoor relief, whilst mostly it was grossly inadequate with part in kind – one or two shillings, in London as low as 7¾d with a loaf of bread weekly.

The situation of the medical officers was made worse by inferior status to the workhouse master, often an imperious retired army NCO, and friction between them on standards of care was commonplace, with the master invariably supported by the board of guardians. The professional and social status of the medical profession was raised after the Registration Act of 1858 and when a Poor Law Medical Officers Board was founded in 1866, of the 40 metropolitan officers concerned 30 attended the first meeting in a militant mood demanding proper recognition.

Any nursing care would be mainly dependent on illiterate pauper inmates in return for an extra ration of food and beer. Even by 1865 there were only 142 paid nurses – few of whom had any training and many were often only made-up scrubbers – to look after 21,000 sick and aged in the London workhouses, and they spent most of their time supervising the pauper staff.

Nursing standards in the voluntary system were revolutionised in the second half of the 19th century with the establishment of nursing schools initiated by Florence Nightingale, but extension to the workhouse system was slow. Her first breakthrough came in 1864 when she sent a Miss Agnes Jones as matron with 12 trained nurses to Brownlow Hill Infirmary in Liverpool, a workhouse with over 1,200 sick paupers, at the request of a local philanthropist, William Rathbone. Within a month she had sacked 35 of the old pauper nurses and quarrelled with both the master and the board of guardians, but she enforced major changes before she died within a year from an infection picked up in the hospital. Nightingale was to keep up relentless pressure on the Poor Law Authorities and politicians of the time, including the Prime Minister, Lord Palmerston, before his death, who was an old friend.

She was joined by bands of charitable ladies, led by a Miss Louisa Twining, who formed a society in London to visit and read to the workhouse inmates, to bring some relief to the total monotony of their life. Many were illiterate, even Bibles were few, cards and gambling were forbidden and there were no facilities for passing the time. Of the inmates in the Cardiff workhouse it was said 'they lead a life that would be like that of a vegetable, were it not that they preserve the doubtful privilege of sensibility to pain and mental misery'. Branches of the society spread around the country. Members compiled information, which they published in a *Journal of the Workhouse*, and joined with other groups to form a National Association for the Promotion of Social Science to press for improvement in social conditions, supported by public figures such as Charles Dickens and the Archbishop of York.

Florence Nightingale drafted an ABC of recommendations for workhouse reform. 'A' was separation in appropriate institutions of the sick, insane, incurable and aged; 'B' that medical relief in London should be under one central management and 'C', the system should be funded by 'consolidation and general rate' and not out of parochial rates. These views were strongly opposed by the parsimonious guardians and an ill-informed Poor Law Board and Parliament that still regarded the Poor Law as a service to deal with the able-bodied pauper. The Poor Law Board had become largely ineffective by 1866 when the ex-officio members stopped meeting, and any decision-making was left to officials. There were only 13 inspectors to cover the country, of whom one had to cover the whole of London, with all real power in the hands of the guardians, who would pick and choose from the thousand Acts that had been poured out from the Board.

Matters were to come to a head with the death of two workhouse inmates from gross neglect, and the various critic factions combined to form an Association for the Improvement of the London Workhouse Infirmaries, with the support of the BMA and the Royal College of Physicians, and lay figures such as Charles Dickens, who had highlighted the state of children's homes in *Oliver Twist*. Under their pressure the Poor Law Board agreed to a review of the situation by Dr Edward Smith, the first medical practitioner appointed as an inspector,

Birmingham Asylum for Destitute Children.

160

and Mr Faunal, the Poor Law Inspector for London. Their radical proposals included a capitation system for paying workhouse doctors 10s per adult, with two children under 16 counting as one adult; and the appointment of another 130 paid nurses in London, with the abolition of pauper nurses, who were described as 'illiterate feeble old women, often with a vicious background and a love of drink that led them to beg and rob the sick'.

It was advocated that separate accommodation should be provided for the infectious, the aged, children and the mentally ill. Six thousand bedded hospital units should be built for London alone, so the sick could be removed from the workhouse, as well as dispensaries for the 'outdoor poor'. The first state hospitals would have trained nurses and doctors, and be able to serve large areas in acute medicine and surgery, which were at present confined to voluntary hospitals. All these measures should be funded from a general fund from the rates, and the Poor Law Board should be given the power to enforce these changes on the guardians.

These proposals aroused a mixed response, with strong opposition from the vested interests of the existing system. The voluntary hospitals feared the loss of their monopoly, with reduced numbers of patients and charity income. The established doctors feared a challenge to their status and to their private practice. The elected guardians resented their loss of power and the increase in the rates involved. Overall they were an uneducated and unqualified politically orientated group compared with the social elite running the voluntary hospitals, more concerned with saving money for the voting ratepayers than establishing a reasonable standard of medical care for the inmates. They adopted a 'coals in the bath' attitude that the poor were used to their present conditions and would not like lofty rooms, bright lighting, ventilation, cleanliness and order.

Although there had been little positive activity in the separation of the sick and aged from the able-bodied workhouse inmates during the middle of the 19th century, there was increasing realisation that disease was related to poverty and living conditions. Chadwick had initiated an inquiry by a medical team in 1842 to study the link, and their detailed reports soon confirmed the facts. In London and the large towns tens of thousands existed in insanitary conditions of overcrowded poverty, with polluted water supplies and rat-infested cesspools overflowing into the streets where all the garbage was emptied, creating breeding grounds for endemic and epidemic infectious diseases. The registration of births, marriages and deaths became compulsory in 1836 and William Farr, a statistician in the Registrar General's department, produced a classification of diseases and an index that related life expectancy to wealth, occupations and hygiene and explained the poor health and short life span of the poor. In the East End of London a labourer's life expectancy was under 20 years, whilst in the wealthy West End it was 46.

Although infectious diseases were still regarded as due to air-borne miasma from decaying matter, Chadwick initiated a range of measures to improve public health conditions nationally. A Royal Commission was set up, and a succession of Acts culminated in 1848 when the first British Public Health Act was passed, by which the Government assumed overall responsibility for public health conditions. Chadwick intended the cost to be met from central taxation and the scheme to be run by trained government servants salaried by the State, with the boards of guardians' role relegated to that of inspectors, but in fact the cost was thrown onto the ratepayer.

The Commissioners had limited powers of enforcement, with no parliamentary representation and lacked any real authority, so the guardians could pick and choose as they thought fit amongst the measures put forward. They could only be forced to adopt them on petition by 10% of ratepayers in any parish, or if the annual death rate was higher than 23 per 1,000. The ratepayers now included every property owner and business, many of whom were satisfied with existing services and could not see any need for new services for the poor, who did not pay rates.

The local authorities were overwhelmed by waves of new Acts and Amendments that were to total over 1,000 over the ensuing years. These ranged from new sanitary measures covering sewage and waste disposal, removal of 'nuisances' and the supervision of 'offensive' trades such as tanneries and slaughter houses. They could appoint a local medical officer of health, provide burial grounds and improve homes considered unfit for human habitation.

By 1853 some of the Acts had been adopted by 103 towns, but there was intense opposition to government intrusion in local politics from vested interests. This was led by *The Times*, which stated 'we prefer to take our chance with cholera than be bullied into health by central government' and labelled the 'lawyer Chadwick' as 'bureaucratic and

Prussian'! He was replaced by a former medical officer for London, Dr John Simon, who became Britain's first chief medical administrator answerable to a newly created medical department of the Privy Council.

The regulations threw the local authorities into serious financial deficits, and public pressure forced the Government to contribute central funding support. Overall the benefits would only begin to filter through in the 1870s as the death rate began to fall decisively, although it was the end of the century before a comprehensive sanitary system was completed in England.

Increasingly the regulations were made compulsory. In 1866 a Sanitary Act compelled local authorities to provide a clean water supply and sewage disposal, and in 1867 vaccination against smallpox became compulsory. All regulations were consolidated in 1875 when a Public Health Act made a local medical health officer compulsory.

London was exempted from these regulations and only developed any central administration long after the provincial cities. It had no effective local government, with seven different commissioners of sewers and over a hundred paving authorities. In the first half of the 19th century as South Bank and Westminster became fashionable, the

St Pancras Infirmary, Highgate.

poor were displaced to St Pancras, where there was no rating support or local hospital and no municipal services. As roads and railways were developed in the second half of the century, Victoria Street, Oxford Street and Charing Cross Road replaced the narrow alleys and slums, with tens of thousands of their inhabitants displaced to the suburbs. A Metropolitan Board of Works was established in 1855. It became the London Council in 1889 (but 28 boroughs did not replace parish councils for a further decade) and was to build a main drainage and sewage system, establishing filter beds in the Thames and Lea Valley from where London obtained water.

In 1867, the new Tory Chairman of the Poor Law Board, Gawthorne Hardy, was induced to hold an inquiry by a committee of leading medical and sanitary experts under the President of the Royal College of Physicians, Sir Thomas Watson. An earlier inspectors' report had drawn attention to the ineffectiveness of the board, which lacked any power over the guardians and had itself largely ceased to function, leaving the officials to pour out orders and advisory circulars which were largely ignored.

Although admitting the existence of many defects, this had pointed out that 'overall the inmates of many workhouse infirmaries were better fed, dressed, housed and cared for than before their admission or the great mass of the working classes who earned their own living'. It had advocated legal powers should be given to the Poor Law Board to enforce the guardians to build hospitals or separate wards for the sick poor, adequately staffed with resident medical officers and trained nurses and supplied with drugs and medical appliances, all funded from a common rating on the metropolis. The new Watson Committee survey reached similar conclusions, in particular emphasising the need to build special hospitals for those suffering from infectious diseases and smallpox, and the insane.

In response Gawthorne Hardy opted for a political compromise designed to placate the guardian boards, who would resent compulsory central regulation. Only 3,000 of the 27,000 workhouse occupants in London were able-bodied, along with 3,000 children. The rest were sick and aged, and rehousing them would leave the guardians with only 11% of the present occupants to spread around 43 large institutions and lead to disintegration of the existing Poor Law administration. He considered a national scheme was not yet feasible, and instead he proposed a pilot scheme restricted to London, where a quarter of the population and a sixth of the rate-aided poor in

England and Wales lived. He also restricted the provision of new hospitals for infectious fever or smallpox patients and the dangerously insane, which merged larger districts and would be compelled to provide from a Poor Fund levy from the rates. Within a month all the unions were pooled into a single hospital region called the Metropolitan Asylum District under the management of a Metropolitan Asylums Board. The term 'asylum' had been carefully chosen as at the time it could cover all forms of medical care. Within a year six 'sick asylum districts', each of four or five unions, had been formed, each obliged to build a hospital for the general sick poor. It was a modest introduction to State responsibility to provide hospital facilities for the poor, which matured 80 years later in care for all under the NHS.

The Metropolitan Asylums Board comprised 60 members, 15 nominated by the Poor Law Board and the rest independent selected by the guardian boards. It was expected to act as a subservient quango to fill a purely managerial role, subject to detailed control from Whitehall. The new board soon showed their teeth. They expected reasonable scope to meet their targets with hands-on management and began a fight with central bureaucracy that was to continue throughout their career, with eventual success. A battle that has been resumed today by the NHS Hospital Trusts against the Ministry of Health with similar outcome.

The first issue was their accommodation. Initially they were lent premises, described as 'cavernous and tavernous', solely at weekends for their meetings, but soon rented their own accommodation – when they were curtly reminded they should have sought government authorisation beforehand. Their remit was to provide hospital beds for smallpox and fever victims and the insane and set up a separate committee to look at each of these and begin to study the basic problems of the siting and design of the new hospitals.

The main killers of the time were the infectious diseases. Smallpox and typhoid were endemic, with frequent epidemics of smallpox, typhus and cholera, for which there was little hospital accommodation. At the time the board was formed there were only two hospitals for infectious diseases, both voluntary in status: The London Smallpox and Vaccination, founded in 1746, rebuilt in 1769 at the present site of Kings Cross Station, and finally moved to Highgate Hill in 1846 with 100 beds – a building now part of the Whittington Hospital; and the London Fever Hospital at Liverpool Road, Islington, founded in 1802 with 182 beds. These would take cases from the workhouses at 1s daily, but were quite unable to cope with epidemics. This situation was reflected generally throughout the country.

By now the wisdom of admitting fever cases to general hospitals was increasingly questioned and it was evident the public authorities had to make provision. In London the buck was passed over to the Metropolitan Asylums Board, which was at once to find problems coming from two directions. The first was the Poor Law Board, to whom any proposals had to be submitted for approval; they would take months to respond, then return them riddled with nit-picking criticism and alterations that made any progress painfully slow. As a result plans were never completed in time and successive epidemics had to be met with panic-stricken temporary emergency measures at high cost. The second problem was intense opposition by the local inhabitants to a fever hospital in their area for fear of the spread of infection, who would turn to lengthy and expensive legal action.

The Asylums Board's master plan was to divide London into a triangle with a separate 200-bedded fever and 100-bedded smallpox hospital at each apex. Located at Homerton, Stockwell and Hampstead, one would be within a three-mile reach for all London's inhabitants, and suitable sites were purchased. Plans for Hampstead were turned down, and after two years' frustrating exchange of correspondence building work on the other two had not been started when an epidemic of relapsing fever began in 1869. This was a distinct condition from typhus that occurred in outbreaks with a five-day fever that settled, only to recur about the fourteenth day, a cycle that was often repeated several times. As numbers peaked, the Privy Council became concerned and leaned on the Poor Law Board for action under the Sanitary Acts; they passed the buck on to the Asylum Board with full powers to provide temporary accommodation. A structure was built in the grounds of the London Fever Hospital within a month. It was rapidly filled and an additional one was set up on the Hampstead site, but both were closed down when the outbreak subsided after a couple of years. They had cost £12,000 to erect. The Poor Law Board also baulked at the cost of nursing staff, obtained from one of the religious orders established around this time to train nursing sisters for the voluntary hospitals at a salary of £3 a month, double the official rate set by the Poor Law Board. They wrote to the Asylums Board to authorise only one fever and one smallpox hospital at this stage, and when warned that the smallpox epidemic that was sweeping Europe had crossed to the East End of London, for which there were no beds, merely responded with two voluminous sets of irrelevant administrative regulations 'defining with minute precision the functions of every officer'. As the epidemic spread, the Asylums Board was again given a free hand, but the only institution for immediate use was Hampstead, which was re-opened in December 1870 at a cost of £13,000 to the great consternation of the local inhabitants. Its 480 beds were soon filled. By January 1871 both hospitals at Homerton and Stockwell were completed and opened for smallpox cases, but could not be brought into use due to lack of nurses for the Poor Law Board's miserly level of pay and complained when the Asylums Board raised this to 10s 6d a week. There were now 1,200 beds available, but these could only house half the cases; many others were crowded into workhouses and chapels. Extra marquees were erected in the existing hospital grounds and an old naval hospital ship, the *Dreadnought* moored off Greenwich, was chartered from the Admiralty.

This epidemic abated after a couple of years. An inquiry showed only a third of smallpox cases had been admitted to hospital, with a death rate of 2,421 per million inhabitants, half the level of those left at home but double that in the provinces, and overall nearly 8,000 died in the epidemic. In Vienna and Hamburg the rates had been 5,369

Dreadnought. The first hospital ship for infectious diseases, with an ambulance boat alongside.

and 10,750 per million respectively. In spite of their efforts to cope, a publicity campaign was started to blame the Asylums Board for the lack of beds. Accused of extravagance in setting up the temporary accommodation and payment of staff, they were also charged with neglect of the patients at the Hampstead site by three of the assistant medical officers who had been employed there but sacked for the time they spent in the local pub when their strong beer allowance was reduced from six to two pints daily and for keeping unlicensed fighting dogs on the hospital premises. The board had had only 34 nurses to look after 800 patients and was completely exonerated at a public inquiry.

In 1871 the Poor Law Board was merged into a new Local Government Board, but the 'Poor Law minded' attitude remained unchanged. Within a year an extensive list of 'amended regulations' was produced that totally undermined the system of individual hospital management created by the MAB, reducing hospitals to the level of workhouse infirmaries and grading all patients as 'paupers'. These orders, prohibitions and advisory injunctions were imposed by the hospital medical superintendent, who was to 'control and govern all the officers, servants and other persons employed in the asylum'. The Asylums Board had adopted their system from the voluntary hospitals, with a superintendent responsible for medical matters, including nurses on duty, and a steward in charge of administrative matters. The matron at that time was little more than a housekeeper responsible for the domestic staff and the conduct of the nurses off duty. There followed two years of acrimonious correspondence. One subject was the class of patients who had been admitted to hospital during the epidemic, which should legally have been confined to paupers with the authorisation of a Poor Law Relieving Officer. In fact, up to 71% of patients in Hampstead had been employed and did not qualify, but had been accepted under 'stress of urgency'.

Meanwhile, the Board had acquired two further reserve sites for emergency use in Fulham and Deptford, and there were plans to convert the temporary Hampstead site into a permanent smallpox and fever hospital. The latter regenerated the intense local opposition that had been led by Rowland Hill of Penny Post fame, who owned the adjacent property, since the site was first proposed in 1869. A legal battle was to continue backwards and forwards through the courts for years, with injunctions to close the hospital overturned on appeal. After a couple of years the matter ended up in the House of Lords, who decided that a new trial should be started from scratch. In fact the hospital had already been closed for four years and the rate payers threatened to strike and stop paying rates if the trial went on. Directly and indirectly through the rates they were meeting both sets of costs, and over £40,000 had already passed from their pockets into the lawyers'. An out-of-court settlement was reached in 1883 by which the board agreed to buy out the Rowland Hill property, open a new hospital entrance and limit smallpox cases to 40.

Meanwhile another smallpox epidemic had started in 1875 and became rampant the following year, rapidly filling up the beds available. Two new hospitals were built on the sites at Fulham and Deptford and by the time the epidemic subsided by the end of 1878 some 13,000 patients had been treated in hospital, with a death rate of 19%. The percentage of non-pauper admissions, technically illegal, had risen to 90% under the 'stress of urgency' escape clause. It was conceded by the Local Government Board in 1875 that they could accept anyone in such a condition that refusal could have dangerous results. In theory these patients were liable to pay 1s 3d a day for their keep, but in practice these charges were seldom levied and the MAB hospitals continued to treat without sanction, as a charge on the poor rate, patients who were legally the responsibility of the local authorities.

The Asylums Board, supported by the local authorities, continued to press for clarification of the position, but the only response from the Government was an Act in 1879 that allowed the boards of guardians to enter a contract with the Asylums Board to supply hospital accommodation for their non-pauper citizens, but there was no take-up as they were receiving the service free although illegally. One benefit was that the Act permitted the board to provide horse-drawn carriages for the transport of patients to hospital to reduce the use of public transport and thus the spread of the disease. Ambulances followed down the street by a band of urchins shouting 'fever' became a familiar sight in London. Ambulance stations were created at the hospital, with accommodation for the nurses and coachmen as well as the ambulances and horses, but strict quarantine regulations were impossible.

Meanwhile, evidence was accumulating that the incidence of smallpox was higher amongst inhabitants in the neighbourhood of a hospital, as much as four times greater within a mile radius at Fulham. This led to a complete review by a Royal Commission of the

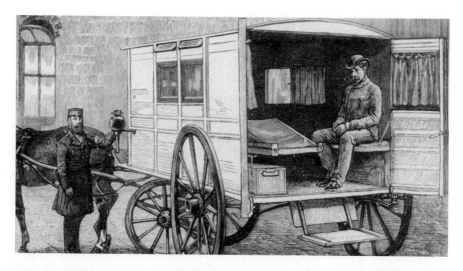
A horse ambulance carriage of 1886, showing the end of the movable stretcher.

policy of locating such accommodation in populated areas, and it was recommended that 1,500–2,000 smallpox beds should be created outside London, or on to floating hospitals on the Thames. Severe cases that could not be moved so far would be confined to strictly isolated wards with a maximum of 40 beds. At the time the cause of the virus' spread was unknown and the same entrances onto busy streets were used by patients, visitors and staff. The Royal Commission also recommended accommodation should be free for all patients.

As usual there was no response from the Local Government Board and a direct approach by the MAB to Mr Gladstone, the Prime Minister, was turned down on the grounds that the matter was outside his province and he had been advised not to receive deputations at the time on medical grounds. During a severe epidemic in 1881 the asylum managers had chartered two retired ships from the Navy, the *Atlas*, an old wooden 90-gun ship, to give 350 beds for acute cases, and an old wooden 50-gun frigate, the *Endymion*, as an administrative centre. With continued pressure they were able to buy these ships, and a disused cross-Channel steamer, for conversion into permanent floating hospitals moored at Long Reach, 17 miles down the Thames, at a cost of £275 per bed. Two paddle steamers were added to serve as ambulance ships, with a pier and wharves equipped with an examination room and isolation ward where cases could be assessed. They also bought land at Darenth within reach of the ships and laid down

170

connecting roads and services. Within a year the next smallpox epidemic struck and a 1,100-bedded hospital encampment had to be rushed ahead. It was soon filled with patients from all over London at the rate of 100 a day. The newly appointed matron in charge arrived to find nothing ready and described how 'patients came pouring in from the ships across the river with their goods and chattels, like children of Israel passing through the Red Sea'. She boasted proudly how she had achieved 'a brush and comb for each patient, a luxury hitherto unknown'.

In contrast to the hospital ships, the cost of each bed provided at Darenth was £100 and it was to become a permanent site. The anomalous position regarding pauper and non-pauper patients in the great majority remained. The Asylums Board proposed the local authorities should pay a fee of four guineas for each case admitted, but the Local Government Board insisted each authority would have to make a separate contract, a policy that they universally rejected. The asylum managers continued their pressure and finally achieved some success in a Poor Law Act of 1889, by which they obtained legal sanction to admit into their hospitals any person suffering from fever, smallpox or diphtheria, and they could be carried freely in MAB ambulances. Technically the parish guardians could claim maintenance charges from patients able to pay, although this was seldom enforced. Another concession was that their hospitals could accept medical students. When in workhouses or MAB hospitals, patients had previously lost citizenship and their right to vote, but this had been restored in 1885.

The same year, compulsory notification of 11 infectious diseases was introduced for all MAB hospitals, although it remained optional for voluntary hospitals for another two years and establishments belonging to the Crown, including palaces, barracks, police stations and prisons, were exempted for another 25 years. It was also optional initially for provincial establishments where development of facilities for smallpox and fevers had been slow.

Until 1891 only 400 of the 1,100 sanitary authorities had made any provision, with great variation in standards. These ranged from excellent in Portsmouth and the 1,000-bedded hospital in Liverpool, to unfit for use when needed in many rural areas, where at most a cottage or shed was set aside. There was then a great improvement all round and by 1913 there were 755 fever hospitals in England and Wales with nearly 10,000 beds. Although the sanitary authorities retained the power to charge, payment was generally means-tested or not enforced. However, some levied high charges that left their infectious disease facilities practically empty. One of these was Eastbourne, which had established itself as a health resort frequented by the wealthy and royalty. A workhouse into which the 'bad, mad and contagious' were incarcerated already existed and there was intense opposition by the local rate payers as to the cost of a separate fever hospital which was generally understood to be solely for the benefit of workhouse pauper patients. Finally, after smallpox and measles epidemics, a hospital was built next door to the workhouse, but the charges enforced ensured paupers could not be admitted.

Cholera had been notifiable since 1875, and the ten added to the list in 1889 included smallpox, erysipelas, scarlet fever, and diphtheria which had replaced smallpox as the primary epidemic. Permission to admit diphtheria cases was only obtained in 1888. By now the MAB had 1,900 fever beds in six London hospitals and nearly as many for smallpox in the hospital ships at Darenth, with three attached depots to house nurses and horse-drawn ambulances, all linked to the head office in Norfolk Street by the newly introduced telephone.

These measures had largely conquered smallpox in London, although it remained in provincial towns. During the four epidemics that had occurred since the MAB's initiation, 57,000 smallpox patients had been treated in hospital, along with 30,000 fever cases, of which 60% were scarlet fever. Alongside these was measles, which killed 133 a week, mostly children, during the winter of 1888–9, although this was not to be registered as a notifiable disease for another 25 years.

In 1891 a Public Health Act finally consolidated the right of the Metropolitan Asylums Board to provide free isolation hospital accommodation and transport for specified infectious disease patients in London, measures first proposed by a Select Committee in 1818, but it remained nominally under the Poor Law without the status of a public health authority.

The board began plans to provide one fever hospital bed for every 1,000 inhabitants, with a reserve to meet any future smallpox outbreak by building five new fever hospitals, each to provide accommodation for 2,000 acute and 800 convalescent cases. But their problems with central authority and local objections remained with any site selected, and permission would often be refused after a lengthy public inquiry which could take ten years. Their existing facilities were overwhelmed by a scarlet fever epidemic in 1892 in spite of temporary hut extensions, and for the first time in their history admissions had to be refused. With the threat of 'Asiatic' cholera and 'Russian' influenza epidemics spreading from Europe, permission was obtained to build the Fountain Hospital at Tooting, followed by the Grove at Tooting, the Brook at Woolwich and the Park at Lewisham, which was formally opened by the Prince of Wales, later King Edward VII, the first state hospital to be recognised by royalty. At the turn of the century after the last of London's smallpox epidemics, a 2,000-bedded hospital was built at Joyce Green to replace the hospital ships, although the River Ambulance service continued.

The pattern of admissions was to change greatly as smallpox was controlled by isolation and vaccination, although there was an outbreak of a minor form in the 1920s throughout the country and London. Enteric fevers were reduced by improved sanitation and typhus in London, but it persisted in industrial areas. Scarlet fever remained a major source of fever cases and was joined by diphtheria, which was becoming increasingly widespread; admission to hospital rose rapidly with compulsory notification and over 75% of cases were admitted. As these infections primarily affected children, admissions of children under 15 rose tenfold over the last decade of the 19th century and became over 90% of the total. The mortality rates initially were high, but more than halved during the next decade as scarlet fever lost its virulence and diphtheria anti-toxin serum, which the MAB itself began to produce later, was introduced. By the end of the 1920s, 10,000 cases of each condition were being admitted annually. The death rate from scarlet fever was to fall to under 10% from a high of 12% in children under five, and 5% overall. Most children with diphtheria were in hospital for 12 to 13 weeks, but the death rate fell from 30% to a mere 3%. Although still not notifiable, measles and whooping cough meanwhile had become rampant, with a death rate of between 7% and 15%. Admission only became legally admissible in 1911, seven years after it was accepted in Liverpool, and there were 2,000 cases of each annually in London.

The scope of the MAB's responsibilities were to be gradually extended. A high proportion of their hospital admissions had always been children suffering from infectious diseases and the mentally handi-capped. They also inherited responsibility for a number of healthy Poor Law boys aged 13–16, housed on training ships owned by guardian boards. Most were initially placed in workhouses and later many were transferred to privately run 'contractors' establishments. These arrangements were unsatisfactory, so they were transferred to 'district schools', large barrack boarding schools run by the boards of guardians. Conditions there and the private schools led to a high incidence of contagious diseases of the skin and scalp, especially ringworm, trachoma and infectious eye conditions. Sufferers were placed into the care of the MAB, along with the educationally subnormal and those in need of long-term nursing care for tuberculous diseases, which a high proportion of Poor Law children contracted. The MAB set up a chain of 'hospital schools' at the seaside and in the country, with children living in cottage homes in the charge of house-mothers. For eight years the MAB was also responsible for the management of young offenders in remand homes until they were transferred to the LCC in 1909.

In 1909 building of the Southern Hospital for convalescent smallpox patients was completed, but not required. It was converted into a 1,000-bedded children's hospital and renamed Queen Mary's Hospital for Children. It was to receive a worldwide reputation as a hospital for children and in particular for orthopaedic care, for which few London voluntary hospitals had special departments. It was also to house the first MAB training school for nurses.

The MAB also became involved in the treatment of venereal disease after a Royal Commission in 1916 recommended management should be in the hands of county and borough councils, with diagnosis and treatment provided free at general hospitals and the Treasury meeting 75% of the cost. In addition, the MAB supplied facilities for the treatment of pregnant women that were not available in the ordinary lying-in wards of the Metropolitan Poor Law institutions, and extended them to non-pregnant women and their babies infected with ophthalmia neonatorum.

From its conception the MAB had been involved in providing establishments for Poor Law 'lunatics and imbeciles', terms used to cover all forms of mental illness and sub-normality, as well as senile dementia or Alzheimer's. The term 'idiot' was reserved for the severely abnormal. Until an Act of 1774, they had been spread in pitiable conditions in prisons, workhouses, public hospitals, such as Bethlem, and private 'madhouses'. The Act applied only to the private institutions, which had a bad reputation and were now to be inspected and licensed in London by five Commissioners, all Fellows of the Royal College of Physicians, and in the provinces by the local Justices of the Peace.

Paupers were excluded from the Act and there was little improvement. Overall standards remained low, with the majority of inmates in wretched conditions, especially in the workhouses in spite of a series of central directives and recommendations. Effective action was not taken until 1845, with Shaftesbury's Lunacy Act. At that time only 20 county asylums had been built, and of 20,600 lunatics in care, 16,800 were classed as paupers admitted into care without certification, and there was no form of official inspection.

This Act set up a Board of Lunacy Commissioners and compelled Justices everywhere to set up asylums, financed from the local rates, to which all lunatic paupers would be transferred, with controls that included certification for admission, proper records and annual inspection by special visitors. A few of the large provincial towns, such as Liverpool, Manchester and Birmingham, complied by building special mental wards in the Poor Law infirmaries, but overall response was totally inadequate. Any asylums built, instead of places of treatment, as intended, became overcrowded, ill-equipped and poorly staffed, and many insane and mentally backward remained in workhouses where the staff could not cope without using illegal mechanical restraints.

The situation was as bad in London as anywhere, and the problem was handed over to the Metropolitan Asylums Authority when it was formed. It built asylums on two large sites in the countryside outside London where land was cheap, each designed for 1,500 and composed a three-storey block, each storey comprising one enormous ward for 500 patients. They were soon filled with acute and chronic cases of all ages, decanted from the Middlesex county asylums at Harwell and Colney Hatch and the workhouses to relieve the guardians of the cost of their maintenance, and an extra 500 beds had to be added. However, over a quarter of the mentally disordered in the county remained in workhouses.

An 1890 Lunacy Act introduced medical certification and a 'reception order' by a magistrate, but left close association with Poor Law and was unchanged for another 70 years.

Although some charitable asylums were set up, there was little provision for subnormal children and the MAB was the first to establish separate centres for 1,000 at Darenth, Kent, to offer education and workshop training in simple jobs, and to provide some means of self-support for those over 16.

Unfortunately, plans to extend asylums throughout the country were blocked in Whitehall and the two institutions became filled with hopeless chronic cases. A separate infirmary was built for the sick and aged, and some public authorities began to provide education and accommodation for deaf and blind children.

The MAB was the first to introduce proper statistics on health and related matters, to supply the facts essential to administrative planning for the provision of public health and hospital facilities, 70 years before the Ministry of Health set up such a department. It was able to attract devoted voluntary service from a wide range of high-calibre people for generations. Two MPs served for over 40 years and many could contribute their specialist knowledge of engineering, building construction and hospital management.

Each voluntary hospital worked independently under separate management, in contrast to overall control vested in the MAB under the direction of a central government authority. Initially there were separate management committees to meet their responsibilities for smallpox, fevers and insanity, but as hospital numbers increased, top-level control became increasingly diluted and unit management was carried out locally. As overheads rose to over £2 million annually, some misuse occurred. One medical superintendent built a private swimming pool in the basement of his private residence. In others 2,500 chickens, lobsters and cigars had been provided for the 'patients', along with £750 for wines and spirits. The children's ward had been supplied with several dozen bottles of beer, with champagne and port, on five consecutive days. The Court of Enquiry found that the chairman of the management committee had disappeared and his clerk absconded. The rest of his staff 'retired'.

But the MAB had achieved international respect for its success in coping with infective disease. It was dissolved in 1929 and its assets and responsibilities transferred to the London County Council, along with the hospitals set up by 25 separate boards of Poor Law guardians, a total of 82 hospitals with nearly 40,000 beds and 120,000 staff. Of these the MAB contributed half the beds and 38 units, which included 10,000 staff; 4,500 were nurses and 200 medical and dispensary staff. Nearly 4,000 of the remainder were in services – domestic, laundry and portering – 600 in engineering and there were 150 teachers in the children's hospitals. Only 400 were clerical, half attached to the head office, and the annual cost of salaries was well under £1 million, 39% of total expenditure. Daily upkeep of buildings amounted to 19% and patient maintenance 16%. Expenditure on drugs and surgical appliances in 1889 for a daily average of 6,500 patients was £1,200, but rose to £6,000 for 10,000 patients with the use of expensive diphtheria anti-toxin, and to £37,000 in 1929 for 18,000 patients. The average weekly cost of a fever patient was 59s 6d compared to under 25s a week for mental patients. Hospitals absorbed 85% of the total £2.4 million expenditure, the total capital outlay throughout its time, of which 46.7% was devoted to infectious disease hospitals, 24.1% to mental institutions, 13% on tuberculosis sanitoria, 8.7% on children's institutions and 4.6% on ambulance services. In the MAB's time more than 79,000 smallpox and over a million other infectious cases were treated, during which a Poor Law system was transformed into a public health service.

Hospital services for the armed services developed independently of the civilian sector from the second half of the 18th century onwards. Their requirements were different, as battle casualties needed immediate attention before transfer to a base hospital for more positive treatment, with the back-up of a permanent hospital system that offered long-term care along with general medical care for the service personnel.

Earlier, army casualties had been largely abandoned on the battlefield at the mercy of the local inhabitants, until surgeons began to be appointed to accompany the troops towards the turn of the 17th century. Then soldiers began to be sent back from Ireland and Europe to the London hospitals, and the Savoy on the Strand and Ely House off Holborn Hill were opened by a Commissioners of Hospitals for a while, along with military hospitals in Dublin and Edinburgh, but were soon closed as they were considered too expensive to run. In 1661 Charles II founded two 'hopitals' for the care of aged and disabled soldiers, one in Dublin, and one at Chelsea. It was another hundred years before field hospitals were established and 'bearer companies' set up to collect the wounded from the battlefield and carry them to nearby mobile field hospitals which were accepted as 'safe havens'.

Fixed regimental hospitals began to be set up in nearby towns for more expert treatment, replaced in the second half of the 19th century by a series of larger permanent general hospitals built on the pavilion plan at the main bases, including Woolwich, Aldershot and Millbank. In time these would be extended to the outposts of the Empire at Hong Kong and Singapore.

Greenwich Hospital.

A few naval casualties were subsidised at St Thomas's or Bart's by their officers, and after the Civil and Dutch wars in the 17th century, contracts were made with hospitals for the care of the wounded at a rate of 2d per head by the Navy, but late payment brought both hospitals to the verge of bankruptcy. Hospital ships were only introduced into the Navy by Cromwell in the 17th century, long after the other European powers. These were to culminate in *Britannia*, designed to serve as a royal yacht as well.

Admirals Drake and Hawkins founded the Chatham Chest in 1590, after the Armada, to which each sailor contributed 6d a month from his pay as an insurance scheme, but it was over a hundred years before the first naval hospital was founded at Greenwich by William and Mary. Designed by Wren, it was primarily planned as an almshouse for the sick and disabled pensioners and was the largest institution of its kind in the world, housing up to 2,700 at the time of Nelson. Reputedly there was only one tap and lavatory to each block that housed several hundred men. It was closed in 1869 and is now the Royal Naval College. Permanent naval hospitals would be built later at Portsmouth, Plymouth and Chatham, along with the civilian voluntary hospitals. The first was Haslar, near Portsmouth, built at a cost of £38,000 in 1761 with over 2,000 cradles, as the beds were called. It was the largest hospital in England at the time, treating over 6,000 sailors a year, and was the largest brick building in Europe, with the 84 wards built round three sides of a square, with a 12-foot wall along the fourth side to prevent desertion by the press-ganged sailors. Initially under the control of medical officers, the wards were described as clean and well ventilated, with 90 women nurses paid £12 p.a. In 1795 administration was transferred to a naval captain as Governor, who introduced strictest discipline with loss of medical standards. Control was restored to the medical staff in 1865. In 1885 Florence Nightingale re-introduced female nurses, who were to become the Royal Naval Nursing Service 17 years later. Haslar opened a Royal Naval Medical School in 1861, which was one of the first to teach tropical medicine. It maintained standards of medical and surgical care that matched the best civilian hospitals.

Within the structure of the NHS the established army and naval hospitals were absorbed and incorporated within their local trusts;

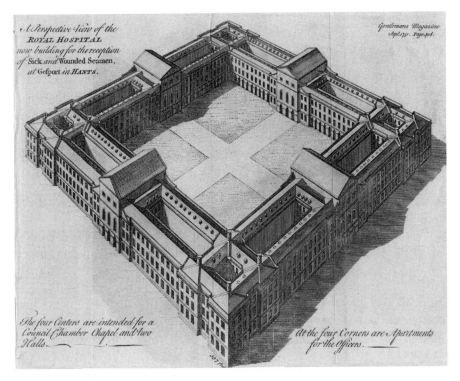

The Royal Hospital for Sick and Wounded Seamen at Gosport, Hants.

179

Chelsea Hospital.

most were closed down as separate units. The last to survive is Haslar, which has been upgraded to a high level of technology. Services have extended to the local community, with staffing divided equally between civilian and service personnel under the direction of a medical naval officer. It was the reception centre for both army and naval casualties in the Falklands and Gulf wars, and runs a tele-medicine unit which links doctors on site in the war zones with consultants at the hospital. Haslar has now become part of an overall Portsmouth Hospital Trust, and it could be tested to cope with the exceptional demands imposed by a major situation with high service casualties.

The Royal Hospital Chelsea was built on the bank of the Thames, 1½ miles from Buckingham Gate, for wounded and superannuated soldiers. Started by Charles II in 1682, building continued during James II's short reign and was completed by William and Mary. The original idea is attributed to Charles' mistress Nell Gwyn, who had been approached by a beggar who claimed to be an ex-serviceman wounded defending the king in the civil war. The hospital was designed by Sir Christopher Wren, and completed in 1690 at a cost of £150,000.

Comprising East and West wings 365 feet long and 40 feet wide, there were 16 wards, each with 26 beds, a small apartment for officers at the end, a large chapel, surgery and hot and cold baths. An area of 14 acres to the north was planted with avenues of lime and chestnut trees, and a 1½ acre burial ground. There were 476 in-pensioners of specified rank, from 336 privates to 16 drummers and 26 captains. The hospital was run as a military station with regular garrison duties. The quarters were comfortable with a fire in every ward, a daily allowance of 1lb of meat and cheese and two quarts of beer, and a uniform of scarlet faced with blue, and a daily allowance according to rank. It was fully staffed with a Governor and administration, medical and domestic teams. Out-pensioners were granted a pension according to length of service and disability, but initially this was paid annually in arrears and they were compelled to borrow from loan sharks to survive, until 1754 when they were paid six-monthly in advance. By 1809 there were over 23,000 out-pensioners paid 5d to 3/6 weekly according to their length of service and the annual running costs met by parliament were £440,000. Burials averaged 60 annually, often aged over 85.

Chapter 7

Specialist Hospitals

Medical specialisation dates back to earliest records. When Herodotus visited Egypt in 500 BC, he commented on the large number of specialists for every organ and part of the body. These priestly physicians were often attached to the court and held in high regard, with their skills passed on by the elders to apprentices. In Babylonia and Assyria there was a three-layered structure: one priest would divine how the patient had incurred the wrath of the gods and which deity was concerned, a second priest specialised in incantations and sacrifices to placate the god concerned and a third was skilled in herbal medicine. These services were expensive and the average person would be treated by laymen.

The Hippocratic era broke away from the supernatural causes of disease and the approach was holistic, based on increasing natural resistance by diet and rest, and contrary to the concept of specialisation. This was followed by the Galenic teachings adopted by the Christian Church, which regarded illness as a penalty for sin, requiring confession and penitence. This would be reinforced by herbal medicines, but shedding of blood or dissection were forbidden. Any surgery was left to laymen such as barbers and bone-setters, who acquired their skills from experience – and often specialised in a particular field such as cutting for stone, eye surgery or manipulation.

The earliest developments in specialisation were in surgery, with the increased knowledge of anatomy from the work of Vesalius in the 16th century and the improved status of the surgeon. It was led by Ambrose Pare, who advocated allowing the healing of wounds in the battlefield casualties of the religious wars of his time, by stitching the injured wound edges together, in place of treatment with boiling oil or cautery which led to infection and necrosis.

Whilst medicine remained stagnant locked in the Galenic era, specialisation in surgery would develop, especially on the Continent. In Britain the established hospitals remained general and few showed any initiative in developing specialist areas of medicine or surgery. Both the management committees and the establishment of the medical staff

183

were opposed to the idea of special departments, and the distinction between doctors remained general, physician or surgeon. The only exceptions were cutting for stone and cataract. During the first part of the 18th century a surgeon was appointed jointly to the staff of St Bartholomew's and St Thomas's as a specialist in stone cutting and was paid extra for each case. An assistant surgeon was appointed at Bart's to look after the blind, although it was laid down he should be paid only the standard operation fee of 8s 6d for each case. This distinction was not absolute as a St Thomas's surgeon detailed his techniques for removal of a cataract and lithotomy operation for stone.

It would only be in the 1870s onwards that the general hospitals would begin to set up any specialised units, and the result was generations of frustrated young doctors who had served sabbaticals studying in European centres, where there were major developments in medicine and surgery. Unable to obtain a post within the closed selection system that existed, on return home many would open up a small specialised dispensary or hospital. This began in London early in the 19th century and spread across the country. By the end of the century there were some 160 specialist centres in England and Wales to cover every distinct organ of the body, of which 29 were in London. Many overlapped in their field, leading to intense rivalry. There were seven hospitals for consumption and chest conditions, six for eye diseases, four for skin conditions and three orthopaedic centres. The overall pattern was to form a committee and obtain the support of an eminent patron, rent a house and appoint a medical staff before launching an appeal for funds by advertising in the press. Subscribers would be given the right to act as governors and give a letter of introduction for patients.

Often the new institutions were set up in unsuitable premises and faced a struggle for existence. Many closed down, but a few developed into centres of excellence through the quality of their work and the dedication of the founder and his successors. This development was aided in London by the Council of King Edward's Hospital Fund, which promoted the amalgamation of smaller special hospitals to secure the provision of one really successful independent centre for each speciality, a pattern that was unique to the British hospital system. Few of these would be able to retain their independent existence within the framework of the National Health Service and would lose their identity when they were absorbed into trusts dominated by the large general hospitals and pleased to acquire their prestige. Often this would result from the specialist hospital being housed in antiquated, badly located premises, requiring heavy rebuilding costs to be brought to up-to-date standards and to absorb the mushrooming departments of investigation, such as radiology and pathology, or new areas of therapy.

The build-up of specialisation was subject to intense criticism from every orthodox quarter, supported by the medical press of the time. In 1857 the *Lancet* ran a leader under the title 'Special Hospital Mania', arguing that division and subdivision had been carried so far there was nothing left to divide. 'These excrescences are being reproduced with all the prolific exuberance characteristic of cancer and soon the metropolis threatens to swarm with nuisances of this kind.'

To some extent many of the specialised hospitals earned their criticism. They were aggressive fund-raisers, competing with the general hospitals largely dependent on public subscription, and were not inhibited in their approaches to the public. There was no Standards Committee to regulate advertising at that time, but when St Mark's added 'Cancer' to its name as 'Hospital for Fistula and Other Diseases of the Rectum' as a fund-raising measure, it was rebuked by the King's Fund.

In 1875 the 36 special hospitals in London raised almost as much money as the eight voluntary hospitals with medical schools, and they also gained substantial funds from the Hospital Saturday and Sunday Funds. They expected a contribution from patients unless they had a letter of recommendation or were too poor to pay, and undercut general practitioners, whose patient base was also threatened by the consultants at the general hospitals. There was also strong criticism of the use to which their funds were applied. As small units, they were expensive, and sometimes run wastefully or even dishonestly. After an inquiry at St Mark's into a fourfold increase in dispensary or alcoholic stimulants, the hospital secretary absconded with £400. At one hospital for skin diseases the secretary syphoned off 15% of all fees collected, amounting to some £450 p.a. Some were openly trading on the fashions and new vogues of the time; the *Lancet* was to pick out the Galvanic Hospital for Stone and the Dispensaries for Ulcerated Legs and Diseases of the Throat and Loss of Voice and recommend the medical staff should resign from such organisations. The hospitals for skin diseases in particular were a constant source of scandal and criticism with their adoption of new methods of light and electricity –

phototherapy; others were 'massage hospitals', little more than brothels, which would soon close. The *Lancet* went on to suggest that next may come Hospitals for Treatment by Quinine, Cod Liver Oil, Hypophosphites – or the Excrement of Boa-constrictors.

Often the special centre would set out with the best of intentions to help the poor obtain the best treatment for conditions which were neglected by the general hospitals, but the altruism of some was suspect and open to criticism that their primary object was self-advertisement to build up a lucrative private practice. The founder of St Mark's, Frederick Salmon, left a considerable fortune on his death and the *Lancet* noted he had a large share of the private practice in the diseases which he had made his special study. The *British Medical Journal* went further and doubted his motives for establishing the hospital, which it considered against the interest of his colleagues.

Along with the *Lancet*, the *BMJ* had always voiced the increasing condemnation of special hospitals within the medical establishment; an attitude felt now towards many of the vogue units that have mushroomed recently. In 1860 it wrote that although it would appear these special hospitals were effected solely on behalf of suffering humanity, anyone who knew anything of their working was fully aware how far this was from the real, vulgar truth. Most were begun as a dispensary by an energetic surgeon who made up his mind to fame and fortune by means of bricks and mortar. First he must hit on some 'striking speciality' such as the treatment of 'inverted eyelashes'. He would then take a quiet house in a side street, canvass for patrons, and in an incredible short space of time a good sprinkling of the aristocracy were found to pledge themselves to suffering humanity. 'Carefully got up statistics' would then prove every tenth person was suffering from this terrible disease. The dispensary could be treating 20,000 patients a year and be expanded into a hospital, although the condition could well be treated in an old well-established hospital close at hand. Another critic of the time stated special hospitals were established for only one purpose – the self-interest of their founder.

Whilst the general hospital attitude was to reject a wide range of patients, the field was open to the development of specialisation, often initially within a dispensary to which in-patient accommodation was added later.

One group of patients universally rejected by the general hospitals were victims of venereal disease, considered a social disgrace at the time. Westminster and Manchester Royal Infirmary had excluded such

186

The first Lock Hospital at Southwark, 1746, where patients were 'thrashed' after the cure.

cases early in the 18th century and the Middlesex restricted admission to the relatively wealthy, charging patients two guineas a week. Only the Lock Hospital, founded at Hyde Park Corner in 1789 with 60 beds, was available for the poor. Some of the new special centres were evidently directed at these patients; St Peter's Hospital for Stone was dedicated to the treatment of 'urinary diseases' and condemned by the *BMJ*, as 'all the medical world knows what they mean in the eyes of the public'. Other special hospitals to welcome such patients included those for skin diseases, and even at St Mark's, one of the surgeons there with an extensive practice amongst the aristocracy and royalty specialised in venereal as well as rectal diseases; his carriage was well known as the 'clap-trap' as it parked outside the houses of notability. A few, such as the Hospital for the Care of the Paralysed and Epileptics, would meet with general approval from the start, whilst others would build up an established reputation from the quality of their medical work and development as post-graduate teaching centres.

The general hospitals had become increasingly selective, preferring acute cases with a good prospect of recovery and of teaching interest. But the challenge of the specialist centres gradually led to a change in their attitude towards specialisation, which an editorial in the *Lancet* in 1873 advocated should be within the general hospital, where other members of the staff would be available, as often patients had a range of ailments and both they and the trainee practitioners would benefit. Many began to introduce special departments during the 1870s, initially as out-patient units and then with in-patient facilities. Guy's had developed a clinic for eye diseases as early as 1831 and for obstetrics and gynaecology in 1842, followed by clinics for skin and aural diseases. The London and St Bartholomew's were to follow course, along with introducing orthopaedic clinics, and by the end of the 1880s the vast majority of both physicians and surgeons at the general hospitals also held a position in a specialist hospital, although some would not mention this in their *Medical Directory* entry.

In an 1889 survey most general hospitals had established out-patient clinics for skin, eyes and ENT, but only women and ophthalmology had small in-patient units. The medical press was unanimous that the ideal solution was for the general hospitals to develop good special departments that would attract talented young men to develop them, as special hospitals increased administrative costs and wasted charitable money.

The first specialist centre would become the leading ophthalmic hospital and teaching centre in Britain, with an international reputation. At the start of the 19th century there was a great increase in eye disease, due to the introduction of trachoma by soldiers returning from Egypt during the Napoleonic Wars. Although cutting for cataract was an accepted procedure, there was little medical aid otherwise and any treatment was mainly in the hands of itinerant quacks peddling a range of eye lotions and salves, some of whom through publicity acquired an enviable reputation. One was knighted by Queen Anne in 1707 for his free services in curing great numbers of soldiers and sailors of blindness. Another to receive royal patronage from George II was Chevalier John Taylor, who operated on cataract and squint in public, standing on a scaffold, dressed and posing as an executioner. His bombastic, self-advertising manner aroused considerable antagonism, especially from the established profession at home,

Moorfields Eye Hospital, c.1910.

but in turn his son and grandson were appointed as oculists by George III and George IV.

It was 1800 before John Cunningham Saunders, a young pupil of Astley Cooper, denied any chance of a general surgical appointment because he had not been articled at the College of Surgeons, started a private practice as a specialist in diseases of the eye and ear. He went on to open a London dispensary, confined to eye disease after a couple of years as there was little he could do for ear patients, and 2,000 eye patients were treated in the first four years. Saunders died early, but his successors opened a new building at Moorfields in 1821 which achieved royal patronage six years later and became the Royal London Ophthalmic Hospital, Moorfields, which was to be a training centre for ophthalmologists across the country and overseas. A number of other eye hospitals were founded in London, notably the Royal Westminster in 1816 on a site leased from Charing Cross Hospital, and the Central London in 1843, which were to be merged with Moorfields within the NHS as one post-graduate teaching hospital within the University of London, with the clinical work concentrated at Moorfields and the Royal Westminster and the teaching and research facilities at the Central.

St Mark's Hospital was established in 1835 as a tiny out-patient clinic in the City of London by Frederick Salmon, with the original title of

189

the Benevolent Dispensary for the Relief of the Poor Afflicted with Fistula, Piles and Diseases of the Rectum and Lower Intestines. Earlier, after years of gamesmanship, he had obtained a post at the Aldersgate Street Dispensary, at a time when such appointments were a matter of bribery and corruption between the applicant surgeons and the institutional governors. He was already a specialist in rectal diseases and had written books on stricture and prolapse, but antagonised his seniors through criticism of the undemocratic structure of the College of Surgeons and the selection methods for medical staff at the hospitals and dispensaries, and was forced to resign. He set up a clinic in Aldersgate, supported by a number of City businessmen and merchants who would contribute up to 20 guineas for a life governorship and the right to introduce two patients. Their entitlement to vote on appointments was restricted and he protected his position by packing the board with his relatives and friends.

At the time, major surgery was impractical and his approach to treatment was holistic, with an emphasis on diet and exercise. He considered a daily bowel action important, but rejected the powerful purgatives in vogue and introduced an enema of a pint of thin water gruel with a teaspoon of castor oil, popular in France but not used in England. He blamed sedentary work and the use of cushions and stuffed seats for many rectal conditions, and when Charles Dickens was a patient, blamed his fistula on 'too much sitting at his desk'. He considered the state of the blood and function of the liver important and would use cupping, leeches and mercury for these. Piles were as common then as today, but he seldom turned to surgery, preferring a combination of excision and ligature as being less painful and easier to handle, whilst any haemorrhage could be controlled by the injection of cold water into the rectum.

The hospital soon moved to a house in Charterhouse Square with 14 beds, having shortened its name to The Fistula Infirmary. In 1868 a rival dispensary was opened, but closed down after ten years due to lack of support, whilst more serious opposition arose from the Gordon Hospital, which opened in 1884 with private beds. Although overall standards were considered lower, the Gordon would be rebuilt and continue until finally it lost its identity when linked with the Westminster Hospital within the NHS.

Meanwhile, St Mark's would continue to enlarge to 93 beds with rebuilding programmes to become a leader in the fields of rectal surgery and radiotherapy of cancer as these advanced.

With the advent of the NHS, colo-rectal surgery failed to achieve recognition as a distinct speciality, but along with the West London, St Mark's was attached to the Hammersmith group. A range of future associations was considered, but half of its beds had to be closed through financial cutbacks within the group, although a total shutdown was prevented through public and political pressure.

In 1995 it moved to a common site with Northwick Park Hospital as St Mark's Educational Trust, an academic unit recognised by the University of London, and part of the North-West Hospital Trust, which also included the Central Middlesex Hospital. Northwick Park had been built in 1971 as two separate buildings, one a new hospital and the other a Clinical Research Centre run by the Medical Research Council. Their partnership began to crumble and the MRC pulled out in the mid-1980s, and St Mark's occupied the vacant premises after an expenditure of some £9 million.

The Hospital for the Treatment of Stone and Urinary Diseases was established in 1860 and after twenty-two years moved to a purpose-built site in Henrietta Street as St. Peter's. Bladder stones were endemic at the time and were treated by lithotomy, before instruments were devised in France to crush the stones through the urethra, and St. Peter's became the leading centre in England for this, as well as the treatment of urethral stricture.

In the next century it led the way in prostatic surgery and would acquire an international reputation. Under the NHS it was united with St. Paul's Hospital for Skin and Venereal Diseases under a Board of Governors as one of the twelve specialist post-graduate teaching hospitals in London. This established the Institute of Urology, as part of the British Postgraduate Medical Federation in the University of London. St. Paul's would develop the first artificial kidney, leading to a full dialysis unit. Their association with venereal diseases would be detached, and along with the Shaftesbury Hospital the Institute of Urology has now been rehoused at a new Centre in Euston Road as part of the UCLH rebuilding programme.

In general phthisis cases were not accepted as they were chronic, usually with a fatal outcome and would be removed from the general medical wards to special hospitals as soon as their infectious nature

191

The Hospital for Consumption and Diseases of the Chest, Brompton, 1865.

became realised. Tuberculosis cases were on the banned list of most metropolitan and general hospitals, including St George's and the London. The Brompton was founded through the efforts of Philip Rose, a partner in a London law firm, when a clerk in his office who had developed tuberculosis was refused admission into any hospital.

There already existed a West London Dispensary for Diseases of the Chest, but this only treated out-patients and agreed to start a joint venture. The promotional literature for the public appeal in 1841 stated 'But consumption, the most frequent and fatal disease in existence, which according to a high authority destroys one third of our entire population, finds the door of our hospitals closed against it.' The Manor House near the Royal Hospital, Chelsea, was rented and it opened in 1842 with an impressive list of patrons that included the Queen and ten nobility. The medical team included six leading physicians from UCH, King's and Westminster Hospitals, and Robert Liston, a surgeon at the University of London, to establish a pattern for consultants at a general hospital also working at a specialist centre.

The main hospital, or asylum, was supported by an out-patient clinic with a domiciliary service in Great Marlborough Street and in the first six months 63 in-patients and 746 out-patients were treated. By 1844 rebuilding was planned and a site chosen at Brompton – 'a village in Kensington, remarkable for salubrity of its air and

192

Mundesley Sanatorium in Norfolk, 1930.

surrounded entirely by nurseries and garden grounds' – formerly part of a botanical garden founded by William Curtis, a noted entomologist. The foundation stone was laid by the Queen and Prince Consort, followed by a bazaar at the Royal Hospital, Chelsea, attended by upwards of 10,000 guests.

By the spring of 1846 the north and west wings had been completed, along with part of the centre including the tower and entrance. The new wards were ducted by warm air to provide 'for the poor a climate nearly approaching that of southern latitudes' and this was in use until 'open-air treatment' was introduced in 1898. The east wing was added in 1854 and beds now numbered 220, although 80 had to be closed for a year in 1857 due to lack of funds.

In 1865 there was a major rethink on admission policy. At that time all cases were admitted, however severe or terminal, but most cases were discharged after three months whatever their progress, far too short a period to achieve maximal benefit. They would be returned to the environment where they had contracted the disease, or to work, and any benefit gained would soon be lost. Their place in hospital might then be taken by one from the workhouse in a terminal state, and this led to the decision to build a new wing.

By 1879 enough property had been acquired on the opposite side of the Fulham Road to build a south wing with 132 extra beds and a new department for out-patients, who had trebled within ten years to over 12,500, connected to the main building by an underground tunnel.

193

In the early treatment of tuberculosis emphasis had been on warmth, but in Germany the value of fresh air became a dominant feature, leading to the establishment of the first sanitoria, the most famous of which was at Nordrach in the Black Forest. In 1861 the Brompton built a small sanitorium in Bournemouth and three years later sent 20 patients to Madeira for three months as an experiment, but as their progress was not improved, plans to establish a sanitorium there were abandoned.

By 1901 the need for a new sanitorium was apparent and one was built with 100 beds on a site purchased at Frimley, near Bagshot, surrounded by pine woods.

The hospital continued to attract leading physicians from the major general hospitals and attracted pupils from early on, and was accepted by 1858 by the main examination boards as part of their educational course. A few students were accepted as patient clinical clerks, but a significant post-graduate medical school was only developed after the advent of the NHS.

It established an international reputation and in 1909 won a $1,000 prize for the best hospital treatment for advanced cases and sanatorium treatment, against international competition, at a congress in Washington. In 1900 a small X-ray unit was established and by 1919 over 1,000 cases were being X-rayed annually. The early staff casualties from irradiation were high before the department was rebuilt in 1925, when X-ray numbers doubled annually to reach 35,000 by 1948.

In 1908 voluntary notification of tuberculosis was introduced and arrangements were made with the Ministry of Health for the follow-up contracts. It became a notifiable disease in 1914 and in 1917 a dispensary was set up under the National Insurance Act for in-patient and out-patient treatment, with home visits by health visitors.

The hospital was to lead in the surgical treatment of tuberculosis. The first visiting surgeon had been appointed in 1884, but his only duties related to general surgical emergencies, and in 1914 there were only three surgeons, one an ear, nose and throat specialist, on the staff. In the early 1920s the first positive treatment for pulmonary TB was introduced, to put the lung at rest by partial collapse through the introduction of air into the pleural cavity. This was to be followed by air into the peritoneal cavity to push up the diaphragm and rest the lower part of the lung and then open surgery to reset the upper ribs and close tuberculosis cavities by direct compression. In 1926, when

The Sanitorium for Diseases of the Chest at the City of London Hospital, Victoria Park, 1851.

operations amounted to a mere 300 cases annually, a new theatre with separate surgical wards was built, and by 1933 surgery was carried out on 1,122 patients. Surgery and collapse therapy would remain dominant until the advent of chemotherapy, and by 1948 there were five leading consultant surgeons with over half of all patients subjected to some form of collapse therapy, continued in out-patient clinics where their pneumothorax was refilled with air weekly.

In 1934 a physiotherapy department was established which was to become a world leader in the management of respiratory disease. The next year ward orderlies for cleaning and domestic duties were employed, freeing nurses to focus on patient care. Pay beds had been introduced from an early stage and in 1925 a proportion of beds were licensed to the London County Council.

The advent of lobectomy advanced surgical treatment for lung cancer, and in 1944 the Brompton teamed with the nearby Royal Cancer Hospital for the joint treatment of lung cancer with deep X-ray therapy. The Brompton retained a degree of autonomy within the NHS; it was able to appoint its own staff, had its own board of governors and became recognised as a teaching centre for diseases of the chest. In 1949 it was affiliated with the London Chest Hospital, Victoria Park, after generations of 'friendly rivalry' to become the Hospitals for Diseases of the Chest and a fully fledged postgraduate teaching centre within the University of London. Later this was to

195

absorb the National Heart Hospital, which had been founded in 1857 as the National Hospital for Diseases of the Heart and rebuilt in Westmoreland Street.

Within the large general hospitals in the early 19th century there was limited orthopaedic facility and none for the common deformities in children such as clubfoot. Any help was in the hands of lay therapists ranging from 'bone setters' to 'sprain walkers' with limited benefit.

Dr William Little had himself developed club foot from poliomyelitis as a child. When he was studying in Berlin his condition was cured by a technique that had become established there but was rejected by the conservative establishment at home. This involved a 'blind' method of cutting the Achilles tendon with a curved knife blade introduced through a small incision on either side of the ankle, instead of cutting the overlying skin, which carried a high risk of infection. He introduced this method on his return home and in 1840 opened a six-bedded Orthopaedic Institute, which was an immediate success.

As would commonly occur in the special hospital orbit, disagreements arose between the management committee and medical staff which led to resignations on both sides, including Dr Little, amid great publicity. The hospital itself continued and, renamed the Royal Orthopaedic Hospital, moved to a new site in Hanover Square in 1856. By then there was a separate City Orthopaedic Hospital for local children and a National Orthopaedic Hospital opened in 1864 at Bolsover Street. All three specialist hospitals expanded and planned further independent development, until King Edward's Hospital Fund recommended they should join into a single unit in Bolsover Street.

The Royal and National merged in 1904, with the City joining two years later, as the Royal National Orthopaedic Hospital, and a new hospital with 200 beds and out-patients department fronting onto Great Portland Street was opened in 1909.

Orthopaedics was to be recognised as a separate branch of surgery four years later at an international medical congress held in London. There was increasing realisation of the value of rest, splinting and apparatus in relieving previously crippling conditions of the spine and limbs, whilst anaesthesia and antisepsis greatly extended the range of operations. Even the general hospitals began to respond. St Bartholomew's had opened an orthopaedic unit in 1864, and was followed later by the other general hospitals.

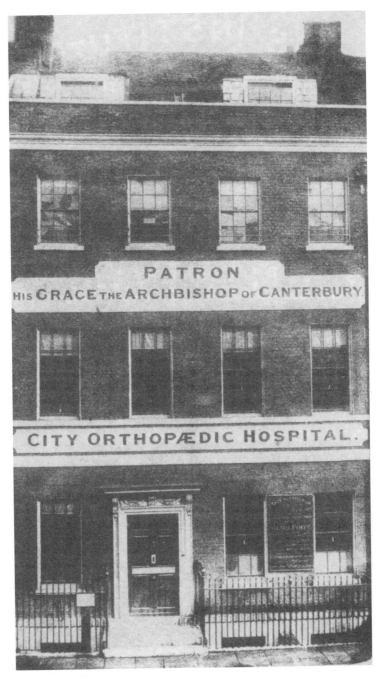

City Orthopaedic Hospital, 27 Hatton Garden, founded 1857.

The National Orthopaedic Hospital, c. 1893.

The Royal National Orthopaedic Hospital in the 1930s.

In 1922 a country branch was opened at Stanmore, which was to grow into the tail that would wag the dog as it became a centre for development over the next 50 years and activities based on the Great Portland Street headquarters were progressively transferred there. In 1947 the Great Portland Street and Stanmore sites were designated teaching hospitals as the Institute of Orthopaedics, but development was focused at Stanmore, where new wards and operating theatres, with a limb fitting centre and rehabilitation unit, were established. Debate on proposals for redevelopment at Great Portland Street within the NHS continued over many years, but owing to the complexity of the leases on the site, in 1980 the Flowers Committee and Government decided the Institute of Orthopaedics should become a member of a vast Bloomsbury Health Authority that would include University College and Middlesex Hospitals, St Peter's Group of Postgraduate Urological and Royal National Ear, Nose and Throat Hospitals. After a short term residence at the Middlesex, the Institute of Orthopaedics was transferred to Stanmore, where a 200-bedded hospital had been built and a £2 million spinal unit would be opened in 1984 by the Princess of Wales.

The nature of the work carried out has changed considerably over its history, and now the majority of surgery is on the elderly under-going a hip or knee implant, with a biomedical engineering unit called Stanmore Worldwide, which manufactures hip and knee replacements. Plans are being considered for a major rebuilding plan and moving the outpatients' department, which had remained in Great Portland Street, to the London Homoeopathic Hospital.

Another neglected area was the management of cancer patients. William Marsden had already established the Royal Free general hospital, and after the death in 1846 of his first wife, Betsy Ann, from uterine cancer at the age of 36, he turned his attention to the relief of sufferers. Reputedly, they had first met on a stagecoach to London when, aged 12, she had been orphaned and was travelling to stay with an aunt, whilst he was going to study medicine, and they were to marry four years later.

In an inaugural meeting to initiate the hospital he is recorded as saying, 'Now, gentlemen, I want to found a hospital for the treatment of cancer, and for the study of the disease, for at the present time we know absolutely nothing about it.' The Royal Marsden Hospital

Royal Marsden Hospital, 1883.

began as an out-patient dispensary in 1851 called The Free Cancer Hospital, in Cannon Row, Westminster. It had a budget of £155, of which £149 was spent on rent, furniture, advertising and drugs, with a salary of £10 p.a. for a resident assistant secretary. In the first year there were 33 desperately ill patients, some having been rejected by other hospitals as incurable. Financial support was slow to develop and an appeal to the Queen for patronage was initially rejected on the grounds that 'she must decline contributing to a hospital for the exclusive treatment of one disorder, sufferers from which malady are not excluded from general hospitals'. Later she changed her mind and became a generous patron. In fact only the Middlesex Hospital had a ward for cancer patients, set up in 1792 from a gift, but in general such patients were discharged as incurable from the general hospitals.

At first any help offered was largely palliative and any active measures, such as local caustics or surgery, without anaesthesia or antisepsis, would cause terrible suffering, and recurrence within 18 months was usual. Marsden was convinced treatment should be a combined medical and surgical approach and toured Europe to study Continental methods, without any great gain. Patient numbers and public support escalated, and the hospital moved three times before a £3,000 loan from Baroness Burdet-Coutts made possible the purchase of the present site in the Fulham Road and the building of an 80-

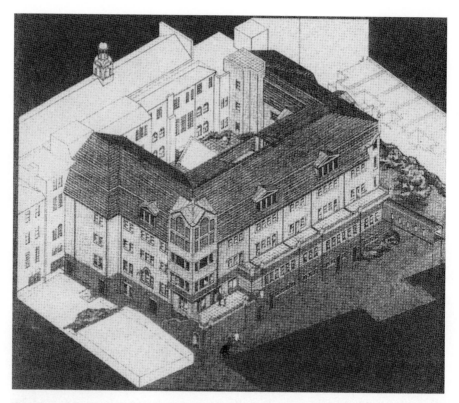

Drawing of the new wing of the Royal Marsden Hospital added to the London site in 1992.

bedded hospital, which was opened in 1862. It was to become a world leader in surgical and radiotherapy treatment of cancer as well as research, as new units were built during the 1920s and a distinct research unit was created in the new Chester Beatty building in 1939.

Within the NHS, the Minister decided the hospital should be grouped as a 'Teaching Hospital Ungrouped' and would only support patient care with research and academic work funded through the Postgraduate Medical Federation. The management of the hospital and the research unit, now institute, were separated. The institute was given the Chester Beatty building and some endowment funds with support from the Medical Research Council and other sources, but in return had to meet all the cost of physics research, half that of the medical records and 10% of the pathology and other hospital departments. The hospital was deprived of the resources of the academic staff and their own team had no right to support research.

There ensued a long period of uncertainty. Plans had been made for extensions to the radiotherapy and radio-isotope units on the existing site, but the Ministry insisted this should be focused outside central London and selected a site in Sutton, Surrey. However, the Royal Marsden was able to survive proposals to merge with the Brompton or be linked with an undergraduate teaching hospital, and became an independent Trust in 1994 with its Fulham Road branch reprieved.

In several other areas of specialist medicine London was to establish leading institutions that achieved international fame. Prior to the mid-19th century there was no facility for the care and treatment of the paralysed or epileptic, especially for the poor who could not afford nursing and medical fees. After the death of their grandmother, who was paralysed, Joanna and Louisa Chandler and their brother Edward decided to set up a hospital for the relief and care of such cases and began to raise funds through City contacts. They obtained the support of the Lord Mayor and established an ad hoc committee. They personally raised £200 by making ornaments of Barbados rice shells strung with pearls and glass beads, and 24 Queen's Square was leased at £110

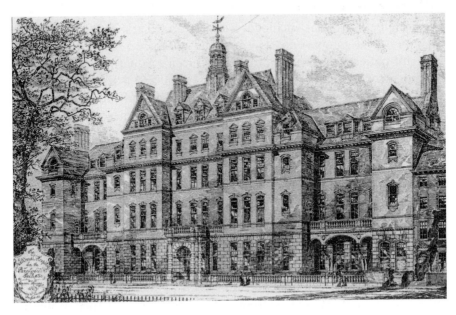

The National Hospital for the Paralysed and Epileptic.

p.a. to provide ten beds and an out-patient department. A secretary was appointed at £50 p.a. basic and 5% commission on funds he raised, and a nurse as superintendent for £21, along with an assistant for £14 with an allowance of a shilling a week for tea and sugar and a pint of beer daily. A couple were engaged as resident porter and general servant, with an unpaid resident medical officer.

Initially it would mainly be a dormitory for the paralysed and epileptic. The first patients were admitted in 1860, paying 7s a week maintenance, later increased to 10s – the first hospital to charge – although later ten beds would be set aside for those who could not afford this. The hospital expanded rapidly to 36 beds by 1866 and 64 by 1870, with a country branch at Finchley, in spite of objections from local residents to patients sitting in Queen's Square, which dated back to 1716 and was one of a nest of fashionable squares surrounded by slums, with the north side an open view to Hampstead. Staff turnover was high initially, and at one time the resident medical officer, matron and dispenser were sacked for incompetence, but a visiting German doctor compared the patient accommodation to a first-class hotel. A Samaritan fund was established, furbishing a day room with pictures and books, and providing music and entertainments that included country drives. As the National Hospital for the Paralysed and Epileptic, treatment was of a high standard from early on, with physical methods that included Russian and Turkish baths, electrotherapy and a gymnasium. The hospital continued to expand, with a new out-patient wing, and took over Queen's Square House in 1948, having absorbed Nos. 29 and 30 in the 1920s, and a Rockefeller Wing built in 1938 (40 and 41 became the Italian Hospital). It is now known as the National Hospital for Neurology and Neurosurgery.

From earliest times orthodox medical treatment was as likely to cause severe side effects as today, when this is responsible for over 10% of hospital admissions. During the 17th century herbalism was gradually replaced by chemical medicine, which was to last for the next 200 years, as the limitations and complexities of herbal medicine became apparent. Only isolated measures such as foxglove (digitalis) Peruvian bark (quinine) and opium remained established. The chemical salts of arsenic, mercury and antimony separated by Paracelsius became generally available and their use spread across Europe and America, with calomel and laudanum as the favourites. Whereas they had used these with extreme caution because of their potential toxicity, the physicians of the time were using dosages that often led to severe symptoms of poisoning and, combined with bleeding and catharsis, could be fatal.

These evident shortcomings led to total loss of confidence by patients in medical treatment, and many doctors were dispirited by this reckless abuse and turned against orthodoxy themselves.

One of the most effective of these was a young German physician called Samuel Hahnemann. During the latter half of the 18th century he totally rejected all lessons of pathology and investigation of the causation of disease as useless. He noted that effective medications such as quinine often mimicked in health the symptoms of the illness for which they were used, and postulated that treatment be confined to a single medication that mimicked these symptoms – the principle of the 'hair of the dog that bit you' – rather than the damaging multipli-

The London Homeopathic Hospital, Great Ormond Street, 1858.

city of drugs and other measures then in vogue. He named this a 'homeopathic' approach, from the Greek for 'same disease', in contrast to the 'allopathic'. Concerned at the aggravation of symptoms which higher dosage could cause, he progressively diluted the concentration of active ingredient in his medications, even to the level of a single molecule, which he considered sufficient to stimulate the vital force which everyone possessed to bring about their own cure. The effectiveness of these dilute preparations could be enhanced by repeated shaking or pounding. He was given the chance to compare his theories with orthodoxy during epidemics of typhus and cholera at this time, with impressive, successful results. His views became widely accepted and by the turn of the 19th century as many as one physician in six was practising homeopathy in the United States.

One of the first physicians to introduce homeopathy to England was Dr Frederick Quin, who had studied with Hahnemann and became physician to the future King of the Belgians. He was a prominent figure in London society, numbering Dickens, Landseer and Thackeray amongst his patients. In 1850 he raised £493 12s 6d to open the London Homeopathic Hospital with 25 beds in Golden Square, Soho. This was one of the main centres to treat patients from the Broad Street pump cholera outbreak four years later, with a mortality rate of 17% compared to 53% at the nearby Middlesex Hospital. As patient numbers grew, the hospital moved to its present site in Great Ormond Street ten years later. It would be rebuilt from 1893–5, and a new wing facing Queen Square was added in 1911.

It was absorbed into the NHS, along with the four other similar hospitals in the country, with its own management, when it became the Royal London Homeopathic Hospital. In 1972, 16 of the medical staff were killed in an aeroplane crash on their way to a congress in Brussels, and this was followed two years later by the loss of its independence under the NHS re-organisation at the time, to become part of the Bloomsbury and Islington Health Authority. Operating theatres and surgical beds had to be closed, along with the children's and geriatric wards, reducing the number of beds from 170 to 75, and it continued to contract to a single ward.

The hospital responded by developing its complementary medicine services to include Iscador therapy for cancer, an acupuncture clinic and relaxation therapies such as manual medicine and autogenic training. Intensive public support and acceptance by the Government that 'patient choice' should include homeopathy and other forms of

206

The Chelsea Hospital for Women, c.1908.

The No.1 Australian Hospital, Harefield, 1918.

The 'Long Ramp', a covered walkway and the main thoroughfare of the Australian Hospital, 1918.

complementary medicine within the NHS enabled the hospital to achieve independent full Trust status in 1993 and the opening of an Academic Unit to study the 'Evidence Base of Complementary Medicine'. Financial pressures compelled the RLHH Trust to merge with the Parkside Health Trust, retaining its name, and to develop contracts for services to 23 health authorities, as well as plans to redevelop the antiquated building, unchanged since 1911, to house the Royal London Homeopathic Hospital along with other organisations with synergistic work.

In more recent times a number of hospitals have achieved a reputation in specialist areas from a general background, often due to the skill and dedication of an individual or team of doctors.

One of the best known of these is at Harefield Park, Middlesex, which began as a mansion house built some 300 years ago. In 1914 it was offered to the Melbourne Ministry of Defence as a repatriation centre for the sick and wounded soldiers of the Australian Imperial Force, by the owner Charles Billyard-Leake. As the 'Australian Hospital' it became a convalescent centre and clearing house which

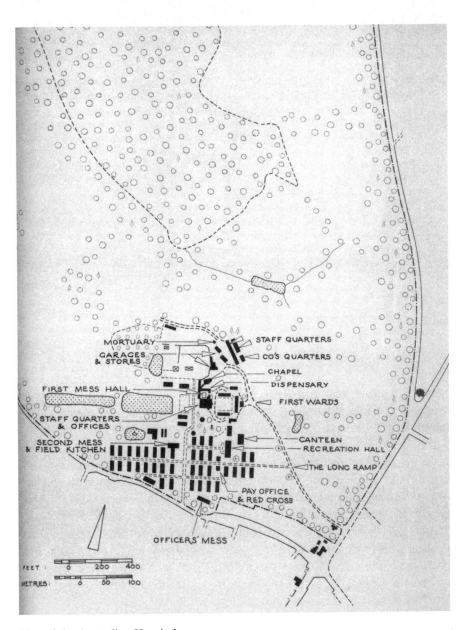

Plan of the Australian Hospital.

209

Aerial view of Harefield Hospital, c.1975.

would handle over 50,000 patients, and a second home for many, even with cockatoos and wallabies as pets. The patients were housed in hutted wards, connected by a long ramp that ran as a covered way the length of the main thoroughfare. 114 soldiers were buried in St Mary's Churchyard, Harefield.

After the First World War it was converted into a sanatorium and, during the surgical era for the treatment of tuberculosis, developed into a unit that attracted outstanding surgical nursing staff that created a leading reputation for the hospital in this field. Led by Sir Thomas Holmes Sellors, it would develop into the major cardio-thoracic surgical unit in the country, where later one of the first successful heart transplants was carried out by Sir Magdi Yacoub. It has so far been able to resist threats to close it down and transfer the work to a London teaching hospital.

A second centre of excellence in the field of cardio-thoracic surgery has been established at Papworth, Cambridgeshire, which has been selected by the Government as one of the twelve sites for their plans to bring the NHS up-to-date, and implement a 'European Working Time

Directive'. It is one of the first hospitals to inform patients, the public and clinical partners about how it measures clinical outcomes following cardiac surgery and is a pioneer in audit and clinical quality.

A National Centre of Excellence for patients with spinal cord injuries that has acquired an international reputation began as an isolation hospital built in the 1920s at Aylesbury in Buckinghamshire. The transformation began in 1944 under the direction of Dr Ludwig Guttman when a National Spine Injuries Centre (NSIC) was opened, which now has 113 beds and has treated over 10,000 patients of all ages. They are admitted as soon as possible after injury and follow-up care continues after discharge for the rest of their lives. The now International Paralympic Games was started in 1952. Patients are referred from all over the country, and from overseas. The NSIC has been part of the Stoke Mandeville Hospital which also hosts many other units, including plastic surgery, and has undergone major redevelopment and is now part of overall Buckingham Hospitals NHS Trusts.

A centre that has looked after chronic disabled patients for over one hundred and fifty years is the Royal Hospital for Neurodisability. It was established in 1854 by Andrew Need, a non-conformist pastor who had already opened four other Asylums for Orphans and Idiots,

Melrose Hall, c.1800, the site of the present Royal Hospital for Neuro-Disability. This original house was bought in 1863 for £18,000.

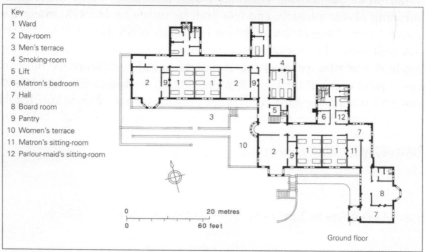

Key
1 Ward
2 Day-room
3 Men's terrace
4 Smoking-room
5 Lift
6 Matron's bedroom
7 Hall
8 Board room
9 Pantry
10 Women's terrace
11 Matron's sitting-room
12 Parlour-maid's sitting-room

Ground floor

The British Home and Hospital for Incurables, 1894, plus the plan of its ground floor.

such as the 'Hospital for Incurables' with the backing of Charles Dickens in raising funds in an old workhouse at Carshalton housing four patients. Within four years it had moved to Putney House where numbers built up towards 200, and finally moved to its present site at Melrose Hall on West Hill in Putney in 1864. It now houses 240 long-term disabled aged over 18, with women predominating four to one, who were initially fee-paying and now supported by Primary Care Trusts and Social Services.

The hospital became increasingly involved in the long term care of chronic neurological conditions either inherited, such as Huntington's Chorea and motor neurone disease, or acquired from accident or illness such as multiple sclerosis or strokes. It developed a Neurological Rehabilitation Management Unit for patients with mixed severe physical and behavioural problems as well as the first dedicated Brain Injury unit in the UK. It has a unit for people who need long-term assisted ventilation and do not need to remain in acute hospital care. In view of its dedicated areas of interest the name was changed to the Royal Hospital for Neurodisability in 1995.

Specified care for the terminally ill was spasmodic historically, but there are now over 240 hospice units with over 3,000 residential beds throughout the United Kingdom. These include the Marie Curie Cancer and Sue Ryder Care Centres, of which twenty-five are for children. The original centre was St Christopher's Hospice started by Dame Cicely Saunders in 1967. A quarter are financed through NHS facilities, with the rest dependent on charity. The average in-patient stay is two weeks, and there are an equal number of palliative day-care units working within the community including specially trained Macmillan nurses. Help the Hospice is a national charity that gives financial support, training and overall help to the United Kingdom network, based at 34–44 Britannia Street, London, and liaises with similar organisations overseas.

Special hospitals in London in 1872 and their subsequent history

	Foundation	
Belgrave Hospital for Children, Cumberland Street SW	1866	Closed 1985. Associated with King's College Hospital 1948
British Hospital of Diseases of the Skin, Great Marlborough Street and Finsbury Square	1864	Closed circa 1906
British Lying-in Hospital, Endell Street, WC	1749	British Hospital for Mothers and Babies, Woolwich 1913, now a charity
Cancer Hospital	1851	Now the Royal Marsden Hospital

Central London Ophthalmic Hospital, Gray's Inn Road	1843	Amalgamated with the Royal London and Royal Westminster Ophthalmic Hospitals January 1947
Chelsea Hospital for Women, King's Road, Chelsea	1871	Rebuilt in Dovehouse Street 1916. Now merged with Queen Charlotte's
City of London Hospital for Diseases of the Chest, Victoria Park	1848	Founded as a dispensary; in-patients from 1855; now merged with the Brompton
City Orthopaedic Hospital, Hatton Garden	1851	Amalgamated in 1908 with the Royal National Orthopaedic Hospital
City of London Lying-in Hospital, City Road	1750	Became City of London Maternity Hospital. Closed 1983
East London Hospital for Children and Dispensary for Women	1868	Renamed Princess Elizabeth of York Hospital for Children (1932); amalgamated with the Queen's Hospital for Children (1942) to form Queen Elizabeth Hospital for Children; closed 1963
Evelina Hospital for Sick Children, Southwark Bridge Road	1869	Building closed in 1973 on relocation within Guy's
French Hospital and Dispensary, Lisle St, Leicester Square	1867	Closed 1965; reopened in 1967 as the Shaftesbury Hospital
General Lying-in Hospital, York Road, Lambeth	1765	Closed 1971 (associated with St Thomas's)
German Hospital, Dalston	1845	Closed 1987. Now MacIntyre Psychiatric Care Clinic
Hospital for Consumption and Diseases of the Chest, Fulham Road	1841	Now the Brompton Hospital
Hospital for Diseases of the Skin, Blackfriars EC	1841	Closed 1948

Hospital for Diseases of the Throat, Golden Square	1863	Amalgamated with Central London ENT Hospital 1939. Closed 1982
Hospital for Epilepsy and Paralysis, Portman Square	1866	Now National Hospital for Neurology and Neurosurgery, Queens Square
Hospital for Sick Children, Great Ormond Street	1852	Still extant
Hospital for Women, Soho Square	1843	Now part of UCHL Group
Hospital for Women and Children, Vincent Square	1866	Renamed the Grosvenor Hospital for Women; joined St Thomas's group; closed 1976
Lock Hospital and Asylum, Westbourne Grove and Dean Street	1746	Closed 1952; beds transferred to St Charles' Hospital
London Fever Hospital, Liverpool Road	1802	Amalgamated with Royal Free Hospital Group 1948; closed 1973
London Homeopathic Hospital, Queen Square	1849	Now Royal London Homeopathic Hospital
London Infirmary for Diseases of the Legs, Ulcers, and Varicose Veins, Red Lion Square	1857	Closed around 1888
Lying-in Institution, Newman Street, Oxford Street	1787	Closed around 1888
Margaret Street Infirmary for Consumption and Diseases of the Chest	1847	Ceased to provide in-patient facilities and finally closed around 1947
Metropolitan Ear, Nose and Throat Hospital	1838	Moved to St Mary Abbot's, 1953
National Hospital for Diseases of the Heart, Newman Street, Oxford Street	1857	Rebuilt as National Heart Hospital, Westmoreland Street; now associated with the Brompton and London Chest Hospitals

National Institution for Diseases of the Skin, Gray's Inn Road	1866	Renamed Central London Institution in 1888; closed circa 1890
National Orthopaedic Hospital, 234 Great Portland Street	1836	Amalgamated with Royal Orthopaedic Hospital in 1905 to form the Royal National Orthopaedic Hospital
North Eastern Hospital for Children, 125 Hackney Road	1867	Renamed The Queen's (1908); amalgamated with East London Hospital for Children (1942) to form Queen Elizabeth Hospital for Children; now part of Hospitals for Sick Children group
North London Hospital for Consumption, Hampstead	1860	Transferred to Northwood and became Mount Vernon Hospital
Queen Charlotte's Lying-in Hospital, Marylebone Road	1739	Rebuilt and opened on site in Goldhawk Road, 1940. Transferred to Hammersmith 2001
Royal Hospital for Diseases of the Chest, City Road	1814	Rebuilt 1863, joined Great (Royal) Northern Group of hospitals in 1924; closed circa 1950
Royal Infirmary for Children and Women, Waterloo Bridge Road	1810	Closed in 1976 when north wing of St Thomas's opened
Royal London Ophthalmic Hospital, Moorfields, EC	1804	Now Moorfields Eye Hospital (City Road); amalgamated under a private Act 1947 with Royal Westminster Ophthalmic Hospital
Royal Orthopaedic Hospital, 315 Oxford Street	1838	Amalgamated with National Orthopaedic Hospital in 1905 to form the Royal National Orthopaedic Hospital

Royal South London Ophthalmic Hospital, St George's Circus	1857	Royal Eye Hospital; transferred to St Thomas's Hospital
Royal Westminster Ophthalmic Hospital, King William Street, Charing Cross	1816	Moved in 1927; now Moorfields Eye Hospital, High Holborn
St John's Hospital for Diseases of the Skin, Leicester Square	1863	Now located at St Thomas's
St Mark's Hospital for Fistula and Other Diseases of the Rectum, City Road	1835	Linked with St Bartholomew's. Clinical Services transferred to Northwick Park, 1995
St Peter's Hospital for Stone and Diseases of the Genito-urinary Organs, Berners Street	1860	Associated with St Paul's Hospital within Institute of Urology
Samaritan Free Hospital for Women and Children	1847	Now managed as part of the St Mary's group
Seamen's Hospital, Greenwich	1821	Initially located afloat in the 'Grampus', then the 'Dreadnought' and finally the 'Caledonia'; came ashore in 1870 to the Royal Hospital. Closed 1986
Smallpox and Vaccination Hospital	1746	Change of use in 1880s; now part of the Whittington Hospital
Victoria Hospital for Children, Chelsea	1846	Largely rebuilt in 1866; because part of St George's group; closed 1966
Western Ophthalmic Hospital	1856	Now managed as part of the St Mary's group

Chapter 8

Cottage Hospitals

The middle of the 19th century saw the initiation of another uniquely British hospital concept, the so-called 'cottage hospital' industry. By then most larger towns had a major general voluntary hospital alongside a network of workhouse infirmaries, but there was no local facility for the acutely ill in the rural areas or the great increase in the number of injured that occurred in the small towns that sprang up with the development of industrial and mining communities.

Those requiring medical attention were faced with a long dangerous journey by farm-cart to reach hospital, where the death rate from infection was high. The concept of a local 'cottage' hospital is attributed to Albert Napper, a GP in the Surrey village of Cranleigh, thirty five miles from the nearest hospital, St Thomas's in London and eight miles from the nearest workhouse at Guildford, a degrading place with no trained staff. He opened a unit in 1859 within a small cottage at the centre of his practice typical of the time, with a kitchen and back shed downstairs and a narrow step ladder leading up to two small bedrooms, one of which would hold four beds and the other would be an operating room. The unit was cheap to run with only one non-resident nurse and patients expected to pay 5 shillings a week towards their maintenance, which the Poor Law Officer would meet for paupers as an alternative to a placing in the overcrowded workhouse.

Within four months this idea was picked up by the British Medical Journal, particularly supporting the concept that patients should pay, in contrast to the situation in the major London voluntary hospitals where beds were filled with the staff of their sponsors who could well afford to pay. The ball was quickly picked up and a second cottage hospital opened at Fowey in Cornwall in 1860 followed by Bourton-on-the-Water in Gloucestershire and Iver in Bucks in 1863. Dr Winter would write an article in the 1866 edition of 'Good Words' and increasingly facilities would be set up, often in a donated cottage, to serve the 'large and deserving class who supported families by honest labour and have no claim upon Parish Relief'. These would be run by a local committee that included doctors and a parson and were

219

Cranleigh Village Hospital, Surrey, 1859.

basically a voluntary cooperative, with paid administrators a later development. The concept would become widely adopted and both Victorian philanthropists and the Unions would set up hospitals in locations ranging from the countryside to industrial and mining communities.

In 1870 Dr Harold Sweet published a handbook that covered every aspect of cottage hospital running and listed 80 around England. They had a range of names besides 'village' or 'cottage' to 'rural', 'miner's accident' or 'quarry' according to the area. The one at Middlesbrough was founded by two Anglican sisters after a serious factory explosion, when the nearest treatment available was at the hospital 40 miles away at Newcastle. The early ones were usually of humble origin, a motley collection of cottages, converted old schools and warehouses. Broadwood House, Capel, was an old house that had housed a flock of sheep at night on the ground floor. Later many would be more grandiose and purpose built. At that time the village doctor was trained in surgery and would carry out a full range of operations at the cottage hospital including amputations, lithotomy and cataract, besides the standard procedures of cupping and bleeding.

220

Trained nurses were opposed as they tended to be bossy and would expect their own room, either too pious or drunk and disorderly, and a neighbourly 'good soul' with some nursing background, was preferred.

Petersfield Cottage Hospital, 1871, along with a plan of its ground floor.

The cottage hospital was faced with all the problems of the large voluntary hospitals. A major one due to their often isolated circumstances was the lack of any proper sanitary system and a big step forward was the development of the Moule's Earth Closet, adapted from the army.

In 1877 Sir Henry Burdett, who had a background of Medical Superintendent at Greenwich Naval Hospital, followed by his establishment of the Prince of Wales Trust, which would become the King's Hospital Fund for London, wrote a book in which he defined the basic principles and standards for a cottage hospital. These included limitation in size to a maximum of six beds, open to all local doctors, which would receive the fees paid by the patients or their unions. He advocated standards of nursing and cleanliness, defining patients' clothing and visiting hours as well as the need for closure to allow regular repainting.

Another problem for smaller units would be their heavier running costs and some would have to close if initial support failed. The main cost was the rent, as wages were minimal with the nurse often paid for with an allowance of beer and wine which was costlier than the drug bill. The medical staff were the local GPs and the only one to appoint a Resident Medical Officer, at Twickenham, nearly went bankrupt. At Fowey the patients or their family would provide the food for the nurse to cook, or run an invalid meal service. In mining and industrial areas the owners might give grants or the workers form a club with a shilling a week deducted from their pay (sixpence for children), from which the doctor would be paid with an income that could match the best town practice.

In all, over six hundred so-called 'cottage' hospitals would be established. Queen Victoria had nine children and this plethora of princesses and princes, along with local gentry, were pleased to lay foundation stones. Her Golden and Diamond Jubilees were great stimuli and Victorian hospitals sprang up all over Britain, with many more to be founded as memorials after the First World War. The church in general would only play a minor part as a 'fairy godfather', although a number of hospitals would be founded by the Catholic clergy and run by nuns, as was the pattern across Europe.

The middle classes began to view their local cottage hospital as a safer place for surgery with better nursing and control of infection. Private beds would be created and some of the hospitals enlarged to as many as 30–70 beds with up-to-date operating facilities and an X-ray machine – usually a small one operated by the doctor or matron and a physiotherapy unit.

There was great publicity at the time about maternal mortality in hospitals where patients could expect every professional care and comfort, compared with the often poor circumstances at home. In 1856 Sir James Simpson quoted the research figures of a Dr Leon Le Fort showing the mortality rate in labour at home to be 1 in 212 compared with 1 in 29 in hospital. Three years earlier a letter to *The Times* pointed out the average mortality in deliveries by the midwives from the Royal Maternity Charity carried out at home was only one third of that in hospital. It was suggested that large maternity hospitals should be closed down and replaced by smaller cottage style ones reserved for maternity cases, and this led to the establishment of many small maternity hospitals over the next 40 years. These would become a popular alternative to home delivery and more than 120 small maternity hospitals serviced by GPs would be started.

The improvement in facilities would attract an increasing proportion of the better members of the profession into country practice with an increase in local surgery at a limited level, whilst links were formed with hospital specialists to visit locally. By 1930, of 73,000 'voluntary hospital' beds over 12,000 were in cottage hospitals.

A rapidly expanding area with no local county or poorhouse hospital might be absorbed or developed by the local authority to establish a full-scale hospital. The Royal Victoria in Bournemouth was built in 1887 and expanded with new departments in 1909. The Princess Alice in Eastbourne became the local hospital until it could be replaced by a new District General Hospital.

With the advent of the National Health Service the country was

The Princess Alice Memorial Hospital, Eastbourne, 1883.

divided into regions, then subdivided into groups in each of which a central hospital was selected as a nucleus. The cottage hospitals were dismissed as peripheral satellites dependent on raising money by charity that would be expensive to maintain. It was not appreciated by the administrators that they were an extension of local primary care rather than a peripheral secondary service and they would be lumped with all other types of small hospital with more than half to be closed down in the early years or absorbed into empires.

Many of the closures aroused violent antagonism initially, before the authorities could achieve their purpose, as at Kingston-upon-Thames and Victoria. In the hospital plan produced in 1962 Enoch Powell planned to remodel 134 hospitals and build 90 new ones, with over 1,000 to be closed or 'amalgamated', including many cottage type, geriatric and small general hospitals. The 'powers that be' decided on large units of 300 beds initially, increased to over 600 later, serving areas of population numbering 150,000, but in 1969 the Oxford Regional Hospital Board decided on a policy of decentralisation with the establishment of 'community hospitals' with beds for selective categories of non-surgical patients and a Day Hospital that could offer some basic services and consultant clinics. Coincidentally, an Association of General Practitioner Hospitals was formed at the same time and within a short time twenty Community Hospitals were opened, with more under development.

A much copied example of this development was Rye, Winchelsea & District Memorial Hospital that was built as a war memorial in the 1920s and closed down in the early days of the NHS. It had a history as a military hospital in Mermaid Street during the Napoleonic wars. A local district hospital was twelve miles away from Rye with poor access by public transport and an appeal raised two million pounds to allow the purchase of a property which could be converted into a Memorial Care Centre. Now the Health Authority, Social Services and voluntary agencies work together to provide a range of community services ranging from out-patient clinics to a base from which the Primary Care Services can operate, including a Day Centre for the chronically ill who can remain in home care.

One cottage hospital that would achieve international renown was the Queen Victoria Hospital, East Grinstead, Sussex, founded in 1863 by a local practitioner, Dr John Roberts, who gave his services free, but received no support from the local establishment who would send their servants there. It was closed in 1874, but thirteen years later a local family rented a house to support a hospital with five beds which would acquire local interest. Patients were fee-paying, and the resident nurse paid in ale only initially, later to receive a salary and uniform. Infectious fevers were refused except for diphtheria cases requiring tracheotomy. Patient pressure on the hospital multiplied and in 1902 it was moved to a building provided by a long standing family of benefactors, the Oswald-Smiths, when it acquired its present name. Thirty years later a further move was made to the present site into a purpose-built hospital, which became the base at which Sir Archibald McIndoe, the famous plastic surgeon, in 1939 set up a specialised treatment centre for war casualties with facial injuries and burns. These would form the 'Guinea Pig Club', whilst a special ward was funded by the Canadian Government in memory of their many airmen treated there during the war.

In the earlier days when funding was desperate, a local benefactor, Mr Gordon Clemetson, had started a Peanut Club in 1931 with the help of a local newspaper that offered a bag of peanuts to anyone who donated 12 new pennies to the Hospital Fund. Within the NHS there was increasing conflict between the remote regional and local management committees, with criticism of the high running costs which were defended by the specialist nature of treatments offered alongside a local general and children's hospital service. This was resolved and the complex remains an international post-graduate training centre for

Queen Victoria Hospital, East Grinstead, 1990.

oral and cornea plastic surgery as well as the burns facility. It has recently been recognised as one of the first to be awarded the status of a Foundation Hospital.

Chapter 9

Maternity Hospitals and Midwifery

Women and children came last in the queue for medical help. In earliest times childbirth was an unaided affair, the mother biting through the cord after her child was born. Later she may have had some help during delivery from her husband, but then he would often claim all the credit for a successful outcome. By the custom of couvade, he would take to the bed for a week or more and be waited upon with as much attention as if he had undergone the labour himself, whilst his wife returned to her normal household duties. Later still, her delivery would be assisted by the elder women of the family, and then 'experienced women' as the forerunners of midwives. The first obstetricians were recorded in the Hindu sacred books of Brahma around 1400 BC as priest-physicians who would help complicated cases. In ancient Greece deliveries were handled by midwives who, under Athenian law, had to be post-menopausal mothers, and were of two levels of experience. The juniors would handle ordinary deliveries, whilst the seniors, called 'doctor midwives', were called in for difficult cases and allowed to carry out abortions, which were commonplace at the time. They also played the role of match-makers, advising men on the young girl most likely to produce the best children. A doctor would only be called at the end of an obstructed labour to cut out the child piecemeal.

The role of the midwife remained dominant in delivery, with little contribution from the medical profession, and it was considered immoral for the doctor as well as the husband to be present. Old 16th-century prints show women, children and even dogs in the birth room, but no men. Although books were published in the 16th century for the guidance of midwives, these were based on second-hand knowledge, even one that became the basis of examinations in Zurich, and were read aloud by a 'well-read woman' when she was attending a childbirth. A Dr Wertt of Hamburg in 1522 was aware of the need to attend a labour if he was to study the process and, knowing that as a man he would not be allowed into a lying-in room, disguised himself as a woman. When discovered he was arrested and burnt to death.

227

There remained a great deal of pagan superstition in relation both to the process of childbirth and the afterbirth, which the Church was determined to stamp out. Stillbirth or a deformed baby and even multiple births were regarded as satanic possession, and the midwife concerned was in danger of being treated as a witch during the time of the Inquisition.

Formal training and regulation of midwives was a later development in Britain than on the Continent and many were uneducated women of low calibre who would include abortion and concealment of illegitimate births amongst their activities. Many an English 'with-woman' or midwife of the 16th century used heather charms and incantations, and in difficult labours a special girdle embroidered with mystic figures from the Druid days would be placed around the mother's abdomen. Henry VIII introduced legislation for the regulation of physicians and surgeons in 1512; apart from graduates of Oxford and Cambridge, they had to obtain a licence to practise from a bishop. This was extended to midwives, who had to apply for a licence to practise to the Bishop's Court. This was more concerned with the soul of the newborn than the quality of care for the mother, and more concerned with character references from the parson and 'honest matrons' they had delivered, than any evidence of midwifery competence, as had become required on the Continent. A midwife had to swear a long and detailed oath as to her standards of conduct and was allowed to baptise any infant likely to die before it could be taken to a priest. She was even expected to remove the child by Caesarean section if the mother died, so that it should not die unchristened and its soul be lost. Any midwife in practice without a licence could be brought before the churchwardens for punishment, although many continued until eventually the Midwives Act of 1902 established a central register.

From earliest times some sort of birth stool or obstetric chair was customary for labour, which the domestic midwife would trundle from house to house. In the middle of the 17th century it began to be abandoned, after the publication of a textbook by a Parisian obstetrician, Mauriceau, who delivered his patients in bed. Many midwives were dangerously ignorant of anatomy and the birth process and would tie the mother to the birth chair, urging her to bear down before the cervix was dilated, or even manually stretching it in the belief that the baby could be 'stuck' to the mother's back, causing severe damage. Another vogue from Roman times, which persisted well into the 17th century, was 'swaddling' to press the baby into good

228

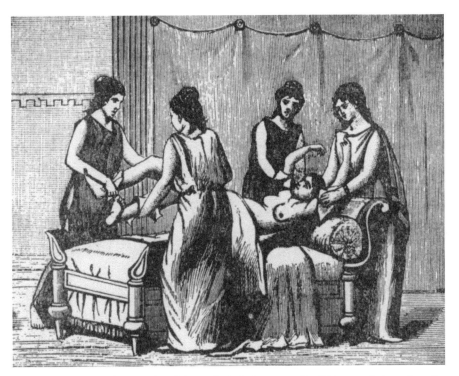

Ancient methods of hastening labour included repeatedly lifting and dropping the woman.

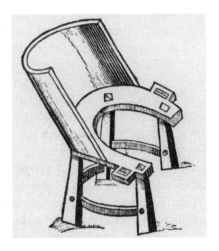

An obstetrical chair.

The obstetrical chair in use.

shape and control any deformities. Each limb was bandaged separately and then the whole body into a state of mummification, after being rubbed in oil of roses if from a wealthy family, or butter and warm wine if poorer in earlier times, and merely salted later in England.

In the 16th century surgeons began to turn their attention to care. Ambroise Pare in Paris re-introduced the art of podalic version, which had been used in ancient times to turn the malpresented child and deliver it by traction on the feet. The next step forward came from the Chamberlens, a refugee Huguenot family who settled in England in 1569. Successive generations became the leading obstetricians over the next two centuries. The first generation of two brothers settled down in surgical practice, but were in constant conflict with the College of Physicians for practising medicine outside their terms of authority. They also supported the midwives who had applied to form a corporation for their education and regulation. One of the brothers was actually imprisoned, but pardoned by the intervention of the Queen, to whom he had become a royal physician. He was probably the inventor of the family 'secret' that was handed on through the next generations and only revealed shortly before the death of the last of the line in 1728. This was the obstetric forceps, which became generally adopted within a few years. It had been steadily improved by each generation and enabled the Chamberlens to deliver women more effectively than any obstetrician before them. They went to fantastic lengths to keep their secret, arriving in a special carriage containing a large box with gilded carvings suggesting it contained large complicated machinery. The woman was blindfolded during labour, with no-one else allowed in the locked lying-in room.

The Chamberlen family was to retain their royal connection, and one was attending Mary Beatrice, the second wife of James II, during her pregnancy. She went into premature labour and was delivered before Hugh Chamberlen could arrive. It was rumoured that the baby was not the Queen's and had been smuggled into the palace by the midwife in a warming pan. King James was exiled shortly afterwards and it was laid down that the chief Ministers of State had to be present to witness the birth of any future heir to the throne. This was eased to their waiting in an adjoining room, a duty passed on to the Home Secretary and only finally abolished at the time of Princess Elizabeth's pregnancies.

Throughout the 17th century the appointment of midwives remained in the hands of the bishops, who continued to license suitable women, mostly married or widowed middle-aged mothers 'of good moral character'. Episcopal authority would gradually be lost; in London by 1720 and the provinces by the end of the century. During this time the state of the midwife, unregulated and mostly without any knowledge or training, steadily declined, in contrast to the rest of Europe, where schemes of training and regulations were being introduced under government control. Although midwifery would only become part of medical study a hundred years later, the advent of forceps required some surgical training, and a role in delivery was attractive financially for the GP as an entry to medical care for the family. By the middle of the 18th century it was stated that 'every young surgeon now intends to practise midwifery' and private schools began to spring up with 'lying-in hospitals'. As more male doctors entered the field it became fashionable for the wealthier to employ them for normal labours. Led by a letter in the *Lancet*, there were even suggestions that the whole of midwifery would be safer in the hands of men, but by no means were all the early 'men-midwives' trained, and some were considered more dangerous than the most ignorant midwives from their misuse of forceps and other instruments.

A man-midwife.

Many of the women who practised as midwives carried out a useful service for the poor and outside the cities, servicing normal deliveries at minimal charges and calling for medical help for any complications, and there was increasing support for their training and regulation.

This had been introduced in Scotland when Edinburgh town council appointed a first Professor of Midwifery in 1726, followed later by Glasgow.

In 1756 Edinburgh began to teach medical students as well as midwives and obtained midwifery beds in the Edinburgh Royal Infirmary. Demand became so great that the school moved to a separate site in 1793, and later to a purpose-built building with maternity wards and a separate labour ward. In 1939 it finally settled in the Simpson Memorial Maternity Pavilion adjoining the Royal Infirmary.

A caricature by Rowlandson of a midwife going to attend a labour, 1800.

There was little progress in England and the image of the midwife as an ignorant drunken woman was typified by Charles Dickens's Sarah Gamp. Gradually efforts were initiated to raise her status, led by Florence Nightingale, who opened a training school in 1861 as an annexe at King's College, but it had to be closed because of puerperal sepsis. A 'Ladies' Medical College' was started in 1862 and began to run lecture courses on midwifery and diseases of women and children, and the lecturer, who had been formerly Professor of Obstetrics and Gynaecology at University College, said his course was exactly the same as for the medical students. The trained midwives formed an elite group who worked privately.

An Obstetrical Society had been set up in 1826 in London to develop an original system of midwife training and regulation, but made little progress until 1872, when it set up an examination board and issued a diploma. This required a training that included 25 supervised deliveries, more than medical students would achieve. It would be 1886 before midwifery was included in the medical student examination curriculum and another two years before they had to spend three months in labour wards, compelling all medical schools to create maternity units.

There was increasing pressure for the formal registration of trained midwives, supported by the British Medical Association, but there was intense opposition from all directions, including many of the untrained midwives themselves, who were afraid they would lose their work. The British Nurses' Association was in the midst of a battle to achieve registration for nurses and considered midwives should be supplemented by a better-trained 'obstetric nurse' working under medical supervision. Many obstetricians were supportive, but most general practitioners, led by a Dr Rentoul in Liverpool, vehemently opposed the idea, as they feared a trained registered midwife would encroach on their private practice with the loss of the 'doctor's guinea' for attendance at labour.

A Private Member's Bill was initially presented to Parliament in 1890, but it was stalled, and modified versions were represented at regular intervals until eventually a Central Midwives Board was established in 1902.

This created a State Certified Midwife 17 years before nurses became State Registered. To practise under the title of 'mid-wife', a woman had to be registered on the board roll, which within three years numbered over 22,000. Less than half held an Obstetrical Society or hospital certificate; the rest were accepted as 'bona-fide' members due to recognition of their experience in practice, although many were totally illiterate and had to have their application forms filled in for them. A few worked for maternity hospitals or charities, but most practised on their own account privately in the patient's home. Illegal attendance would continue for some time, often with the collusion of the local general practitioner, who would continue to collect his fee, as 'cover'.

Proposals that the midwife's licence should be renewed annually and the board should be placed under the authority of the General Medical Council were rejected and it was placed directly under the Privy Council. The board laid down strict regulation of the midwives' conduct and practice in minutest detail, from the clothes she wore to defining her duties to the mother and child at birth and for the following ten days, including the records she had to keep and when to send for a doctor. Even their private lives were regulated. They were expected to be virtuous and were liable to be struck off for any reported lapses in 'moral behaviour'. Supervision was in the hands of the local civil authorities, ranging from the medical officer of health to the sanitary inspector, and many would be harassed from jealousy or chauvinism. As a result, during the earlier years many were brought before the board on disciplinary charges of a trivial nature, but it would be 1947 before these rules were reviewed.

The initial training period laid down by the board for its examinations was three months, and the three London lying-in hospitals negotiated to provide this for a fee of £25, extended to five months for £33. This was steadily extended to two years, and in time most midwives would be trained nurses. During the initial years maternal deaths remained stubbornly high at 4 per 1,000 live births, in spite of the increase in trained midwives, although infant mortality had halved. In an effort to bring about an overall improvement in maternity services, the Government brought in a 1936 Midwives Act under which the local authorities were to introduce a salaried whole-time midwifery service for all, free or at reduced cost where necessary. The midwife would become a salaried professional employee of the local authority, extending ante-natal and post-natal care, and with an increasing proportion of hospital deliveries, especially where any complications might be present.

The first specific maternity hospital was founded in Dublin in 1745 by Bartholomew Mosse, an Irish surgeon with no funds, wealthy contacts or experience in hospital management. With help from friends he was able to rent a house that had been used as a theatre and opened the Dublin Lying-in Hospital with 10 beds, increased to 28. The early results were exceptional in economy as well as medically, with maternal and infant death rates far superior to its early London counterparts. But he envisaged a hospital with 150 beds and, realising that concerts and lotteries would have to be the main source of income, opened the hospital office for the sale of State Lottery tickets in London, relying on the charity of prize-winners to donate their stake to the hospital committee. He raised enough money to rent a large estate where he established a walled-in entertainment and leisure centre similar to the Vauxhall Gardens in London with great success, and the hospital building was started in 1751. Due to recurrent financial crises it was 1757 before it would be opened and granted a Royal Charter by George II, after support by large grants from the Lord Mayor and the Irish Government, who also awarded a tax levy on all licensed sedan chairs and coaches within a mile of the hospital. In 1757 the Rotunda was built to include a concert hall with an auditorium 80 feet in diameter and 40 feet high, with 18 Corinthian pillars 25 feet high; a ballroom was added later.

The hospital expanded rapidly and became a major teaching centre for medical students and midwives. As elsewhere, epidemics of puerperal fever would occur, although not to the peaks in other European centres. In the 1860s the maternal death rate averaged 3.4%, but the hospital was closed on two occasions for cleansing when patients had to be refused admission and treated at home. Admissions were to fall from over 3,000 annually to 1,000, and a retired Master suggested in 1867 that the large hospital was dangerous and should be closed and replaced by 30 small cottages with three beds in each for two patients and a nurse. This idea was rejected, and the problem of puerperal fever was gradually overcome with the introduction of antiseptics and disciplines in cleanliness. Puerperal sepsis had bedevilled maternity hospitals since their origin and made delivery in them far more dangerous than at home, where it rarely occurred.

At no time did the Rotunda's level of maternal deaths approach levels common in Europe. Puerperal fever would begin shortly after childbirth, with a high fever and symptoms of 'blood poisoning', and was epidemic in the lying-in hospitals that developed in Europe during

The house in George's Lane, Dublin that became Dublin's first Lying-in Hospital for Poor Women on its opening in 1745.

The Rotunda Hospital and Round Rooms, Dublin, c.1785.

The New Hospital, 1754.

the 18th century. In the Hotel Dieu in Paris and in Vienna as many as 20% of women admitted died within a week of delivery during an epidemic that peaked in 1772, when it was said that in Lombardy not a single woman survived childbirth and it was seriously suggested all lying-in hospitals should be closed.

From 1840 in Vienna obstetric work at the hospital was carried out in two clinics. The first was restricted to teaching medical students, who were taught on the female cadaver and then went on the wards to examine the women; and the second was confined to training midwives, who were not allowed in the dissecting or post-mortem rooms. The average mortality from puerperal sepsis in the first clinic, to which women begged not to be admitted, rose to four times as high as in the second. The problem was studied by a new assistant appointed to the clinic, Dr Semmelweis, who concluded the only possible explanation was that infected material was carried by students and doctors from the dissecting room to the patients they examined in labour. Against intense resentment he ordered them to scrub their hands in a solution of chloride of lime before touching a patient, and within a year the death rate had fallen from a level as high as 30% to 1%, the level of home deliveries. He went further and advocated that any midwifery teaching should only be started after the student had completed his pathology and post-mortem studies.

His views were naturally criticised by many in the profession, but gradually the evidence became overwhelming and his principles became widely adopted and it was realised that besides the birth attendants, infection could be carried by the patient herself, her family, or dust in the cubicles where infected patients had been nursed. Puerperal fever could be largely eliminated by the strictest standards of discipline in the medical attendants, scrubbing up, cleansing cubicles and the isolation of any infectious cases.

The first maternity beds in England were provided at the Middlesex Hospital in 1747 and these created a crisis. Dr Sandys had been appointed as 'man-midwife extraordinary', with five beds for lying-in cases. He had promised to restrict himself to these, but was found to be plotting with the chaplain to turn the hospital into maternity cases only. As a compromise the proportion of lying-in beds was increased and a separate maternity department included when a new hospital was built in Berners Street on its present site, whilst Sandys went on to found the Lying-in Hospital in Long Acre with William Hunter.

Over the next few years a number of hospitals confined to midwifery were to open in London through charitable support. The first was the lying-in hospital with 20 beds, renamed the British Lying-in Hospital for Married Women when it moved to Endell Street in 1845. The cost of maintaining a maternity patient was double that of a general case and the hospital ran into financial problems that forced it to close and merge with the Home for Mothers and Babies in Woolwich.

The next was the City of London, which opened a school for midwives in 1771. In the 18th century women were admitted up to four weeks before term, and kept in for three weeks after delivery in some hospitals, except at the Rotunda, where they were only admitted when labour started and discharged after a week. The City of London would admit them as soon as they presented, but this was so misused that the women could be turned out and fined 20 shillings if not delivered within a month. At first delivery was in the general ward, and when separate labour wards were added later there was an increase in puerperal fever. As at other lying-in hospitals unmarried women were generally excluded and, when accepted, restricted to a single pregnancy for fear of earning a bad reputation which would put off respectable married women. Its premises at the junction of City Road and Old Street, comprising 42 beds in three large wards built largely of wood,

The City of London Lying-in Hospital, 1771.

had to be rebuilt in 1907 when it became structurally unsafe through the construction of the underground railway beneath it. It was destroyed by bombing in 1941 and re-sited to Harley Road until it was finally closed when it joined with the Royal Northern Hospital.

The hospital that was to become the most famous maternity unit in London was of uncertain conception and suffered very unsettled initial years. It was founded as the General Lying-in Hospital in 1752 at Duke Street, but records suggest an earlier origin. In a letter dated 1739 to his godfather Hans Sloane, a famous obstetrician, Richard Manningham refers to the financial state of a lying-in apartment he had rented in Jermyn Street and the same year he advertised classes to teach young doctors and women midwifery (on different days) in a pamphlet *The Institution and Economy of the Charitable Infirmary for the Relief of Poor Women Labouring of Child and During the Month of Lying-in*. It refers to the Foundling Hospital lately established and adds that 'our little hospital has its praises too and maybe the means

240

of saving the lives of many poor distressed mothers and their offspring'.

At first it was only for married women referred for admission by subscribers who paid two guineas a year subscription. Non-subscribers would have to send two guineas with their nominee and 10s 6d a week extra if they stayed more than a month. Teaching was important, students paying £21 for a course of lectures, including the dangers of using instruments, demonstrated on a model. Then followed the first of a succession of moves, first to Grosvenor Square, where unmarried women were accepted, and then to Quebec Street ten years later. The policy to accept single women was very unpopular with the parish as the bastards would be eligible for Poor Relief and it started legal action to enforce closure. This failed, but a scandal arose over charges of neglect and cruelty when the bodies of newly born babies were discovered buried in the hospital back yard. This cast doubts on the claim of the man-midwife then in charge, Dr Macclonogh, of a low mortality rate of 1 in 160 patients, less than half the rate at other London hospitals and the Rotunda. He escaped prosecution and remained in charge for 38 years, but moved to Oxford Street, within a few yards of the Tyburn Gallows where criminals were hanged, for a short time before a further move to Bayswater close to a burial site.

By now medical standards had degenerated to a low level and following a 1773 law whereby bastard children should be removed to their mother's settlement, the General Lying-in Hospital moved again in 1791 to an elegant country house, Bayswater Hall, where it was known as the Bayswater Lying-in Hospital. The lease was controlled by two doctors, one of whom appointed himself as physician without the knowledge of the subscribers and used it as his own private residence; any patients were confined to two small attic rooms.

When subjected to a special inquiry in 1809, the hospital had almost fallen into disuse as subscriptions had declined and it was faced with closure. However, it was saved by the Duke of Sussex, who took charge of the management committee. Strict standards were laid down to attract high-quality medical staff and strict rules for nurses were hung in every ward. Proper records were kept and teaching resumed, including midwifery instruction for women. The hospital rapidly attracted top patronage; there were ten royal patrons.

Bed numbers rose to 145, with separate wards for married and unmarried mothers, and in 1809 Queen Charlotte became a patron. The patients were the wives or widows of servicemen, working poor,

241

and women in labour off the streets or from outside parishes. In spite of the change, criticism remained. The hospital was vilified by the editor of a local scandal sheet, who was found guilty of libel and sent to prison for a year. Later the hospital had to be evacuated for six months due to an outbreak of puerperal sepsis, and as the building had become very dilapidated it moved to new premises in Marylebone Road when the lease ended in 1813.

By now the admission system had become cumbersome. To comply with the 1773 Act, any applicant had to apply a few weeks before confinement, with a letter from a subscriber, who was now paying three guineas p.a., as well as an affidavit sworn before a magistrate and signed by the hospital secretary, with an official seal.

There were other problems affecting both nursing staff and medical standards. The hospital suffered a series of dishonest matrons who would demand money from patients, one who let her family live in the hospital and sleep in the wards, and subscription collectors who stole their receipts. As at most maternity hospitals, the death rate from puerperal sepsis was far higher than with home deliveries. One of the medical staff strongly opposed any use of forceps 'however slow' labour, and his influence was responsible for the death of Princess Charlotte, daughter of the Queen, and her baby from obstructed labour and haemorrhage through his refusal to allow any mechanical intervention.

The number of patients rose to 200 in-patients and 300 out-patients a year and outgrew the existing facilities. It moved in 1857 to a new building in the Marylebone Road which, although purpose-built with separate small lying-in and convalescent wards, had no accommodation for nurses, whilst the wards and toilets had a common ventilation system. The death rate from puerperal sepsis rose sharply and the hospital had to be closed in 1865 for a new ventilation system, when an extra floor was added to house the nurses. Administration was changed, with the matron becoming a Lady Superintendent freed from midwifery duties and a resident midwife and medical officer. In spite of improved hygiene standards and separation of toilets from the wards, in 1879 there was a serious rise in the death rate from puerperal sepsis. This was traced to a breakdown in the rules for the disinfection of bed linen and within a year the death rate had fallen from 48 to 3.3 per 1,000 births.

A new financial crisis arose when it was calculated that the two patients a subscriber was entitled to propose for a subscription of

ABSTRACT ACCOUNT

OF THE

WESTMINSTER LYING-IN HOSPITAL,

NEAR THE BRIDGE,

Inſtituted A. D. 1765, and ſupported by Voluntary
Subſcription.

Right Hon. Lord GROSVENOR, Preſident.

Duke of Rutland,			
Lord Hood,	Vice	Rt. Hon. C. J. Fox,
Hon. Gen. W. Hervey,	Preſidents,	Maj. Gen. Sir R. Boyd, Hon. T. Groſvenor.

IN the year 1765, Dr. *John Leake* of
Craven-Street, London, purchaſed a
piece of Ground on a Building Leaſe, and
afterwards preſented to the Public, the *Original Plan for the Inſtitution of this Hoſpital*. Soon after the Building was raiſed, he
voluntarily, and without any conſideration,
aſſigned over to the Governors, all his right
of the above Ground, in favor of the ſaid
Hoſpital.

G

Being

Westminster Lying-in Hospital.

New General Lying-in Hospital, 1828.

three guineas cost the hospital £8. It was salvaged by Saturday and Sunday Club funds and fees from trainee midwives when a midwifery school was opened in 1876, and became the first after the Rotunda to offer obstetric training to medical students. The Marylebone Road site was developed to cope with over 1,000 patients and more than 100 students by adding an additional floor and a separate nurses' home.

A laboratory was opened in 1905 and the first female resident medical officer was appointed in 1915. The hospital continued the policy of admitting servicemen's wives free. During the war years there was a serious outbreak of diarrhoea and vomiting amongst both patients and staff with an alarming rise in stillbirths and infant deaths. It was eventually controlled by strict isolation measures, separating infected cases and banning any nurses with symptoms from work, but was an example then of how any relaxation of hygiene standards in a maternity unit leads to serious consequences, a lesson that continues to have to be relearned today. In 1924 the name was changed to Queen Charlotte's Maternity Hospital and ladies joined the management committee, whilst a separate ante-natal clinic branch opened.

Many other maternity hospitals would be established to serve their local communities. One of these in London was The New Westminster Lying-in Hospital in York Road, Westminster, founded by Dr John

244

Leake in 1765, a respected lecturer who wrote a number of books on obstetrics. From the start it accepted unmarried women and is referred to in Pennant's *London* in 1773 as 'a haven not merely for the honest matron who can depose her burden with the consciousness of lawful love, but also for the unhappy wretches that some villain in an unguarded moment hath seduced, and then left a prey to desertion of friends, poverty, want and guilt, and tempted to destroy themselves or murder their child'. Midwives were trained from 1769 and in 1818 it became the General Lying-in Hospital, rebuilt in 1828. It was ravaged by puerperal sepsis for most of the century and had to close down for a time in 1878 when the mortality rate reached 25 per 1,000, although this was lower than the maternity units of some general hospitals. After an inquiry stricter standards of hygiene were introduced and by 1886 the level had fallen to under 3 per 1,000. It was closely associated with St Thomas's, by whom it would be absorbed in 1971 and closed.

Although 10 lying-in hospitals were founded across provincial cities between 1745 and 1800, only 15 more that still survive were added to the list over the next hundred years in spite of the enormous growth in population. In 1900 there were 25 lying-in hospitals, rising to 36 by 1921, with 4 in Southern Ireland. All were dependent on charity, and made a modest beginning in rented accommodation. Expensive to run and riddled with infection, many had to close permanently or temporarily. Birmingham opened in 1842, but had to close after 25 years until a new hospital was opened in 1907. However, many general hospitals opened small maternity units and some of the Poor Law infirmaries had quite large obstetric wards.

Springfield Maternity, Lancashire, opened in 1918. Numbers then rose rapidly and by 1962 there were 172 maternity hospitals and 152 nursing homes in Britain and Northern Ireland. From 1773 lying-in institutions had had to be licensed by the Justices of the Peace at Quarter Sessions and display an inscription over the entrance. Now they have to obtain local planning permission and be registered with the Public Health Department under the Maternity and Child Welfare Acts of 1936.

There was national concern in the early 20th century at the high maternal and new-born death rates, and Queen Charlotte's launched a campaign to fund a new up-to-date maternity hospital under the title of a 'National Mother Saving Campaign' with the registered trade mark of a stork holding a baby over a cot. A five-acre site was purchased in Goldhawk Road, London, and an ambitious plan drawn up with four blocks, two for 100-bedded units with additional labour wards, and a private block of similar size. There would be a separate isolation block, out-patients and laboratories. Appropriately work was first started on the isolation block in 1929 with a reluctantly given £15,000 from the Ministry of Health, carefully allocated for child and maternity welfare to avoid any exposure to capital expenditure. This block was to open in 1930, along with laboratories to lead the attack on puerperal sepsis, taking in cases from a wide area. The main hospital was to remain at Marylebone Road until the funds had been raised to start the next stage of the new building. With over a hundred medical students and midwives in training, there was increasing competition for cases to manage.

Another problem that was to emerge was the 1929 Local Government Act that abolished the board of guardians and transferred their hospitals to local authorities. Many of these began to develop large maternity departments in competition to the voluntary hospitals such as Queen Charlotte's. Within ten years such institutions had doubled and were covering a third of pregnant women, who would be seen six or seven times during their pregnancy in ante-natal clinics. This was at the expense of training hospitals with districts to cover, and intense rivalry developed between them, especially Queen Charlotte's and the London County Council Postgraduate School in Duchene Road. The problems were defused by The Midwives Act of 1936, by which it was agreed to allocate domiciliary midwifery between the municipal authorities and established voluntary maternity hospitals into agreed zones or 'districts'. The surplus of midwives that resulted was 'downsized' by early retirement or allowing them to practise privately. Later the Central Midwives Board doubled the period of training, with the first part on theory, some practical to be spent in hospital and the rest in domiciliary practice under supervision. Queen Charlotte's was granted full recognition for training in both aspects.

A start was made on building the remaining blocks and a new nurses' home in 1936 on the Goldhawk Road site. It began to admit patients in 1941 and by the end of 1945 had expanded to 135 beds when the old hospital was closed. After the war it was decided to plan a merger with The Chelsea Hospital for Women to form a combined postgraduate teaching school incorporated within the Postgraduate Federation. This became the Institute of Obstetrics and Gynaecology in 1948 and trained many specialists under difficult conditions. It was here that Ian Donald was the first to use the clinical applications of the ultrasound. Space was cramped and the hospitals widely separated; formal teaching had to be housed for the next 30 years in a 'temporary' prefabricated unit before the building of some new facilities for teaching and pathology. A major rebuilding at the Queen Charlotte site to house both hospitals was planned, but abandoned with the onset of prolonged and frustrating negotiations with the Ministry, regional hospital boards, local authorities and the University of London.

In 1968 the Todd Report by a Royal Commission recommended all London postgraduate teaching hospitals should be integrated with undergraduate medical schools, and many were to be closed. Queen Charlotte's was amongst these, which stimulated immense public support for a 'Save Queen Charlotte's Hospital' campaign. Another suggested scheme was a move to the new King Edward Memorial Hospital being developed at Ealing.

The ultimate decision after another Flower's Commission, supported by the University of London, was a merger with a larger unit at the site of the Hammersmith Postgraduate Medical Centre. Both the Queen Charlotte's and Chelsea Hospital for Women were to lose their

Queen Charlotte's Hospital, Hammersmith.

247

separate identities, although the authority was to be called 'The Hammersmith Queen Charlotte's Special Health Authority'. A new Institute of Obstetrics and Gynaecology was created, with the largest team in Europe working on the health of new-born babies, studying genetic disorders such as cystic fibrosis and muscular dystrophy by screening embryos before their placement in the uterus by in-vitro fertilisation.

There has been a radical change in the pattern of childbirth since the 1960s. Now fewer than two babies in a hundred are born at home, compared with a third in the 1960s – a level that still holds in the Netherlands with equal safety. The trend started in the 1920s, when hospital deliveries doubled to over a third over ten years as puerperal sepsis was controlled. The move was accelerated by a government recommendation that childbirth in hospital was safer for both mother and child. Hospital stay has shortened progressively; now patients are often discharged within a day or two if all goes well.

At the same time there has been a great increase in 'active management', with increasing intervention in the natural course of labour. This had been a feature at the time of the 'man-midwife' with the use of forceps. Mechanical intervention was to peak in the 1970s with episiotomy (cutting the opening of the vagina), which had become a general routine measure in the USA in the 1950s for a forceps-assisted delivery under general anaesthesia; in the UK this was only carried out in an emergency, but would be used increasingly, especially in teaching hospitals where medical and midwifery students had to carry out a set number in the course of their training. The grounds were shortening delivery time, preventing possible perineal tears or pelvic floor damage and trauma to the baby's head. It is now performed less often as it has been shown to be more painful, taking longer to heal than a tear, with re-suturing often being required.

Epidural anaesthesia for pain relief entails the injection of local anaesthetic into the mid-back into the space between the vertebrae and the membrane enclosing the spinal cord. The transitional 'full' anaesthesia is used for Caesarean section, but now a modified version known as 'mobile' epidurals is used for pain relief in about a quarter of all deliveries. A new generation of anaesthetics has greatly reduced side effects, and the need for forceps. They require an anaesthetist, and analgesia lasts for a couple of hours when it can be topped up through an in-dwelling catheter.

Of more concern is the increase in Caesarean sections which now range from 12% to 30% between hospitals, with an average of 22%, double the level considered beneficial by the World Health Organisation. Obstetricians deny this is for their convenience, although natural deliveries are higher during the week than at weekends or bank holidays. The grounds advocated can include a simple breech, slow progress in labour and foetal distress, whilst 7% are requested by patients in the absence of any such indication.

The big factor in the incidence of assisted deliveries seems to be the cultural attitude of the maternity unit towards childbirth being a natural event, with one-to-one emotional support from the midwife. Video recordings have shown she may be in the delivery room for only 15% of the time, and the emphasis is on record keeping and watching the monitors, for fear of litigation. There is an increasing trend to 'active' childbirth, where any intervention in the absence of complications is avoided and the attendant's role merely to give support. An Association for the Improvement in the Medical Services (AIMS) has been formed, calling for more personalised maternity care and the right to home deliveries with proper medical back-up. In France in support of closer mother–child bonding, Dr Michel Odent created a *salle sauvage*, or primitive room, in his hospital, painted in warm colours, dimly lit and well heated – a return to ancient practice, with all emergency equipment nearby but out of sight.

Chapter 10

Children's Hospitals

Great Ormond Street

One of the specialist areas in which the English hospital system lagged behind was in the care of children. With the Industrial Revolution, there was a large shift of population from the countryside to the developing industrial and mining areas, which became overcrowded slums. Under these appalling living conditions up to half of children in the larger cities would die before the age of five, many under two, from malnutrition, infectious diseases and gastro-enteritis. Deformities such as clubfoot from poliomyelitis and rickets were rampant, as was tuberculosis. Many aged eight or younger were working up to sixteen hours a day for a few pence in mines and factories or sweeping chimneys before this was restricted to six and a half hours for children under ten by a Factory Bill in 1844.

A National Children's Hospital had been founded in Dublin in 1825, but at the time of the Great Exhibition in 1851 this was the only children's hospital in Britain. Across Europe there were at least 16 in the capital cities, many large and often under royal patronage and attached to a medical school. The oldest was *L'Opital des Enfants Malades* in France, which had opened as a foundling institute in 1676 and been converted to a hospital with some 600 beds after the Revolution. In all these hospitals the mortality rate from cross-infection was unacceptably high. Between 1775 and 1790 in Paris 25,476 of 31,957 admitted died before their first birthday, and in Dublin Foundling Hospital only 45 survived from over 10,000.

In Britain the general policy of voluntary hospitals during their formative years was to refuse admission to children except for accidents, and an inquiry in 1843 revealed that of 2,363 patients in the London hospitals, only 26 were under ten years old. Guy's was the only hospital to have had any beds – 15 cribs in a wooden building over some stables, which were pulled down in 1848. The cots were dispensed within the women's wards until these in turn were demolished four years later. The London Hospital excluded all children

251

under seven except those requiring 'cutting for stone' or amputation, whilst the Oxford Radcliffe would refuse any. It was a policy dictated by a belief that children were best cared for by their mothers at home, however squalid their accommodation, whilst the hospitals were afraid of spreading infection and the increased nursing demands.

In 1741 a London Foundling Hospital had been opened by a retired naval officer, Captain Thomas Coram, to tackle the common practice of infanticide and to maintain and educate children abandoned in the streets. Initially all infants were accepted and the mother would leave an identity tag with her child, such as a marked coin or piece of clothing, but as numbers grew there was a system of balloting with red, white and black balls based on an interview by a selection committee. The hospital was supported by many leading artists and musicians of the time, including Hogarth, who painted several decorations, and Handel, who held regular concerts of the *Messiah* which attracted the social elite of the time. Its art exhibitions were probably the background to the foundation of the Royal Academy, whilst later it formed a juvenile hospital band that trained many musicians for the Army and Navy.

To meet the pressure on numbers, the governors in 1756 appealed to Parliament for financial support. This would be the first State support for hospital care and was to prove disastrous for both the establishment's reputation and the standards of care. It was a condition that all children offered had to be accepted, and local receiving centres were

The Foundling Hospital, Lamb's Conduit Fields.

Receiving Day at the Foundling Hospital, 1883.

set up all over the country with a basket hung outside the hospital in which babies could be abandoned. Within four years 14,934 children were poured in from the workhouses, mostly under six months old, of whom 10,389 died from infections and malnutrition in the overcrowded and insanitary conditions. The Government withdrew the open-admission policy and funding in 1771 as the cost rose to £500,000 p.a. and the hospital had to return to voluntary support. The governors responded by progressively reducing admissions to 40 p.a., restricted to the first-born of abandoned unmarried mothers of previously good character. These were brought up in the country homes until the age of five and then educated in the London Foundling Hospital until they were apprenticed at the age of 16 as servants or mechanics. It was to become recognised in Europe as a small, well-run establishment supported by voluntary contributions and became a model for the organisation of children's hospitals in the next century. It finally closed in 1951 to become an adoption charity and the playground became the site of the Wolfson Centre for treating handicapped children.

It was 1769 before the first children's dispensary was opened by Dr

Armstrong in Red Lion Square, and within a few years it was treating 4,000 patients annually. Single-handed and overwhelmed by the work and lack of funds, he fell heavily into debt and suffered a stroke. The clinic closed, and it was 30 years before another was opened by Dr John Bunnell Davis. He had trained in Paris when trapped there during the Napoleonic Wars and returned home to become a physician at the London Dispensary. Five years later, in 1816, with the financial support of 107 governors, including royalty and the Lord Mayor as President, he was able to open the Universal Dispensary for Children in a rented house on St Andrew's Hill, Doctors Common, staffed by himself as physician, two surgeons and a resident apothecary, paid £50 p.a. with £25 for medicine, as well as a 'collector' at 5% poundage. It became a teaching centre for medical students and postgraduates, and trained mothers to care for their children, along with carrying out domiciliary visits. These activities continued when the dispensary moved to a site in the Waterloo Road, but were given up when Dr Davis died in 1824 at the age of 44 and the funds dried up.

In its first three and a half years the dispensary had treated nearly 7,820 children, with 130 deaths and 7,000 claimed as cured. It was to be revitalised 15 years later when Dr Charles West was appointed as physician. Dr West had written an internationally recognised book on diseases of children and was convinced that some of the sick should be removed from their overcrowded, insanitary slums into hospital care, although they would be parted from their mothers. At the time there was considerable debate in the medical press about the value of children's hospitals and the fact that London was the only capital city in Europe that lacked one, or provision for the admission of children to a general hospital. Most parents could not afford private care and dosed their children with proprietary medicines, many based on opium, with fatal results. When his proposals for in-patient beds were rejected by the management committee Dr West resigned in frustration after ten years, and the dispensary again slumped before it was revived as part of the Royal Waterloo Hospital for Women and Children, now absorbed into St Thomas's Hospital. During its first 30 years it treated over 175,000 children at an estimated cost of under one shilling per head.

However, Dr West retained his ambition, and achieved it. He was walking along Great Ormond Street and passed the former house of Richard Mead, a famous Bart's doctor who had been physician to Queen Anne 150 years earlier. This seemed to him the perfect site and after a successful advertisement in *The Times* for funds to start a 100-

bedded children's hospital, he was able to take on a lease for 21 years at £200 a year on 49 Great Ormond Street. This house had special features, including extensive grounds with a large old plane tree, which remained until it had to be cut down in the rebuilding of 1938. The Hospital for Sick Children opened in February 1852 with 10 beds, soon increased to 20, in a ward created from Dr Mead's famous library. At first admission was restricted to children between the ages of two and twelve, as those younger were considered too great a feeding problem and the death rate in this age group was horrific. Strict rules were laid down for the care and clothing of the children, with a gymnasium in the garden and some education. The lower limit was widely ignored by the medical staff from an early stage: the upper limit lasted well into the 20th century before it was raised.

One of the major problems was to obtain suitable nursing staff, for whom high standards had been set. They were expected to be able to read, and to repeat the Lord's Prayer and the Ten Commandments, and the sister-in-charge had to be able to write. Such staff were hard to find on the terms offered and in the early years there were many complaints that they were incapable, dirty and disrespectful. However, they had to sleep on the wards at night, with a single ward nurse on duty night and day, for a salary of £12 p.a. with board, until a stone-floored basement room was converted into a dormitory as numbers increased. Meanwhile, the unpaid resident house surgeon had to sleep in the boardroom and the porter in the hall behind a screen.

Sanitation and heating in the original house were poor, with no main water supply and drainage that caused inspecting governors to note 'an unpleasant smell'. Matters improved when the house next door was bought in 1858 with funds raised by the help of Charles Dickens, and bed capacity was raised to 75. Patient numbers doubled over the next decade and staff numbers grew from two physicians and one surgeon to seven physicians, five surgeons, a dentist and a pharmacist, and conditions became increasingly overcrowded and unhygienic. By 1871 the hospital was treating 678 in-patients a year, with over 7,000 out-patients who were seen in a large basement room that would hold up to 500 children and parents at a time. It was calculated that a new patient occupied five minutes and a follow-up only one and a half. A surgical ward had been opened, but the surgeon's changing room also housed the coal supply for the adjacent wards, which were old-fashioned and often had to be closed from outbreaks of infection.

The first Hospital for Sick Children at 49 Great Ormond Street.

The big breakthrough came with the opening of a new Hospital in the Garden in 1875 after several years of planning. It was designed by the son of Sir Charles Barry, architect of the Houses of Parliament, and was a state-of-the-art paediatric hospital with a purpose-built operating theatre and sophisticated under-floor heating. Six wards achieved the original target of 100 beds, and a separate 16-bedded isolation block opened in 1880. Initially this was used for scarlet fever and whooping cough cases transferred from the general wards, where outbreaks were common, but later there were separate

One of the wards at 49 Great Ormond Street.

Nurses and patients under the plane tree at Great Ormond Street.

The 'Hospital in the Garden' at Great Ormond Street, 1875. One of the original houses can be seen on the left.

wards for diphtheria and whooping cough, which became increasingly endemic.

Within the Garden Hospital was built an outstanding Gothic chapel, which was moved on its concrete foundations by hydraulic skates when the hospital was demolished in 1990 to make room for a new Variety Club building. The original houses were replaced in 1893 by a red-brick building fronting onto Great Ormond Street, built in memory of Queen Victoria's Silver Jubilee. This still remains and was extended in 1908 with a new free-standing out-patient department funded by the American newspaper owner Lord Astor, when the sites of the adjacent Working Men's College and Convent of St John & St Elizabeth were acquired.

A nursing school was opened in 1878, named after Charles West, and became a national centre for paediatric nurse training. Preliminary studies were moved to Queen Elizabeth Hospital in Hackney until this was closed down, and the whole school was transferred to South Bank University in the mid-1990s. The school hired out nurses privately, and they may have been the first to wear the famous pink uniform that was to become standard hospital wear. The grim accommodation for the nuns in the convent was used to house the nurses until the

Great Ormond Street Hospital, 1908-1936.

present Princess Royal's Home was built on Guilford Street in the 1930s.

In 1869 the hospital acquired the lease of Cromwell House in Highgate village, which had been built in 1630 for some of the General's army and was converted into a country home for convalescent and long-stay patients. This proved too expensive and impractical to run and was replaced by Tadworth Court, a country house on the Surrey Downs, which remained in use as a centre for orthopaedic and rheumatic conditions until 1982.

The hospital was to weather recurrent financial crises and continued to extend through donations. Plans to rebuild on the nearby Foundling Hospital site were frustrated and delegates at the third International Paediatric Congress held in London in 1933 were amazed to find the staff working in such cramped old-fashioned conditions. An on-going rebuilding programme on the existing site was initiated in 1938 when a new Southwood Building replaced the long open wards of the Victorian Hospital with multiple ten-bedded units considered to be more patient-friendly and to reduce the risk of cross infection. It also included a 36-bed unit for private patients. The building was

259

Annie Zunz Ward at the Hospital for Sick Children, Great Ormond Street, c.1920.

severely damaged by bombing in 1940, but extensive rebuilding was started after the war, culminating in major redevelopment between 1991 and 1996. This included purpose-built accommodation for the specialist departments, among them a separate cardiac block with buildings for the Institute of Child Health and the Charles West School of Nursing. A national 'Wishing Well Appeal' raised the funds for a new clinical block called the Variety Club Building with the emphasis on patient friendliness. Opened in 1994, it included single-bed units where a parent could stay with the child.

Increasingly the hospital has become a centre of excellence in research and medical innovation rather than a local service unit. It became the postgraduate teaching centre when the University of London's Institute of Child Health was created. At present there are 320 beds with a staffing of over 1,700, treating 20,000 in-patients and 80,000 out-patients a year.

The hospital's future was assured through its children's image. Many cots and beds were endowed in memory of famous people, such as Lewis Carroll, and the copyright income from *Peter Pan* was given by Sir J.M. Barrie, and now endowments cover some 10% of the current annual budget expenditure of £100 million. Its prestige and financial strength enabled it to be one of the few specialist hospitals to retain independence within the NHS, retaining its own management and facing down proposals to include it on a common site with The Middlesex and University College Hospital. It remains a specialist 'Tertiary Referral' hospital, with contracts for its services with regional health authorities across the country and worldwide references.

A number of children's hospitals were established across London in the second half of the 19th century. These were mostly located in the more affluent areas, leaving a disorganised and expensive system that gave an inadequate service to the poorer East and South London areas. Some established a high reputation in their district and in the course of time would be absorbed by the teaching hospitals as these belatedly began to develop children's departments. Amongst these was the Infants' Hospital, founded in 1903 in Hampstead before it moved to Vincent Square, with 50 cots and a large out-patients' department and research laboratories. It was specifically concerned with infants, and studies in nutrition. With the advent of the NHS it was absorbed within the Westminster Hospital Children's Unit. Others of note were the Evelina, to be merged with Guy's, and the Paddington Green and Princess Louise, which joined St Thomas's.

Children's dispensaries also began to be established at this time in most major towns across the country as precursors to hospitals, mainly through the dedicated efforts of individuals. They would fill the gap from the lack of involvement by the general hospitals, where children's departments would only become established by the 20th century. By 1888, 38 hospitals had been opened in most major towns across the country, largely adopting a common pattern; at first they were primarily dispensaries, with at most a few in-patient beds, which would be gradually increased as the demand grew. Initially few would accept infants and restricted admissions to children between the ages of two and ten, in contrast to Paris, where there was a special hospital for babies. There was a general attitude that it was irresponsible to separate infants from their mothers, whilst in hospital they would need especial nursing care and feeding, which would be expensive and diffi-cult to provide. In fact a few would be admitted by the medical staff, often leading to rebuke by the governors.

During the last quarter of the century many hospitals began to relax this policy, although the infants were placed in the general mixed-age wards. At Great Ormond Street Dr Ward was against any proposal to open a separate ward, and in 1878 only 28 of over 1,000 admissions were under the age of two, although the proportion was over 20% eight years later. One of the problems was the high mortality rate in the group. An exception was the East London at Shadwell, which opened in 1868 and had a special ward for infants. But as late as 1898, 38.6% of infant admissions died in hospital, although this was attributed to 'malnutrition and unavoidable neglect at home', rather than any hospital neglect, as many were brought by their parents when they realised their child was dying. Birmingham refused to accept any children under the age of one until the late 1870s.

Many children's dispensaries would carry out domiciliary visits on an increasing scale and in 1865 Manchester carried out over 5,000 visits, averaging six per patient during the year. The level aroused increasing complaints from the local doctors at their loss of income from paying patients, and from the dispensary doctors that it was taking too much of their time. As a result a means test was introduced whereby patients with a weekly income above 18s a week plus 1s 6d per child were referred on to a private dispensary. Many other children's hospitals were to reduce or give up domiciliary visiting, although home nursing care was continued. Glasgow appointed two hospital dispensary sisters to spend their mornings in the out-patients and afternoons doing domiciliary work. Many charitable institutions were to join in providing home nursing care for the poor, and by the end of the century a widespread district nursing service had been established.

Outside London, the first children's hospitals were established at Norwich, Manchester and Liverpool. A small dispensary for out-patients had been opened at Manchester in 1829, and was treating 1,500 children a year with a subscriber's letter of introduction. About one patient in ten died, but the overall death rate in the city for children under ten was over 50%. After several earlier moves, a hospital with six beds for in-patients was started under the initiative of Dr Borchardt, a political refugee from Germany. This would be increased to 25 beds, but as patient numbers rose to over 7,000 out-patients annually, along with 350 in-patients and as many home visits, facilities were totally inadequate and funds were raised to build a

262

The Royal Manchester Children's Hospital, 'Pendlebury', 1879.

Manchester Children's Hospital — the Godfrey Ermen Memorial Dispensary, 1879.

hospital at Pendlebury in nearby Salford, with a new dispensary within Manchester at Gartside Street. The hospital comprised six wards of twenty beds, built in two phases, on a pavilion design identical to the new St Thomas's Hospital in London. Florence Nightingale described it as 'one of the best constructed hospitals in Europe'. Each ward had a balcony on which long-term patients would spend much of their time throughout the year. Discipline was strict, with the children dressed in a uniform of blue and red flannel jackets with blouses and collars. There were four open tiled fireplaces in the centre of each ward built back to back, and one of the nurses' duties was to keep the fires alight. It would become the first paediatric nurses' teaching establishment in Britain, and by 1879 there were 13 probationers paying £50 for the privilege of one year's training.

Under the NHS there were initially several restructurings of management within the health authorities, until in 1995 it was granted

Royal Manchester Children's Hospital, Pendlebury, c.1920s.

Trust status within the Manchester Children's Hospitals NHS Trust, and after 50 years achieved total management of its own affairs, including the budget, paediatric services and research. In 1959 the tertiary services were moved to the Central Manchester Hospital site, whilst local services remained at Pendlebury.

After London and Manchester, the next city to open a children's dispensary was Liverpool, where social conditions became even worse than Manchester as the population quadrupled from Irish immigration. The first medical officer to an English town was appointed to Liverpool in 1848, several months before London. He initiated a dispensary in 1851 and five years later an eight-bedded hospital was opened. This was moved 14 years later to a specially built hospital, the Royal Liverpool Children's Hospital, to be renamed The Alder Hey in 1914 and remain as an independent authority. In 1889 another hospital was opened in the town, The Liverpool County Hospital for Children. In contrast to the general pattern of children's hospitals which were concerned with acute illness, this focused on chronic cases such as bone and joint diseases that needed long-term surgical care and nursing.

The first children's hospital in Scotland was opened in 1860 in Edinburgh with 20 beds and a dispensary. Three years later it moved to larger premises and received royal patronage. Bed numbers were increased to 72, but it was forced to close through an outbreak of typhoid fever related to suspect plumbing and was eventually demolished. A new hospital was built and opened in 1895 on the site of the present Royal Edinburgh Hospital for Sick Children, and within the NHS it initially became part of Edinburgh Central Hospitals Group. It is now under the South Lothian District of the Lothian Health Board.

A children's hospital would only be opened in Glasgow after more than 20 years' controversy, and its story highlighted the problems that many others had to face. Edwin Chadwick, when Commissioner for the Poor Law Board, stated he had never seen misery equal to Glasgow's in any other British city. It had become one of the most densely populated, with over 200 people per acre in places. Many lived in windowless cellars with earthen floors and emptied their excrement into the streets, continuing to draw water from wells as they were unable to buy a key to one of the taps which carried clean water from a local loch. Epidemics were frequent and the bodies were buried in common pits.

An eminent group, including doctors and clergy, met as early as 1861 to discuss a children's hospital, but in spite of public and press support the proposal collapsed due to intense opposition from the profession itself, especially the Royal Infirmary staff, who were afraid of the competition for charitable funds. The subject was raised again four years later, but negatived by the Senate of Glasgow University, who had been offered a government grant for rebuilding, provided a new general hospital was built in conjunction. There followed ten years of frustrating correspondence from which it was evident that any children's hospital would only be an annexe to the new Western Infirmary. However, sufficient funds were raised to open a Glasgow Hospital for Sick Children in 1882 at Garnethill; initially a tiny hospital based on the site of two small houses. At first infants were not accepted, but eventually they packed 74 cots into the wards.

The site was carefully chosen and the conversion planned to ensure 'perfect drainage, freedom from damp, good ventilation and an equitable temperature'. There were three wards, one on each floor, each painted with reproductions of Randolph Caldecott's illustrations of nursery rhymes. The lower part of the walls was lined with cream tiles with a narrow red border and each ward had its own scullery and bathroom. There was a separate isolation ward, with a small room attached for the nurse in charge, where she remained 'until all danger is past'. On the ground floor was a reception room where the children were admitted, stripped of their dirty old clothes, washed and put into a smart ward uniform. There was a mortuary designed on the principle that such places should be 'not repulsive and dismal, but decorous'. The floor was of marble mosaic and round the walls ran a dark grey wreath-patterned frieze with the words 'Not dead but sleepeth', whilst the room had an amber light with a white star cut in it. Relations who wished could have the child's funeral service conducted from the chapel.

The standard of the nursing staff was exceptionally high for the time, and all were 'ladies', according to the hospital authorities. They were interdenominational and set a high moral tone, with morning and evening prayers for the children and grace before meals, and Bible stories on Sundays. Work was hard and they had to do all the chores until two cleaners were appointed in 1904, but there was no shortage of applicants prepared to pay a guinea for training. Visiting was restricted to one hour two days a week, and visitors had to remove their boots before entering the ward in socks, until regulations were eased in 1909.

NATIONAL ⎰Hospital, No. 45 (Douglas).
TELEPHONES ⎱Dispensary, No. 384 (Douglas).

TWENTIETH ANNUAL REPORT

OF THE

ROYAL HOSPITAL

FOR

SICK CHILDREN, GLASGOW,

AND REPORT OF THE

LADIES' AUXILIARY ASSOCIATION,

FOR YEAR ENDING 31st DECEMBER, 1902.

HOSPITAL, 45 SCOTT STREET, GARNETHILL.

Miss Wilson

COLLECTOR FOR THIS DISTRICT, WILL CALL WITHIN A DAY OR TWO
TO RECEIVE DONATIONS OR SUBSCRIPTIONS.

☞ Should Contributor be from home, it will be esteemed a favour if the Contribution is
left with the servant for Collector.

ANNUAL SUBSCRIBERS OF ONE GUINEA TO LADIES' AUXILIARY ASSOCIATION ARE
ENTITLED TO RECOMMEND A PATIENT. Form of Recommendation may be had
from the Hon. Lady Treasurer, who will also supply Collection
Cards suitable for Children and Sabbath Schools.

SUBSCRIBERS UNDER 2/6 WILL NOT BE NAMED IN REPORTS.

**Cast-off Clothes, Boots, Shoes, Slippers, &c., are very acceptable, and will
be judiciously dispensed by the Ladies' Committee.**
OLD LINENS or WHITE COTTONS are at all times much needed.

An annual report for the Royal Hospital for Sick Children, Glasgow from 1902.

267

The Royal Hospital for Sick Children, Garnethill, Glasgow, c.1900.

A new wing was added and a county branch built, but the hospital was serving a population of over two million and as the waiting list grew longer in time and numbers and the hospital became more out of date and overcrowded, a move became inevitable. Next door was a veterinary college and the unpleasant smell made a local expansion unsuitable, so a large fund-raising exercise was started for a new hospital. Over £140,000 was raised from charity sources that ranged from the Scottish Football Association to an Ice Carnival and a Fancy Dress Fair that raised £1,500. A 16-acre site at Yorkhill near the university was found and in 1914 a carefully planned children's hospital built on the pavilion style was opened by Queen Mary. Three storeys high, it had 12 wards with 300 beds, and large verandahs where tubercular patients would spend most of the winter. It was the largest children's hospital in Britain apart from Great Ormond Street.

In 1965 the hospital had to be closed for six years and totally rebuilt at a cost of £5 million when the lightweight cement used to clad the steel made the structure a 'potential avalanche'. The new hospital is eight storeys high with two 24-bed wards on each of the upper six floors; a third of the beds are in single rooms where parents can stay. With the Queen Mother Hospital Maternity Centre, it forms the Yorkhill Division NHS Greater Glasgow. Amongst the many services allocated are Glasgow's Emergency and Accident unit, a centre for

Aerial view of Yorkhill Hospital complex. The only remains of the Royal Hospital for Sick Children on this site are its laundry block.

Scotland's paediatric cardiac surgery and an Institute of Medical Genetics.

Another hospital to achieve an outstanding reputation and retain its independence as a Trust within the NHS was established as the Birmingham and Midland Free Hospital for Children, which was opened on New Year's Day in 1862 by Dr Thomas Pretious Hislop. He began his career locally as resident medical officer at the Birmingham General, and later as a Professor of Physiology at Queen's Hospital, but resigned from both in turn because of disagreements over administrative policy. He summoned up enough interest amongst local dignitaries to support his scheme for a children's hospital and a lease was taken out on a property in Steelhouse Lane. The location, in a slum area, with a tannery at the rear, was criticised, but the local tradespeople and manufacturers completely furbished it from cots to cleaning materials and drugs within a few days. In partnership with C.E. Matthews, a young local solicitor, as honorary secretary, Hislop established the hospital as a working model of good management for the future, separating administration from medical practice. The process by which the honorary staff were elected was reformed to selection by professional qualifications, in place of local contacts or canvassing, when up to £1,000 could be spent by applicants with election carts trundling through the streets with placards bearing the message 'vote for Dr X or Y'.

Another radical change was the abolition of subscribers' patronage with the right to recommend patients for admission and pass out 'tickets' as favours for their servants, whilst the less privileged sick would be left begging to find admission.

The hospital was intended for the group between paupers entitled to parish relief and those who could afford a private doctor. A system was introduced where a patient had to bring a certificate of eligibility signed by two 'respectable householders', but the out-patient services would soon be swamped as the locals were only too happy to endorse anyone who asked for a signature. The hospital tried to limit numbers by only issuing tickets to the first 30 patients in a queue, but those who forced their way to the front were often the least deserving.

In 1863 a form of means test was introduced whereby the house surgeon would question the applicant on the family circumstances, but paupers would deny they were on parish relief, so in 1871 a charge of sixpence was introduced which would remain until the move to Ladywood in 1914.

270

Birmingham and Midland Free Hospital for Children at new premises on Broad Street, 1869.

In 1869 the hospital was moved to a new site in Broad Street on a 50-year lease, converted from an old lying-in hospital, where a proper isolation unit was built. As the end of the lease approached, plans were made to build a new hospital on a site at Ladywood. Building started in 1913, but it would take over four years before the first patients could move into a state-of-the-art purpose-built hospital. During the 1920s and 30s it was transformed into one of the leaders in paediatric development, under the direction of Dr Leonard Parsons, its leading physician. A nurses' training school was opened in 1920 and an X-ray department that included a Sunlight Clinic. In 1925 the first Massage and Therapeutical Department was created, and with grants from the university and the Medical Research Council new department laboratories opened up developments in clinical medicine and research, as well as a separate infants' block with 66 cots, with the babies in separate glass cubicles.

Teams were formed that would take the hospital into the lead in many paediatric specialist areas. The cardiac unit is now one of the

271

Birmingham Children's Hospital, Ladywood, 1917.

largest in Europe, carrying out over 400 major operations a year, and was the first in Britain to perform a successful hole in the heart operation, as well as the present techniques by cardiac catherisation. The liver unit has been a pioneer: it was the first to carry out a 'cutdown' operation where a portion of an adult liver is transplanted into a child. It is also a leader in oncology and the treatment of leukaemia. All these developments were carried out in a deteriorating environment; the site was becoming an unconnected collection of buildings, some of them Portakabins in the grounds. 'The Covered Way', a plastic corridor that connected them and saved the patients from being pushed out into the open from one place to another in all weathers, was only built in 1986 with the funds from special appeals, helped by a Paul McCartney concert. Eventually a move had to be faced, and at a cost of £30 million a new hospital was created on the site of the old Birmingham General Hospital in Steelhouse Lane. It was opened by the Queen in 1998 and renamed the Princess of Wales Children's

The Princess of Wales Children's Hospital, formerly Birmingham General Hospital, Steelhouse Lane, 1998.

Hospital. Much of the lovely facade of the old Victorian hospital has been retained, but a new purpose-built central block houses the latest technology to form one of the leading paediatric units in Europe. Meanwhile, the hospital also continues to function as a local service unit and a centre for community healthcare services.

In their early years children's hospitals largely restricted their intake to medical cases, and injuries or patients requiring serious surgery were admitted to the general hospitals. With the development of anaesthesia, followed by antiseptic and aseptic techniques, the high mortality of active surgery was reduced, and the surgical innovations initiated in the general hospitals passed down to the specialist children's hospital. But it was only towards the end of the 19th century that major non-acute surgery became general.

At Great Ormond Street Charles West opposed the early appointment of a surgeon to the staff, who left after a few months, replaced by a surgeon-to-outpatients who stayed longer. Although the first resident doctor was labelled a 'house-surgeon', it was only when the Hospital in the Garden was built that an adequate operating theatre and separate surgical ward were included.

This was the general pattern, with any surgery largely restricted to minor procedures such as drainage of abscesses, and the creation of special operating facilities only developed with later rebuilding programmes, often related to closure of fever blocks. The early exceptions were lithotomy for bladder stones and amputation or excision of the hip, for tuberculosis. Lithotomy had been carried out extensively in the 18th century before anaesthesia, with the child bound and trussed like a chicken. A staff would be passed along the urethra and a cut made between the anus and the scrotum down to the staff, the base of the bladder opened and the stone removed with a finger. Increasingly during the second half of the century, major non-acute surgery that had only been considered at general hospitals would be adopted and developed at the children's hospitals.

Tuberculous infection of the knee and hip joints was common amongst poorer children, and with the advent of anaesthesia and antisepsis during the second half of the century there was a vogue for excision of the joint as an alternative to amputation. Healing led to considerable deformity and towards the end of the century excision was replaced by simpler exploration and drainage, followed by the prolonged effective splinting techniques devised by Hugh Owen Thomas working in Liverpool. At the same time surgery began to be undertaken for the commoner congenital malformations such as harelip and cleft palate. Operation on the former was relatively safe and successful; but at Great Ormond Street, of 38 operations for cleft palate in 1899, only half were successful, with many left worse off and two deaths from infection. Later, new techniques developed in America were introduced by Sir Arbuthnot Lane, with overall improvement. Other neglected deformities were club foot, until tenotomy was introduced by a surgeon at the London Orthopaedic Hospital, and congenital hernia, which had earlier only been controlled by a truss. The surgical treatment of both deformities were developed at children's hospitals across the country. Limb deformities from rickets were also commonplace, and surgery that involved osteotomy to straighten the bones, if necessary removing a wedge of tissue, was introduced.

The commonest minor surgery was for circumcision and the removal of tonsils and adenoids. At Pendlebury there was only one tonsil-lectomy in 1888, but by 1900 the number increased to 141, leading a vogue that was to be followed across the country after the introduction of the guillotine for clipping off the tonsils. Often the tonsils would be removed without anaesthesia, followed with removal of the nasal adenoids by a finger passed back into the throat.

From the beginning the attitude of paediatric hospitals to the infec-tious diseases was ambivalent and changeable. Until bacteriology developed towards the end of the 19th century, a contagious basis for even smallpox and measles was not generally accepted and spread was attributed to miasma, air polluted by foul emanations from human or animal bodies and decomposing matter encouraged by overcrowded and insanitary conditions. It was even debated whether a specific child-hood fever such as measles or scarlet fever was spread from patient to patient, or if a basic miasma could lead to a range of fevers depending on local and individual circumstances. Apart from smallpox, for which exclusion was strict, few excluded feverish children altogether, as measles and whooping cough could cause life-threatening complica-tions which could be managed in hospital. They would be nursed in separate rooms or wards, but epidemic outbreaks were a constant threat, leading to close-downs of the ward or even the hospital. Often these were blamed on visitors, and severe restrictions were often imposed. As the opening of specific fever hospitals in London under the Metropolitan Asylums Board extended throughout the provinces, isolation facilities became available, although the authorities were slow to accept measles and whooping cough cases as eligible for acceptance. The main exception was diphtheria, with a mortality approaching 50%, mainly due to laryngeal obstruction from the false membrane that was formed throughout the respiratory tubes, and former fever units would continue to treat these cases at several children's hospitals. The only possible relief was surgery; but in the special unit set up at Great Ormond Street, 30 of the 40 cases admitted in 1893 died after tracheotomy and the outcome was only improved with the introduc-tion towards the end of the century of an anti-toxin developed by teams of researchers working in Germany and Paris.

In general hospitals, around a third of the patients were convales-cent, and increasingly a chain of country and seaside houses were set up across the country to which they could be decanted. This released beds and delayed the return of the patients to their previous squalid environment. Children especially would need long-term care, and most hospitals followed Great Ormond Street in setting up country homes to which they could stay long-term. One of the largest groups attending out-patients were suffering from rickets, and as the beneficial effect of sunlight was recognised, many sunshine hospitals were opened as country branches of the children's or orthopaedic centres. In their enthusiasm for fresh air the wards would often be built without a wall, and the rickety or tubercular patients would be wheeled outdoors summer and winter.

Along with other specialist centres, paediatric hospitals were subjected to a range of criticism, although overall they established a role as general hospitals for a specific and neglected age group. A writer in *The Times* stated that the children's hospitals achieved nothing that could not be done as well, or better, in the wards of the established general hospitals. Both general hospitals and general practitioners complained about the diversion of funds, and one GP wrote to the *Lancet* to say that his practice of giving advice in his surgery for 1s or 1s 6d a time had fallen by 30s a week since Great Ormond Street had opened. Means-testing to restrict patients who could afford private medicine was introduced, but this was only loosely enforced and overall children's hospitals continue to expand their out-patient facilities. They were expensive to run, although the doctors were largely voluntary. Nursing ratios could be as high as one for each two patients, but nurses were badly paid and their work was menial, mainly attracting women of low calibre until training schools were started.

Whilst overall nursing standards then became exceptional, the mortality rate was slow to fall, due to winter chest and summer intestinal infections amongst the impoverished children. The visiting physicians and surgeons whose initiative had led to the establishment of the hospitals were dedicated, but there was little they could offer medically. As charitable workers at the voluntary hospitals they were dependent on private practice for income, and as children's diseases were not a remunerative area, they had to rely on their general hospital appointment for connections rather than specialising in paediatrics.

The position was aggravated by the attitude of the major London teaching hospitals, which were slow to respond to medical specialisation in general and paediatrics in particular. Initially they might appoint an assistant physician of lower status with 'an interest in children's illnesses'! One was appointed at Guy's in 1911, but it was

1923 before a children's ward was opened, and not until 1934 was there a modern department with 46 cots. Most teaching was carried on at the nearby Evelina Children's Hospital, which had 80 beds, with which Guy's was joined. St Thomas's appointed an extra assistant physician in 1890 to initiate a children's department, but it would be 1949 before a new dedicated paediatric unit was formed by the union with two long-established children's hospitals, Paddington Green and Princess Louise. Bart's appointed two physicians already working in specialist children's hospitals to an out-patient department in 1904, and by 1920 two cots had been introduced into each medical ward. A children's ward was only opened in 1938 when a physician solely concerned with children was appointed to a dedicated Department of Child Health. It would be 1972 before a Professor of Paediatrics was appointed, jointly with the London Hospital Medical School. Although the Middlesex was reputed to have held lectures on diseases in infancy and childhood as far back as 1835, it was 1891 before a children's ward was opened, followed by a department in 1935.

These hospitals were independent units and lacked any co-operation with the University of London. It was in the provinces that the leading children's hospitals would form links with their local university and the establishment of paediatrics as a speciality would take the lead.

In Scotland the Royal Hospital for Sick Children forged links with Glasgow University, and their medical students were encouraged from an early stage to attend lectures and clinical instruction in medical and surgical diseases of children for a fee of one guinea. This became a compulsory part of their training when Yorkhill was opened in 1914, and organised teaching, along with postgraduate studies, was introduced after the war. Lectureships were endowed and a University Chair of Medical Paediatrics, linked with hospitals, was founded in 1929. This was the first such chair to be established and, as the only academic paediatric centre in Britain during the 1920s, Yorkhill developed as a major teaching and research centre.

The lead set in Glasgow was followed at Birmingham under Dr Leonard Parsons. He insisted paediatrics should be a compulsory subject in the medical curriculum and made the Children's Hospital a vital teaching centre for medical students and nurses. He was appointed as Lecturer in the Diseases of Childhood at Birmingham University in 1915, and in 1928 the medical faculty made him England's first Professor in the Diseases of Childhood. He also linked the hospital and university with the child welfare and school medical services to form an Institute of Child Health. He would be knighted for his work and was acknowledged by the British Paediatric Association as the most notable contributor of his time to our knowledge of disease in childhood.

At the advent of the NHS the number of specialist paediatricians was low compared with the rest of Europe and the United States, due to the lack of systematic training. Much of children's care was in the hands of general practitioners or physicians, and the new-born were looked after by the obstetrician. Special units for premature babies were few and far between.

Most of all, the emotional needs of children in hospital had not been reviewed. Many were still placed in adult wards, with parental visiting confined to an hour on Saturdays and Sundays. Pressure led to a committee under the chairmanship of Sir Henry Platt to study hospital arrangements for children. It reported in 1959, recommending separate out-patient departments, with admission avoided where possible and then only into separate wards under the care of paediatricians and specially trained nurses, whilst parental visiting should be unlimited. The result was a radical change in the professional status of paediatrics and the numbers entering the speciality. Separate departments would be extended within the district hospital, and increasingly paediatrics would be divided into sub-specialities located in seven regional referral centres across the country. Neo-natal units under the care of a paediatricians would be attached to all maternity units.

Chapter 11

Mental Hospitals

In the Middle Ages the overall attitude towards mental disturbance was probably as understanding as it is today. People realised that it was often the outcome of emotional upset and accepted the principle of diminished responsibility, rather than holding the earlier belief of possession by 'the devil'. In 1270 at a trial in Norwich of Richard Blofot, who had killed his wife and two children and then tried to hang himself, the jury concluded he was not responsible for his actions and committed him to prison. His case was reviewed by a Royal Commission six years later, which decided it was too early for his release. Sadly he was to kill a friar who had befriended him by smashing his skull with a trestle table and was convicted of 'killing by misadventure during a fit of madness' and retained in prison. A century later a boy who had seriously injured his father with a sword was acquitted on the grounds that the father was to blame, as he had provoked the lad through constant criticism.

Around this time one of the first hospitals dedicated to mental cases was established at Gheel in Belgium at the shrine of St Dympna, who was the patron saint of those with mental illness. She was the daughter of a pagan Irish chieftain, by whom she was murdered, along with the priest who advised her, in a fit of insane rage when she fled to escape an incestuous marriage.

The first comparable institutions in Britain were related to the monasteries, for priests 'who suddenly fell into a frenzy and lost their memories and novices who suffered a breakdown under the stress of the strict religious regime'. At the end of the 13th century a priory that had served as a base for the Bishop of Bethlehem on his visits to London was converted into a hospital under the direction of the City of London, and in 1403 was found to have been treating mental patients when there was an investigation into a scandal about its finances. All documents before the Reformation relating to the hospital's treatment of mental patients are lost, but it is probable that in the 15th century it was functioning properly, with any physical restraint restricted to violent cases and removed when they settled. The warders were reputedly people of calibre, as Henry VII maintained one of his staff 'that is mad' there for 6s 8d a quarter.

Only the violent who were a danger to themselves or others would be sent to prison, a workhouse or house of correction. Poor families could apply to the county justices for public assistance to support their mentally unbalanced relatives and receive 'family care', with financial aid for their care at home. Where the disturbed had assets, they were taken over by the 'King's Prerogative', which claimed any rents and profits during his lifetime from which the necessities of life would be provided. This was succeeded by the Court of Wards, which appointed neutral trustees for idiots and lunatics in legal matters. Bethlem was the first public institution for the insane jointly managed by the City of London with Bridewell, a house of correction for the dissolute. Early in the 17th century it began to acquire a reputation for the callous and cruel treatment for mental patients for which the name Bethlem (or Bedlam) became synonymous under the direction of the appropriately named Helkiatt Crook, who would be sacked for stealing the funds supplied by the governors and parishes, as well as levying admission fees from patients.

In 1678 Bethlem was moved from its site at the future Liverpool Street Station to a newly built hospital at Moorfields to house 250 patients, described as the most palatial building in London, with the portico entrance flanked on either side by statues depicting Melancholy and Maniacal Madness.

Overall it is difficult to obtain a balanced picture of conditions for the majority of patients relative to Bethlem's reputation for 'inhuman animalisation'. Anatomically there were long broad corridors along which patients could walk, with single cells with a small window which would open, and even a garden for their use. Its policies were impeccable as a charitable institute open to paupers from the whole country, with an emphasis on the admission of curable cases who were examined by the board of governors beforehand and only accepted for a year. Records show most were discharged within the year, with about one third labelled as cured; those regarded as incurable were returned home or transferred to the beds allocated at Guy's. Many would have nowhere to go and became professional beggars dressed as Tom O'Bedlams, touring fairgrounds and markets dressed up as clowns.

The majority of patients were aged between 20 and 60, of whom half were labelled as 'mischievous'. These included violent murderers and

'New Bedlem' in Moorfields, 1676.

many who had attempted suicide. Many were suffering from depression due to domestic and social problems, then considered the 'English disease'. Bedlam's problems arose from the lack of any proper administration or discipline. For over a hundred years it had been run by five generations of Munros, who took little interest in their responsibilities and seldom appeared. As physicians, they were only paid £125 p.a. but they ran their own private asylum, into which they fed any patients who could afford to pay. The result was a corrupt, demoralised institution run for the benefit of the staff, who behaved as jailers. Although strict rules had been posted for the regulation of staff and care of the patients – such as their freedom to walk in the corridors or outside in the gardens and have regular baths, with the incontinent being given fresh straw – these were largely ignored. Bethlem contained some government-funded criminal lunatics, who were kept in the basement and upper floor in solitary confinement, manacled with handcuffs and chains, along with the more violent patients. Although their death rate was 10%, conditions were probably not worse than in Europe at the time, where cages, whips and chains were standard and the inmates kept in vast prisons of the worst kind, confined in dark cells, denied any outside communication or even religious consolation. The Paris Hopital General housed over 6,000 lunatics and imbeciles within ten years of opening in 1656, mixed up with vagabonds and criminals.

The main reason for the notoriety that Bethlem acquired was that it opened its doors to public viewing and it became the freak-show of the period; it was open every day except Sunday for a 2d admission fee. The crowds attracted would be sold refreshments and bait the patients, who would probably respond by 'insane behaviour' to attract atten-

A mentally ill patient restrained.

The Royal Hospital of Bethlehem — the gallery for women.

The Royal Hospital of Bethlehem — the gallery for men.

283

tion. Admission was restricted to ticket-holders only after 1770, but these could include a whole family. Any medical treatment was standard for the time, with emetics and purgatives, bleeding and blistering and sedation with opium and hyoscyamus.

In 1815, after increasing press exposure and pressure from reformers, a House of Commons Committee held an inquiry into Bethlem, precipitated by the death of James Norris, an American sailor who had been confined for 18 years in a purpose-built harness of rods and chains that virtually prevented all movement. He was considered a dangerous and uncontrollable violent lunatic, and had attacked the staff and bitten off the finger of another patient. The Munro in charge at the time was called as a witness and admitted he used chains for the restraint of patients to cut down on staff, but did not use these in his private asylum as they were 'only fit for paupers, and gentlemen would not like it'! As a result of the inquiry, conditions were improved, with patients no longer woken at 6 a.m., to be put back to bed two hours later and left to rot in their cells all day. In spite of its splendour, Moorfield's Bethlem had been jerry-built, and as the fabric started to decay it was moved to a new building in Southwark, now part of the Imperial War Museum. As early as 1820 it admitted medical students and doctors for training, which was only otherwise available at Edinburgh.

New Bethlem Hospital, St George's Fields, Southwark, 1815.

At the turn of the 18th century relatively few insane were confined to workhouses or Bridewells and the rest remained within the family, or roamed the countryside as vagrants jeered at by the public. In 1714 the Vagrancy Act linked lunatics with 'rogues, vagabonds, sturdy beggars and vagrants' and empowered JPs to confine the furiously mad and dangerous in some secure place where they could be physically restrained. Their only concession was that they would not be whipped. The Act was amended in 1744 to cover keeping, maintaining and curing mental patients, but the decision was entirely in the hands of JPs without any medical opinion. Lack of public or state facilities spawned the establishment of private madhouses, very much an English phenomenon. A few had been started earlier, but they multiplied during the first half of the century without any regulation. Many were small family affairs and even doctors would take in a patient at home, but others became a major business investment both for doctors and entrepreneurs. Standards varied immensely, with conditions related to the fees paid. These ranged from 7s 6d a week for parish paupers, who were usually housed separately in an outhouse, on a scanty diet and sleeping on straw more than one to a bed, whilst an average private patient paid a guinea a week, and a few lived in luxury for five guineas a week.

The number of private asylums was to double over the next 50 years, although there is no evidence of any increase in insanity in the 18th century; this was merely a matter of supply meeting demand, as with homes for the elderly at the present time. Standards varied greatly, with no inspection and a strong profit motive. Some acquired a bad reputation when scandals were exposed in the press; a feature in the *Gentleman's Magazine* described them as 'evil' in 1763. Wrongful and illegal impoundment by the families of the elderly, or heirs by their families to gain access to their funds, and husbands or wives of their partner for personal reasons, became common.

As early as 1773 measures of control were considered, but these were strongly opposed by the College of Physicians through self-interest, as many members owned their own madhouse into which they directed and retained their own private patients. Eventually a Bill for the Regulation of Private Madhouses was passed. They now had to be licensed annually and open to inspection, whilst only paupers could be admitted without a doctor's certificate. It was only designed to protect against illegal confinement, not to impose any standards of care or treatment, and was to prove totally ineffective. Five members of the

Royal College of Physicians were appointed as Inspectors, restricted to the London area, and their inadequate powers were to continue for the next 50 years. It was 1828 before a doctor was forbidden to sign a Certificate of Admission to an asylum in which he had a personal interest.

Up to 1850, pauper inmates outnumbered private patients, but their numbers were steadily reduced as they were transferred initially to workhouses and then to county asylums. Many of the private homes would become absorbed into the county system, and in 1959 only 20 remained under licence. In contrast, some were to acquire more favourable publicity. When George III suffered his first attack of insanity in 1788, possibly due to the metabolic disorder porphyria, and treatment by orthodox doctors failed, he turned to a clergyman, Dr Francis Willis, who had established a madhouse in Lincolnshire. A visitor to this unit described how he had passed many clean and smartly dressed people happily farming in the surrounding fields and found they were the hospital patients. Regarded as a quack by orthodox doctors, he insisted on exclusive medical control of the King. Although he used the regular measures of mechanical constraint with a straitjacket, gag and restraining chains, he combined these with a programme of mesmerism and semi-hypnosis, and when the King recovered he was awarded a pension of £1,000 annually for 21 years.

A more forward-looking approach was developed at York Retreat, founded by William Tuke in 1795 for Quaker patients and designed to offer them the comfort of treatment by their own community. Although limited mechanical restraint was accepted, medication was discounted and patients were encouraged towards self-discipline by bonding with the staff, who were in a ratio of one to every three patients, in a family atmosphere. On each ward the patients were housed in small separate units, with day rooms leading into a central area.

Alongside private madhouses was the development of public asylums on the lines of the general and specialist voluntary hospitals. The first of these was St Luke's, opened by subscription to relieve pressure on Bethlem, on a site later to become the Bank of England printing works. It was the first to call itself an 'asylum' in place of 'madhouse' or 'hospital', banning casual sightseeing and admitting students. Unfortunately the founder, Dr William Battie, also owned a private home into which he diverted the wealthier patients. He left an

St Luke's Hospital, Old Street Road.

estate valued at £200,000 on his death, setting a pattern that was to bedevil many of the asylums opening throughout the provinces.

The first of these was in Manchester in 1752, with 22 cells for private and parish pauper patients and under the management of the General Infirmary. It was successful and became Cheadle Royal Hospital. Others in Newcastle and Hereford would become privatised and be taken over by the physician-in-charge for his private patients. The York Asylum was to acquire a reputation for evil far worse than Bethlem's, although it was designed by a leading architect as a purpose-built unit and was initially described as a 'truly noble institution'! When it was under the control of an ineptly named Dr Best, scandal began to spread and the secretive atmosphere led several townsmen to buy a subscription for governorship and demand to inspect the asylum. They found the patients in appalling conditions, and concealment of deaths, as well as financial embezzlement. The stench is said to have made the inspectors vomit, with some patients manacled naked and lying in straw fouled by their excrement, and in one case 13 women cooped up all day in a cell eight feet square. A subsequent fire, suspected as arson to destroy the evidence, killed several patients. It was later rehabilitated to become Bootham Park

Psychiatric Hospital. In contrast St Patrick's in Dublin, founded by Jonathan Swift in his will, was described as 'clean and in good order'.

Across Scotland seven subscription asylums were opened, the first in 1781, and achieved a high reputation. All received a Royal Charter, and as a group were known as the 'Royal Asylums'. But they could not handle the numbers involved, and due to resistance to state asylums from public funds on financial grounds, Scotland developed a system of billeting out patients into unlicensed private homes which were often of poor quality, whilst many of the more disturbed suffered in prison or poorhouses. It was only in 1855, when general agitation about the poor facilities for mental patients became general, that district asylums began to be developed, and boarding-out clinics supervised.

In Ireland district asylums were opened from 1820 with 100–150 beds, but later ones were much larger, with up to 1,000 beds, and patients labelled as difficult and dangerous were restrained, only later to match changes in English legislation.

Asylums in Wales were only developed later in the century; until then, mental patients would remain in the family, who received a weekly payment for their care.

Although the Georgian century earned a reputation for the abolition of family care for the mentally ill – and their confinement under mechanical restraint in custodial institutions riddled with sadism and embezzlement with no effective treatment, epitomised by Bedlam – in fact at the turn of the 19th century only a few thousand were in institutions. It was Victorian psychiatrists who were preoccupied by asylums as therapeutic institutions, and a century later they held over 100,000 patients.

Examples of neglect and ill treatment were increasingly exposed by the press and social reformers, but there was stubborn political and professional opposition to any reform at the start of the century, when a previous lax system was replaced by a century of legislation and psychiatric theories by straitjacketed doctors and magistrates as much as the patients.

Until 1800, social regulation and welfare, raging through education, public health and insanity, devolved around the shires and squires, Justices of the Peace and the parish. Most disordered people were kept at home, boarded out or left to roam in public, with only a few frenzied chained up in a workhouse, Bethlem or private madhouse at the cost of the parish or family. In 1800 a Criminal Lunatic Act was passed as an urgent measure when a religious maniac, James Hadfield, was acquitted on the grounds of insanity from a head wound suffered in the army, when he shot and wounded George III two days after he had tried to murder his son. Until then there were no grounds to detain him, but he was now able to be confined for the rest of his life to Bethlem for his own and public safety.

Increasingly it was realised that a combination of private and charity asylums and the Poor Law did not cover the care of the insane, emphasised by successive Royal Commissions in 1808 and 1815. As a result, Acts of Parliament entitled local authorities to set up lunatic asylums, controlled on a county basis and administered at public expense by the local JPs. The pattern envisaged was 300-bedded units to hold private, charity and pauper patients, but the response was limited and only 10 were initiated within the next 20 years, none within the London region. However, private licensed houses mushroomed to over 150 asylums, many with parish contracts for paupers. At Hoxton House and Bethnal Green in London, patient numbers rose to several hundred, in appalling conditions, which led to the establishment of a Metropolitan Commission in Lunacy, with increased powers of inspection. Subsequently there was an overall improvement in standards, and the first London asylum was set up at Hanwell.

In 1845 a new Act initiated by Lord Shaftesbury was to begin a new era in mental health care. Based on the York Retreat, the plan was to create a national network of asylums with improved care, expected to be largely self-supporting, with the inmates working to keep labour costs to a minimum. Supported by medical and legal experts, the paid Commissioners were entitled to inspect and license all institutions for the insane, who had to keep proper records. Counties and their boroughs were compelled to provide accommodation for their insane, and this led to a boom in building over the next 15 years, but the original concept of relatively small units located close to town with easy access to properly trained doctors was frustrated, and most of the vast mental hospitals inherited by the NHS date back to this mid-Victorian period. They would become overwhelmed by the masses of chronic cases decanted from the workhouses and become 'lunatic colonies' holding up to 3,000 patients.

Overall conditions were to improve. The criminal element was removed to secure prisons and there was a progressive change in the attitude towards patients. There was increasing controversy about

Colney Hatch Asylum, Barnet (later Friern Hospital), 1845-1951.

physical restraint since Dr Pinel in 1792 had taken charge of the two Parisian hospitals, where he found the inmates in animal conditions, lying naked in chains on stone floors, deprived of air and water, and ordered the removal of their chains. He initiated a division of the insane into acute and chronic, with separate accommodation and isolation of the criminal, and separate institutions for the epileptic and simple-minded.

Led by Germany, the pattern of cells opening onto a corridor began to be replaced with attractive dormitories and separate villas with public rooms, schools and shops, and grounds to develop farming and cottage industries. Although restraint was to some extent continued until early in the 20th century, it was gradually phased out throughout the county asylums, including Hanwell, which was to become the first London county mental hospital, led by the influence of Dr Hood at Bethlem.

Whilst the first county mental hospitals were built on the prison pattern and based on rows of single rooms opening onto a gallery, some would be modelled on the York Retreat pattern. At the West Riding Asylum, Wakefield, Dr William Ellis was appointed as resident Medical Director in place of a workhouse-style master, and he pioneered a scheme to employ patients in industrial and occupational training with 'after-care homes' and 'half-way houses' for re-integration into society. This pattern was only gradually to become standard, and many retained a workhouse regime, with only a visiting physician or a junior resident medical officer with little authority. Admissions were restricted to paupers; there were limited facilities for patients above this level, and the subscription hospitals such as Bethlem, renamed 'registered hospitals', expanded under reformed administration. Their criminal patients were relocated to Broadmoor, and there was a complete change in the calibre and attitude of the attendants, with facilities for occupational therapy. A ballroom was opened at Bethlem and plays were produced quarterly by the patients, with a billiard table for the men, who were allowed to smoke.

By the time of the Metropolitan Asylums Board there were 39 privately owned licensed asylums in Britain, each with over 400 beds and contracts with the parochial authorities for Poor Law patients, and the charitable institutions of Bethlem and St Luke's each had over 300 beds.

It was never intended that the majority of mental patients should be packed away into asylums, which were planned for those who needed treatment or were a danger to themselves and others. The incurable chronic and mental deficient should have remained in union workhouses, or where possible stayed in the community with medical aid and Poor Law relief. But there was no system to ensure reasonable classification, and allocation was at the mercy of the boards of guardians and their officials, whose primary motive was to cut costs to a minimum. For many, conditions at home were wretched, whilst in the workhouse mental cases would be mixed in with the able-bodied without any nursing or medical care.

The smaller units envisaged by the 1845 Act were uneconomic, and although special mental wards were attached to some workhouses, the county asylums would become progressively packed with chronic cases decanted from the workhouses. By the turn of the century many housed over 2,000 patients whilst at Colney Hatch (now Friern Barnet) and Hanwell numbers exceeded 3,000. Routine management and treatment were impossible. One failed experiment in London was to build two long dreary units at Caterham and Banstead, to hold the harmless and chronic, but ended up housing the subnormal.

Staffing at the county asylums was quite unable to cope within the large, overcrowded, grim-walled establishments that these became from the influx of patients, 90% of whom came from the workhouse, with many dependent on nursing care. The asylums had been planned as small 300-bedded units on a model of a mixed grade of patients divided into separate villas each holding about 60, and largely self-supporting from the farm produce they could produce themselves. They were considered uneconomic and by the 1890s vast asylums with more than 2,000 beds had been built around the country, holding over 60,000 pauper patients, often packed in three rows of beds in each ward, on sites well out into the country, chosen for cheapness. The Metropolitan Asylums Board institutions at Leavesden and Caterham each held over 2,000 beds and comprised three-storey blocks, each floor forming one enormous ward. The patients would be under lock and key, with the emphasis on security instead of treatment, and private asylums became increasingly expensive to run. Many closed, or moved out into the countryside, as with Ticehurst. Although a medical superintendent would now be appointed to run the asylum, he would have had no previous training experience in psychiatry, and would often only be allowed a single assistant. The poor pay and conditions would restrict the quality of the medical staff.

In Catholic Europe, many of the insane were in institutions run by religious orders, as at the Hôtel Dieu in Paris staffed by the Augustinians. Their compassionate approach was reflected in a few cases in England, such as the Quaker York Retreat and Dr Cotton's asylum at St Albans, but in the county asylums the nursing staff were of the lowest calibre.

Judgement of insanity and the decision to retain in custody was entirely in the hands of the Justices of the Peace at Quarter Sessions, independent of any medical assessment. In Britain psychiatry in general was of low esteem in the public mind and remained retarded in development as a profession throughout the Victorian era, rejecting the advances in psychotherapy and dynamic treatments that were developing across Europe and in the United States.

Although doctors could attend Bethlem and Edinburgh asylums for experience as early as 1820, mental illness did not form any part of medical training. It would be 1885 before a Medico-Psychological Association was established under the aegis of the General Medical Council and a national scheme set up to train doctors for a Certificate in Psychological Medicine. This was extended to cover all levels of attendants, who would receive a certificate after a two-year course, but this proved of little practical benefit and led to a general strike by asylum mental nurses early in the 20th century for improved conditions and to establish a professional status. In 1911 a Diploma in Psychology was established by several universities, initiated at Durham, leading to increased numbers entering psychiatry, whilst in 1920 asylums were designated as 'mental hospitals'.

The First World War exposed the limitations of the asylum system when thousands of servicemen were shipped home suffering from 'shell-shock'. Early in the war they were liable to be shot as deserters, but later this became a recognised state. Their management established the principle of psychotherapy, and the condition of anxiety neurosis was recognised. Special centres to handle them were established, exemplified by a small villa-pattern asylum at Maghull, near Liverpool.

Maghull Hospital had been purpose-built in 1912 as a colony for epileptics. It was taken over by the War Office and converted into a centre that was to treat over 4,000 'shell-shocked' soldiers and become a training centre for Army psychiatrists under the direction of Dr 'Ronald' Rows. A pathologist who converted to working in mental hospitals, he was one of the first in England to research neuropathology. He also criticised the lack of any psychiatric training and advocated the need for local out-patient clinics, which were being set up in Germany and the US, where mental patients could obtain early treatment before the need for committal to asylums. Rows established the diagnosis of traumatic neurasthenia, covering 'shell-shock' and the label 'lacking moral fibre' which was attached to the Voluntary Flying Corps air crew who broke down under their stress and would be cashiered. The condition is now generally recognised in civilian life as a sequel to train crashes and other traumatic experiences. Maghull has now become Ashworth Special Hospital, housing the criminally insane.

Criticism of the mental hospital standards after the war led to an inquiry and, following a classical status dispute between the Medico-Psychological Association and the newly established General Medical Council in 1919, a Nurses Act set up a training course leading to a Certificate as a Registered Mental Nurse.

Following the war, two clinics were set up to offer early treatment independent of the asylum system through psychotherapy. The Cassell Hospital was run by a Dr Ross, who had established himself at Maghull during the war and later at Springfield, a sister hospital in

London which did not survive. The Tavistock Clinic was founded by Dr Crichton-Miller with a background of Freudian and Adlerian staff.

The first asylum to offer any laboratory and research facilities in psychiatry was Claybury in Essex, built in 1893 and planned to service the other mental hospitals throughout the Home Counties, which were all taken over by the new London County Council in 1889. It became increasingly evident that a central laboratory allied to research facilities and a postgraduate training centre with university affiliation had to be established, but Claybury was considered too far out of London to be suitable. A reputable private psychiatrist, Henry Maudsley, offered the LCC £30,000 towards the cost of a new acute teaching hospital with laboratories as early as 1908, but it was five years before it was to be built opposite King's College Hospital.

The wards were used for service casualties throughout the war and it was 1923 before the London Psychiatric Hospital opened for psychiatric clinical work and teaching. For the first time, voluntary patients would be admitted to a mental institution controlled by a public authority. It became confirmed as a university school the following year and as the Institute of Psychiatry of London University in 1948 when it joined the British Postgraduate Medical Federation. At the same time it linked with the Bethlem Royal Hospital nearby, doubling the number of beds to over 500. Bethlem had been rebuilt in Beckenham in 1930 and was now located in a 200-acre park with its own laboratory and nurses' accommodation; any trace of the past was confined to the museum of memorabilia. It had considerable wealth from London property holdings, which was carried into the union to finance major rebuilding of laboratories or lecture theatres, with offices for the Institute of Psychiatry. It had developed a broad range of activities, from neurosurgery to clinical psychology, psychotherapy and analysis, and became the predominant centre of training for British psychiatrists.

It was only in 1926 that a revolutionary Royal Commission Report concluded physical and mental disease were not separable and the mentally ill needed to be offered medical treatment, not just confinement, and needed specialist medical attention both at home and in hospitals, which were small and comfortable for the patient – as well as out-patient clinics and facilities in general hospitals.

It would be a long time before these goals were achieved. Although out-patient clinics for the mentally ill had existed at Wakefield and St Thomas's since 1890, the Lunacy Act that year, designed to eliminate abuses and safeguard personal liberties, restricted admissions to legally certified patients. Assessments had to be carried out in the workhouses as many suitable cases could not be admitted, and voluntary admission to licensed and certified houses was the only route for the great majority before the 1930 Mental Treatment Act, which allowed local authorities to open out-patient clinics, sponsor research and admit voluntary patients. There was increasing realisation that the vast dreary asylums had become anti-therapeutic, and by the turn of the century a few had begun to develop small self-contained units within their grounds, as at Hellingly and Napsbury, whilst later others added independent villas in cottage garden suburban style, complementing or even replacing the larger units, as at Shenley and Runwell, and an open spread-out plan stepped backwards to give a southern aspect became standard. The improved design would include dayrooms, recreation halls, playing fields, a chapel and workshop. But admission to county asylums would remain restricted to paupers, and many backward boroughs would continue to use licensed private houses.

During the Second World War there was a further improvement in the liberal attitude towards the mental casualties amongst the forces, initiated at the Millhill Emergency Military Hospital, where a more therapeutic approach spread generally, with greater interaction between staff and patients, more liberal regimes and increased freedom for the patients. This was linked to the introduction of new health professionals – physiotherapists, occupational therapists and psychologists – to rehabilitate the bored and unstimulated patients, in preparation for return to the community.

The advent of the NHS should have provided central finance to upgrade wards and improve training and conditions for the nursing staff, and to develop auxiliary services such as day hospitals and rehabilitation centres for discharged patients. But the mistakes of a hundred years before with the foundation of county asylums would be repeated, and they became packed with chronic and geriatric patients. With continued low pay and poor working conditions, and lack of support from their union and the General Nursing Council, the morale of the mental nurse remained low and trainees voted with their feet, 80% leaving before completion of their course to switch to general nursing. Care was left in the hands of untrained nurses, managed by authoritarian senior staff who were opposed to any improvements to the old system they had run, and treatment was restricted to electro-therapy and medication. The low standards of care and management were exposed by public inquiries during the 1960s and 70s, leading to a change in political attitude, but effective action was slow and protracted.

During the early years of the NHS over 150,000 mentally ill and handicapped were locked away in large forbidding institutions, often with decrepit infrastructure and sanitation, and the patients were packed into large, overcrowded units with little to occupy their time. The disposal of the Medical Superintendent system with his overriding authority often led to a breakdown of staff discipline, whilst the great majority of acute mental cases would continue to be admitted with little facility for their treatment. The first proposals for improvement were put forward in the 1962 Hospital Plan, which included the provision of units with up to 80 beds for acute short-stay psychiatric patients in the new district general hospitals that were to be built, which would work alongside the local authority social service departments.

There was no immediate action, but a succession of scandals involving the old mental hospitals and those housing mentally handicapped and the elderly would lead to the creation of a Hospital Advisory Service, whose team would regularly inspect the hospitals concerned. In 1967 a book *Sans Everything* was published on behalf of an organisation called Aid for the Elderly in Government Institutions (AEGIS), detailing six hospitals in particular where conditions were especially bad and there was staff brutality and dishonesty. An inquiry was held and the charges were largely dismissed as isolated cases, with the support of the medical and nursing professions; but a complaint by a nurse about conditions at Ely Hospital, Cardiff, was investigated by a committee, which issued a damning report on conditions and management.

Other hospital scandals included Farleigh in Somerset, for the mentally handicapped, where several nurses were charged by the police for cruelty; and Whittingham, where it was confirmed that patients would have a wet towel wrapped round their neck until they were unconscious. At Napsbury Hospital, following an inquest on a patient who had died from severe injuries, it emerged the consultant would routinely treat schizophrenics by behavioural therapy that included withdrawal of routine nursing care so that conditions became dirty and unhygienic. At Normansfield Hospital for the mentally handicapped in London, the low standards of care were only exposed when the nursing members of their union went on strike.

The value of the Hospital Advisory Service was limited as it was restricted to the team descending on a hospital for a few days, making a report and then moving on. It was realised a proper supervisory policy was essential and in 1975, the Minister of Health, Barbara Castle, published *Better Services for the Mentally Ill*, a long-term plan to halve the number of mental hospital beds and build up facilities for community care.

As the older hospitals became more 'open door' in attitude, there was an increasing problem with severely disturbed patients, many of whom had to be placed in prisons due to the shortage of beds in secure hospitals such as Broadmoor. One solution was the development of smaller 'secure' units in each region, an expensive programme unpopular with people locally.

Over the next 20 years there was a great improvement overall in the management of the mentally ill. Half of the 130 large mental hospitals had been closed, with most of the rest time-dated and their bed numbers decimated to an average of 233 by 1993, reducing pressure on staff. Hospital beds had fallen to 50,000 and the average length of patient stay halved to 76 days. Supervision was shifted into the community, with a care plan and key worker for each patient. Housing and hostel accommodation would be made available, and there were small special residential units for those requiring secure conditions, with extra facilities for home-care patients and adolescents. Inevitably new problems arose. Many of those discharged were unable to cope with resettlement in the community and the streets of the larger towns would be littered with homeless living in cardboard boxes and begging, comparable to the time of the closure of the monasteries.

Overall psychiatric services were transferred to separate units attached to the district general hospital which would include residential accommodation for acute cases.

Of more concern to the public has been a small number of highly publicised murders and attacks by discharged patients. Although medical treatment of schizophrenia and manic depression has greatly improved, control is dependent on the patients continuing their medication. Failure to do this, without supervision after discharge from hospital, leads to a relapse when they can become dangerous, although, in fact, they are far more likely to commit suicide than harm others. At present they can only be compelled to take their medication in hospital, and measures are under way to extend this into community care, with those refusing to attend treatment centres to be compulsorily returned to hospital. Anyone who refused voluntary treatment could be detained for 28 days, after which further detention and treatment must be agreed by a Mental Health Tribunal, an independent body with two doctors and a specialist, and the patient has the right to an independent consultant opinion.

Apart from the problem of finding suitable extra accommodation, there has been considerable criticism both from within the psychiatric system and groups that represent patients, such as the Mental Health Alliance, a group of 50 voluntary and professional organisations. They point out one person in four would suffer some form of mental health problem in their lifetime, and in some their behavioural pattern could be strange enough to attract a label of personality disorder without being a threat to themselves or others. There was no direct link between severe personality disorders and dangerousness, whilst many people who were potentially dangerous did not carry such a label, and it was wrong to present them as a group. Doubts have also been expressed as to any possible treatment, although patients with the condition have been successfully treated in therapeutic communities under court orders in Canada and the Netherlands.

Roehampton Priory, c.1835, before its conversion to a private asylum by Dr William Wood in 1872.

Cygnet Health Care's 36-bed intensive care and acute treatment hospital at Black-heath, southeast London. It was opened in 1998, specifically for NHS funded patients.

Amongst all these changes has been a great increase in mental care back within the private sector, such as the Priory & Cygnet Hospital groups. These are providing an increasing proportion of NHS funded acute psychiatric care, reaching 50% of such cases in London and the Home Counties with many transferred as NHS facilities cannot cope. Cygnet, with eleven centres, is the largest outsourcing provider to the NHS and provider of heroin detoxification services. Priory owns Roehampton, the oldest private mental health hospital in the UK, and now has a chain of 15 hospitals that specialise in addictive and stress care. It offers education facilities and residential schools for young people with emotional and behavioural difficulties, and has set up a Fellowship for psychiatric training attached to several London teaching hospitals.

Chapter 12

Evolution of the Medical Profession

Quackery was to reach its peak in Tudor times when different divisions of the medical profession began to be established through a series of Acts passed by Henry VIII, each assigned separate duties and privileges. These were respectively the barber-surgeons, apothecaries and physicians, but they would become preoccupied with a struggle for their own respective status and it would be centuries before they worked out the working relationships of today. Initially, many had little more background than the mixed bag of quacks they sought to replace. The barber-surgeons led the way in 1509 when they united to form a company so that only their members could practise within a mile of the City of London any 'barbery or shavery, surgery or letting of blood', the only exception being drawing of teeth.

In 1565 a member of the Worshipful Company of Surgeons, John Halle, wrote that for every surgeon or physician that was fit to practise his art, there were ten tradesmen and women running round the country like 'pedlars, tinkers, rat-catchers and vagabonds', and although there were legal regulations for making cloth and tanning leather, there were none for surgeons. He suggested the surgeon should have 'the heart of a lion, eyes like a hawk and the hands of a woman'. Training was a haphazard seven-year apprenticeship which might teach them next to nothing, except to pull a tooth or shave, and some 'sea-professors' would set up as a fully fledged surgeon after a couple of trips as a surgeon's mate. The development of anatomical knowledge and practical experience through the constant wars of the time led to a general improvement in standards and rise in status. After the Barber-Surgeons' Company became chartered in 1540 their education became organised, with anatomical lectures and demonstrations in dissection, although it would be 1800 before surgery would finally be accepted as a fully respectable profession.

In 1511 a statute restricted medical or surgical practice within a seven-mile radius of the City of London to doctors approved and admitted by the Bishop of London or Dean of St Paul's, acting on advice from a medical panel, whilst outside the City bishops had

301

A physician and patient of the sixteenth century.

similar powers. In 1518 Henry VIII was persuaded to give a Royal Charter to the College of Physicians, along with the authority to license physicians within the seven-mile limit.

Apothecary is a term derived from the Latin for a shopkeeper, and the word used by Galen to denote the repository in which he kept his medicines. It became used to describe someone who prepared,

The apothecary.

prescribed and sold drugs. These roles would be passed on to qualified chemists and druggists, whilst the apothecary himself would become the general medical practitioner of the future. Many responsible fringe practitioners were harassed by the members of the College of Physicians and Barber-Surgeons as 'quacks', and in 1543 an Act was passed for their protection and toleration; they were labelled apothecaries as many kept shops to sell medicines. An early advocate of apothecaries was Henry VIII, himself labelled a 'physician's cook' who dabbled in pharmacy. He had contributed a number of prescriptions to a medical book in relation to the treatment of leg ulcers, by which he was constantly afflicted. In 1606 the apothecaries were incorporated by

James I as one of the city companies; at first they were united with the grocers, but obtained a separate charter as 'Master, Wardens and Society of the Art and Mystery of the Apothecaries of the City of London', and won the right to treat the sick and Plague victims in 1665.

There were few doctors at the time and the apothecaries played an increasingly important role in medical care. Whilst one in ten would attach himself to a physician and make up his prescriptions, the remainder earned an independent existence, including domiciliary visits. Relationships between them and the physicians became increasingly fractious. Inside their range of seven miles around the City of London, doctors were accused of abusing their monopoly to protect their fees, charging 10s 6d against an average apothecary charge of 3s or 4s for a prescription, making their services unavailable to the average working-class patient. In their turn the apothecaries were accused of exceeding their province by prescribing as well as dispensing drugs and that, without any regulations for quality, some were selling 'worm-eaten' and superannuated drugs.

In retaliation the College of Physicians at the end of the century opened three dispensaries offering free advice, which attracted a large number of patients. But they were closed due to the cost of supplying drugs and problems in staffing. The dispute eventually had to be resolved by the House of Lords, when the apothecaries acquired the right to give advice without charge and prescribe as well as dispense, and the Apothecary's Company was empowered to send in inspectors who could destroy medicine unfit for use. Their powers were increased in 1748 when practice as an apothecary within seven miles of the City of London was restricted to those licensed and examined by the Company, and in 1815 this power was extended throughout England and Wales, although chemists and druggists were exempted. The rights of the universities and Colleges of Physicians and Surgeons were protected, and apothecaries were compelled to fulfil any prescription from a physician.

The 1815 Apothecary Act planned to create a class of practitioners with the right to practise medicine in collaboration with physicians and surgeons. Until then, any general educational background or medicine training was optional. Although many had studied at a university or college, the majority had no qualifications or were even illiterate. The Act gave the Company the power to enforce anyone intending to practise as a GP or apothecary to obtain their licence beforehand, unless they held a university degree. The terms before entry to its examination were stringent and included five years' apprenticeship to an apothecary, with a certificate to confirm they had attended courses in anatomy, physiology, chemistry and materia medica which covered the source, preparation and use of drugs – although surgery and midwifery were not included until an 1886 Medical Act.

The General Medical Council and Medical Register were established in 1858 to enable the public to distinguish qualified from unqualified practitioners, and the Council was given the power to require all licensing bodies to define their study and examination standards before awarding a licence to practise, bringing all entitled to practise in Great Britain onto one register. Three levels of hospital staff had been created, with a distinct pecking order. The Royal College of Physicians had been licensed in 1518 to control the practice of medicine, but became a monopolist guild. The Royal College of Surgeons had been successively licensed in Edinburgh in 1778, Ireland in 1784 and London in 1800, and later in the rest of England.

The early role of the apothecary in the hospital system was rigidly defined and arduous compared with that of surgeons and physicians. He would be a full-time salaried resident responsible for admissions and treatment, including bleeding, cupping and blistering. He supervised baths and looked after the surgical instruments, providing and dispensing medicines out of his meagre pay. He would not be allowed to leave the hospital without telling the matron where he was going and carried the main burden for daily hospital administration.

Since their formation, the divisions of the profession had gone their individual ways. The 1886 Act was designed to eliminate this situation and specify training and examination for all medical students before practising. This would lead to the establishment of medical schools throughout the country and became the background to modern teaching. The background to medical training was poor; Oxford and Cambridge held a monopoly from early times, but this was a 14-year course, proceeding from BA to MD in a very general range of humanities in the widest sense, covering philosophy, logic and metaphysics and history. Any medicine was purely galenic, with no clinical aspect and little anatomy, and the only science was chemistry. Any professor responsible for medical teaching would seldom, if ever, lecture. Often, this would be the limit of their studies and the end result would be an arrogant and ignorant hospital physician who at most would examine the patient's tongue and pulse and write out a complex prescription.

To obtain any proficiency in medicine, students would have to go overseas to universities in Leiden, Holland, founded in 1685, and other European centres, returning to Oxford and Cambridge to 'incorporate' their degree. Medical training in Britain began in Edinburgh University, founded in 1582. In 1670 a Physics Garden was established near Holyrood Palace and became a Centre for the Study of Botany. Two honorary professors were appointed to teach the Principle and Practice of Medicine, but gave few lectures or demonstrations. A significant medical school was initiated in 1720 when a Dr Monroe was appointed Professor of Anatomy, followed by others in turn that included the facilities of materia medica, midwifery and the principles and practice of medicine. By 1726 a complete medical school had been established, and the same year a six-bedded hospital was opened by public subscription. This was to become the Edinburgh Royal Infirmary within ten years, and would be rebuilt in 1741 with 228 beds and a professional staff who began clinical teaching. It would become the

Edinburgh Royal Infirmary, 1738.

Edinburgh Medical School, 1877.

premier medical teaching centre in Europe over the next hundred years, offering systemic and clinical teaching in all aspects of medicine including midwifery, whilst anatomy and physiology schools were established. The Doctorate of Medicine examination included pharmacy and materia medica – with a thesis in Latin which could be excused by a fee and recommendations from two physicians. In 1759 Goldsmith wrote 'if poor and needs to work, send your son to Leiden or Edinburgh, if rich send him to Oxford or Cambridge, where there is the best chance of education and becoming famous'.

Legally Scottish graduates were not allowed to practise in England until the 1858 Medical Act, but this was largely ignored and at Leeds in 1767 four of the five physicians had trained in Edinburgh. It introduced clinical teaching in the form of ward rounds, which had been developed in Leiden, and it became the premier medical school in the 18th and 19th centuries, attracting many eminent students and graduates. On the surgical side these would include Simpson, appointed a Professor of Midwifery at the age of 26, who introduced chloroform for childbirth in 1847; Lister, who developed antiseptic at Glasgow before moving on to Edinburgh on his way to King's College; and Charles Bell, who was to open a famous private anatomy school in

London and become Professor of Anatomy and Surgery at the Royal College of Surgeons. On the medical side were Bright and Addison, whose names were to be attached to kidney and pancreatic conditions; and Mackenzie, who became a leading cardiologist. More contentious was James Meranda Stuart Berry, who graduated in 1812, served for 46 years in the armed services and became Inspector General of Military Hospitals in Canada, but when he died in 1865 was found to be a woman. Officially women graduates were accepted in 1864, but had to attend separate lectures and were only granted a certificate of professional competence until 1876, when an especial Act of Parliament allowed universities to grant women a degree.

It was not until the earlier part of the 19th century that proper London medical schools would be established in close alliance with the larger general hospitals. Before then any training was haphazard, expensive and hazardous. It would entail an apprenticeship to a general practitioner before an attachment to a hospital surgeon as a pupil, or for a higher fee as a dresser or 'cub' who might assist at operations and be on call under the apothecary for emergencies.

When Bristol opened in 1737 the fee was 20 guineas for a seven-year apprenticeship; it had risen to 150 guineas by 1813. In St Bartholomew's Museum a formal sealed document records the apprenticeship in 1799 of William Lawrence to John Abernethy, a famous surgeon of the time, for seven years at a fee of 400 guineas. He was to serve his master faithfully, keep his secrets and do his lawful commandments, whilst he must not commit fornication or marry. In return Abernethy agreed to teach Lawrence his 'art' and provide him with food and lodging.

For additional fees the students could also attend lectures and anatomy dissections, but before proper facilities were added, conditions were usually foul and unhealthy. At St Thomas's until 1819 teaching dissections would be carried out in an overcrowded, unventilated room linked to the cutting room and mortuary, foul wards and brewhouse. Many students would become ill during the course and drop out altogether, whilst the life expectancy for those attending anatomy demonstrations was low.

As a result of the lack of proper teaching facilities, private schools flourished towards the end of the century and attracted many eminent men to the staff. The Grainger brothers opened the Webb School near St Thomas's, and the Windmill Street School was founded by William Hunter, to be taken over later by Charles Bell and his brother. The

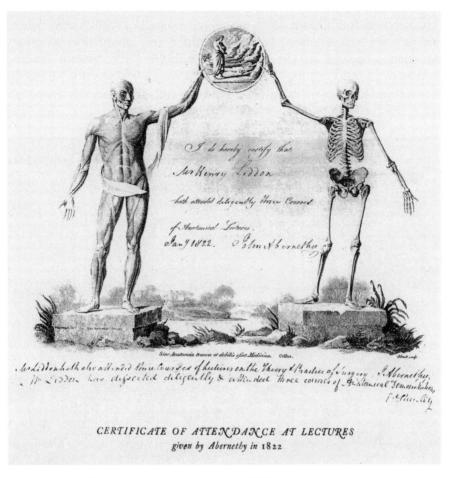

CERTIFICATE OF ATTENDANCE AT LECTURES
given by Abernethy in 1822

A student's certificate of attendance at lectures, 1822.

increase in anatomical teaching led to a shortage of bodies for dissection, exaggerated when the 'Paris method' came into vogue, and revolutionised teaching in that each student dissected a whole body.

In Elizabethan times physicians could include human tissue in their medicines, as powdered bone in red wine for rheumatism and the skull for epilepsy. In the Middle Ages anatomy was a theoretical subject based on Galen's dissection of animals during the third century, when human dissection was not allowed. The first published study in 1543 on human anatomy by a Belgian, Vesalius, was based on a skeleton stolen from the body of a hanged criminal. Later in the century anatomy could be studied at Padua, or Leiden, where the Anatomy

Theatre was founded in 1592 in a large classical amphitheatre where the lectures were attended by a large public and recorded in paintings by such artists as Rembrandt. This established the custom for the bodies of hanged criminals to be handed over for dissection. Later in France and Germany there was a ready source of bodies for dissection from hospitals as well as the destitute criminals. In 1745 this was

The Reward of Cruelty.

extended to the Royal College of Surgeons, who for 10s 6d had the right to the bodies of those hanged at Tyburn. They would make a formal incision from sternum to pubis and then pass the body on to a hospital for dissection. There is at least one recorded case of a hanged criminal being still alive when delivered to Barber-Surgeons' Hall. Edinburgh Medical School was granted the bodies of foundlings and stillborn as well as paupers, criminally insane and suicides, provided the intestines were buried within two days and the remainder of the body within ten days.

But such sources were totally inadequate to deal with the demands of the mushrooming private and hospital anatomy schools, and a black market in bodies built up in England and Scotland. They would be imported from Ireland and France and coached around the country, although they would often arrive unfit for dissection. In Scotland the scarcity was so great they would salt them in the summer and hang them up to dry like kippers for winter use. Grave-robbing became general, led by the students themselves to earn money for their fees, but it became a professional career and it is estimated there were over 200 'resurrection men' in London alone. They were totally ruthless, the most notorious being Burke and Hare in Edinburgh, who may have murdered as many as 16 lodgers in their boarding house to sell on the bodies; Burke himself ending up on the dissecting table after being hanged.

In England there were open resources for their activities as rapid urban development led to the burial facilities for towns in church and hospital graveyards becoming overwhelmed. Corporations would rent land from the churches to bury their dead, but the numbers increased so much during epidemics that bodies were stacked in heaps at the workhouses. In the graveyards, bodies were piled on top of one another and pauper graves were left open until given a scant covering. The graves would be easy prey for the robbers, who dug up the bodies to sell off their teeth, in demand for dentures at the time, grind down the bones as fertiliser and break up the coffins for firewood, before selling on any bodies still fresh enough for dissection, stripped of their clothes.

The anatomists, amongst whom there was intense jealousy and competitiveness for supplies of bodies, often positively encouraged their activities. In Edinburgh a surgeon called Knox, who was a brilliant teacher with as many as 500 students in a year, would pay up to £10 for a body to meet his needs. He was suspected of being aware of the source of the bodies obtained from Burke and Hare. Another famous surgeon suspected of collaboration was Sir Astley Cooper, who became President of the Royal College and was known as the 'King of the Resurrectionists' through his arrangements with the grave-robbers, paying less than the overall average of ten guineas a body. Families would go to great efforts to protect the bodies of their loved ones from being snatched, ranging from armed guards to lowering concrete stone slabs in heavy iron cages or mort-safes onto new graves for a week or two until the bodies were too decomposed to be attractive. More than a thousand bodies a year were being lifted from the burial grounds in Scotland and England in the first decade of the 19th century, and there was an increasing public revolution against grave-robbing with attacks on the homes of suspected anatomists and their schools. In Aberdeen an anatomy theatre was burnt down and anatomy schools in Manchester and other towns were attacked. Some anatomists were accused of direct personal involvement, and one Glasgow surgeon after being acquitted was forced to emigrate to America, where he founded the Bellevue Medical Centre in New York.

Strict measures were introduced in Scotland to ban the practice, but the students left their universities to move south, where medical schools were being established in London and several provincial cities. In 1832 an Anatomy Act was finally introduced into England and Ireland by which all anatomy schools had to be licensed and inspected, and make quarterly returns and detailed identification records to the Home Office of all bodies dissected. These had to be medically certified and decently interred within six weeks. The bodies of executed criminals were no longer sent for dissecting, but those who died in hospitals and workhouses and were not claimed after three days could be sent to licensed anatomy centres. Executors could also send bodies, unless the deceased had expressed conscientious objection to dissection. Heavy penalties were imposed for grave-robbing, and the practice died out. The same year saw the foundation of the first authorised London cemetery at Kensal Green.

Increasingly hospital governors allowed their staff to take on pupils, and later assisted them by building dissection rooms so that anatomy could be taught. By 1830 students were gaining clinical experience in seven major London hospitals, which became intensely competitive, with individual ups and downs in success; there was bitter rivalry between them, only finally resolved recently. It was realised by clini-

312

cians that a hospital with teaching facilities and a medical school increased in fame, as well as providing a better education.

Several had established a close connection with the private schools as the surgeon-anatomist founders were joined by medical colleagues to lecture in medicine and therapeutics and give a broader curriculum, including St Thomas's with Grainger's and The Middlesex with Windmill Street. Lane's Grosvenor Street School would lead to the founding of St Mary's Hospital with its medical school. But the independence of private schools would be undermined as medical training changed with the emphasis on clinical examination, and around 1828 the College of Surgeons passed a devastating blow by a regulation that all candidates for its Diploma had to present a certificate of attendance for a course of lectures from one of the London hospital surgeons. The private schools and their staff merged into the newly founded medical schools, which would themselves tend to function in a private capacity. Started by the medical staff with less than enthusiastic support from the authorities, they would pay rent for their facilities in the hospital, whilst the students' fees were pooled and the profit shared out amongst the teaching staff. This was often considerable if one of the teachers was famous, and the number of clinical students mounted as they came to London after their pre-clinical training at the university colleges that were opening in a number of provincial cities. Whilst Oxford and Cambridge offered degrees, in London only the conjoint exam was available at that time.

Apart from being a source of income, students would benefit the hospitals themselves by acting as unpaid assistants and junior staff after qualification. As well as the fees to the surgeon and for attending lectures, the hospital could charge a student articled as a hospital apprentice £800, and if resident £1,000, to gain first claim for a surgical appointment later. Patients' medical care would be better from the attention of the students, whilst hospital wards would be redesigned to give more space between beds to allow for the invasion of 50–100 students on a teaching round. On the other hand, hospitals became selective in admissions, choosing patients for their teaching interest and even closing wards during vacations on economy grounds, leading to complaints led by the *Lancet* in 1840.

The *Lancet* had been founded in 1823 by Sir Thomas Wakely, priced 6d a copy. He was unable to afford the apprenticeship to a leading surgeon which was essential for a top job and had to go to Webb

Street School, run by Grainger. He was attached to a local GP whilst he worked the wards of borough hospitals, but after being assaulted in the first year and having his house burnt down, he turned to journalism.

He had radical views and targeted the elitism of hospitals and Royal Colleges, nepotism in the choice of staff, and a rigid attitude of mind that was adverse to the care of the poor and education. It was a journal for the reform of the medical system and education, recommending the abolition of quackery and the rights of the average doctor, few of whom could afford, or were able, to attend the practice of hospitals, and advocating free publication of lectures. The *Lancet* was frequently in conflict with the 'trade' and was often sued in court for libel. It referred to the Society of Apothecaries as 'Rhubarb Hall' and the Royal College of Surgeons as the 'Bats Cavern'. However, it was backed up in the courts and by charities.

The *Lancet* was in the forefront of the campaign to improve medical education with better clinical teaching, regular examinations throughout the course and free access to the hospital practice. It published an annual guide comparing the quality and cost of teaching hospitals, with frank criticism of the staff, who were often unpunctual and extortionate in fees, especially the lecturers appointed by the Royal College of Surgeons. They demanded certificates of attendance at their lectures before examinations could be sat, whilst the examiners were the ten senior members of the college, who would then pocket most of the £22 admission fee. The *Lancet* advised students not to be influenced by low fees or the imposing appearance of the school, but to pick a hospital to attend lectures and choose a dissecting room nearby, either within the same complex or at a local private school. In 1834 it recommended St Thomas's, which had rebuilt the old premises, where the students were well treated and received good clinical teaching on the wards.

In 1800 only three London hospitals had schools attached. Thomas's and Guy's had established medical schools as early as 1768, allocating subject matter between themselves, sharing students and co-operating as the 'United Hospital' until they parted in 1826 over academic disputes. The London and St George's started medical schools at the end of the 18th century, and by 1858 there were 12 London hospitals with medical schools, containing 80% of general hospital beds.

The Middlesex opened a medical school in 1836. Most of the

students and staff were inherited from the former Windmill Street private school. It accepted students from University College, which had been established in 1832, but regarded this as an 'upstart' and refused to amalgamate their facilities. This led to the college starting a dispensary and then building its own hospital and medical school which would poach both students and medical staff from the Middlesex. University College was considered too radical and King's College became an 'establishment' alternative, teaching pre-clinical subjects. After the rejection of several approaches to Charing Cross, which had started a medical school when the hospital was rebuilt in 1834, King's went on to build its own hospital.

There was increasing demand, led by the heads of most of the medical schools themselves, for the reform of an archaic system with a chaotic training structure. In 1833 a Select Committee of the House of Commons dissected the whole structure of medical education, from the restricted practices of the three great orders of surgeons, apothecaries and elitist physicians, to the curriculum and standards of training and examination and the cost for the student. At the time, finals consisted merely of four viva voce exams, each lasting a quarter of an hour.

It was accepted that teaching hospitals should have a minimum of 100 beds, threatening the status of the Westminster until it was rebuilt in 1834, whilst the Charing Cross was accused of filling up its beds on inspection day as it could not afford to admit genuine patients.

The curriculum was also attacked; an initial higher general educational background was advocated, to be followed by a basic scientific training with less emphasis on botany and more on clinical experience, as well as free admission to hospitals and regular examinations throughout the course. A central body with a national examination was also recommended. The colleges themselves began to accept some of these recommendations and the establishment of the General Medical Council in 1858 made progress easier. There was increasing emphasis on a scientific background in chemistry and physiology as well as anatomy, establishing a pre-clinical programme that required appropriate teaching staff.

At the time there were 11 medical teaching centres, and a Medical Teachers' Association was formed which proposed these centres should be amalgamated to make pre-clinical teaching more concentrated and attract a higher quality of professor. Guy's and Bart's had not joined the Association and it was accepted their long-standing prejudices would probably interfere with any such proposals, whilst The London was too separated. It was suggested the remaining eight medical schools should be split into northern and southern groups, each comprising four medical schools, but rivalries were too intense for any progress at that time.

In 1873 the *Lancet* launched an attack on hospital administration, pointing out medical staff were often excluded from the management committee, with financial control and general administrative powers in the same hands, leading to wrong expenditure at the wrong time. Professional knowledge was kept private for individual gain rather than made public and widely diffused. Medical and surgical knowledge were 'mysteries' and closed to all who could not afford the fees, and any new advances were confined to a small group in one hospital. Lectures were private property, the views of self-opinionated men with no common knowledge. Whilst major cities had many hospitals, small towns would only have one institution with a specific purpose. The whole British hospital system was bad, relying on charity, with the State providing nothing, and had no control apart from providing workhouse infirmaries. A Parisian model of a centralised system was advocated, with all hospitals pooled with a large financial grant from the municipal authority and open to the sick poor with the right of admission. All staff would be employed by the local authority and could be moved between institutions. Prophetically, it was said this would be efficient if over-administered.

Although any proposals for union were rejected, teaching standards were individually to improve greatly as a succession of outside pressures were imposed. The University of London was established by charter as an examining body with the authority to grant degrees in arts, law and medicine, and in 1873 it was enabled to offer a register-able medical qualification. The General Council of Medical Education and Registration had been initiated in 1858 with the power to super-vise medical training, and in 1884 the Royal Colleges of Physicians and Surgeons formed a conjoint examinations board granting the qualifications of LRCP and MRCS. In 1886 a Medical Act stretched the powers of the GMC to ensure all registerable qualifications were of a proper standard and all students must qualify in medicine, surgery and midwifery. Diplomas in sanitary science and public health or state medicine were approved, to become the Diploma of Public Health compulsory for all medical officers of health. Medical standards improved at all levels, and generations of eminent physicians and

The examination hall of medicine and surgery at Savoy Place on the Thames Embankment.

surgeons would be initiated who would advance the quality and standards of medical and surgical care.

In 1898 the University of London was established as a teaching university with a federal constitution of eight faculties that covered University and King's Colleges as well as ten London teaching hospitals. Although the 1913 Commission on university education in London considered it necessary to appoint and pay professors in the various branches of medicine and surgery who could devote their time to teaching or research, this proved too controversial for any action to be taken before 1926.

As early as 1922 a Ministry of Health Committee on Postgraduate Medical Education recommended ambitious plans for the establishment of a central postgraduate medical school and institute of state medicine, but the only measure adopted was to initiate the School of Hygiene and Tropical Medicine in 1929, concerned with public health, industrial and forensic medicine. Earlier, abortive efforts had been made to set up private postgraduate colleges at the West London Hospital in Hammersmith and other hospitals, with ward teaching and lectures, and a fee of three guineas for a one-month course, but all

317

'A Great Surgeon' (Dr Bland Sutton).

'Orthodoxy' (Sir William Henry Broadbent).

closed down at the onset of the First World War. After the war, Sir William Osler founded a Postgraduate Medical Association offering a month's course of instruction at a range of general and specialist hospitals for a fee of six guineas, which was attended by over 1,000 demobilised doctors over the next three years.

The matter of postgraduate education was raised again by a Ministry of Health Committee, which concluded that a school should be established on an existing site capable of expansion, with a hospital of over 400 beds near the medical centre of London and teaching confined to postgraduates. All 12 major teaching hospitals turned this down and The Hammersmith Hospital, which was due to be taken over by the LCC in 1920, was chosen as the site. The British Postgraduate Medical School was granted a Royal Charter and after the inevitable argumentation over funding between the LCC and the governing body, the school opened in 1935. Recognised by the University of London, it had a dean and a full-time staff of professors and readers, and within a year over 500 students had enrolled, half from overseas.

The Hammersmith Postgraduate Medical School was opened in 1935 by George V as an independent unit within the University of London, linked with the hospital and various autonomous units of the Medical Research Council, each with their own staff, administration and finances. As the pioneer academic institute of postgraduate teaching in London, it was to become a leading international centre for clinical teaching and research, after facing difficult patches.

In 1944, the appropriately named Goodenough Report commissioned by the Government was published. It advocated that every medical school should have a university attachment and become a teaching centre, which would be grouped with hospitals and clinics also providing teaching facilities. Each school admitting 100 students should have access to 1,000 beds, far more than most had at the time, whilst Charing Cross and St George's should be relocated. The same plan should apply to postgraduate education and research, and it noted that recognised specialist hospitals in London varied greatly in size and staffing. Many had organised schools or received university grants to develop postgraduate education, and if recommended one specialist hospital in each subject should be brought up to university standard.

As a result, in 1947 a Postgraduate Medical Federation was established, with 13 separate institutes, one of which was The Hammersmith, which ceased to be an independent school of the University of London. As a teaching hospital, The Hammersmith Board of Governors was answerable to the Minister of Health, whilst the school was funded through the University of London and the Postgraduate Medical Federation. With their relationship interlinked, there ensued an unseemly argument as to who was responsible for the staff salaries, as at The Marsden. In 1951 it was agreed that the Minister would only pay the Medical Superintendent and the staff of selective departments, including radiology and radiotherapy and the chest and dental clinics. All other senior medical staff would be funded by the university, which would run the hospital clinical services on a voluntary basis, whilst their juniors would be paid by the NHS. The agreement proved unworkable as it was not realised that if the school were to increase the number of lecturers indiscriminately, they could not expect their junior staff automatically to be paid through the NHS.

Meanwhile the school was undergoing rapid expansion. The Medical Research Council Radiotherapeutic Unit had moved there in 1942, and in 1954 it erected a new building for a linear accelerator and cyclotron with three floors of laboratories. A division of medical mechanical and electrical engineering was also established that was to make a number of inventions ranging from the first mass spectrometer to measure gas concentrations in the lungs, to a catheter for insertion into the umbilical artery of premature babies, and an artificial finger joint in reconstructive hand surgery. As any expansion had to be confined within the overall existing 14-acre site, the school initially had to add huts or build on top of existing buildings to house expanding departments such as pathology and a new library. Rebuilding became essential and fund-raising brought in £1 million over six years. A new 12-storey school was opened by the Queen in 1966, named the Commonwealth Building. The concrete used in its construction was defective and new expensive foundations had to be built when these began to fail under the strain of added floors, and the cladding resurfaced.

Within ten years it was to face a serious financial crisis. The school had to commit itself to forward planning and would make a quinquennial submission for funds. Of its money, 42% was from outside sources, mainly the Medical Research Council, whilst the rest came from the Government through a supply chain that began with the University Grants Committee, then passed to the University of London and was finally received by the school through the Postgraduate Medical Federation. In 1973 after the inevitable Royal Commission, Keith Joseph, the Minister of Health, re-organised the NHS on a so-called 'managerial basis', with a three-layered structure replacing the single boards of governors. University hospitals with an interplay between research, teaching and patient care were most affected when a system of cash limits was introduced. Planned areas of research were disrupted; six had been initiated at The Hammersmith, in addition to the fifteen already under way in 1971. There were 13 academic departments in several buildings on the hospital site, with 740 paid employees and 180 honorary staff, plus 24 professors. The departments were centred on a general hospital integrating a wide range of specialities, with its clinical work firmly based on basic studies.

In 1974 the Hammersmith School, by a new Charter, reverted to its previous 1935 status within London University as the Royal Postgraduate Medical School, retaining the right to use the site and buildings in the hospital grounds. It had started a series of short courses in specialist medicine and surgery that attracted over 1,000 students a year. More than half of these came from Europe, but in 1979 the Tory Government under Margaret Thatcher introduced a range of 'volume cuts' to reduce public sector expenditure. These included overseas students having to fund their own fees of up to £10,000 p.a. and a severe cut in the finances of the University Grants Committee. The school had also built, after a ten-year battle for permission, a block of 481 single-bedroom flats and 64 three-bedroomed maisonettes to house students and visiting professors with their families.

The school faced bankruptcy, and after a review of the situation in the 13 departments it was advised it would have to cut down on activities and 'down-size' the academic staff by half. It defended itself on the grounds that it was the main source of supply of professors and readers across the UK, and important internationally, with a vast output of publications in research areas, and the cuts would seriously damage its role in medical research, whilst two thirds of its costs were through 'earned' income support. It managed to continue through an increased grant from the University of London, support for the Department of Clinical Pharmacology by the Wolfson Foundation, money from the Nuffield Foundation and £500,000 from the British Heart Foundation for the Department of Cardiac Surgery. It was awarded research group status by the Medical Research Council, who underwrote the cost of four further research programmes.

This support enabled it to survive the financial crisis and become cost-effective. It continued to promote developments in scientific medicine and attract overseas postgraduate students on an economic basis, and became a tertiary referral centre for patients referred by outside specialists. Most of the research was largely the result of individual initiatives, but in two areas it was involved in 'operational research', and this was dictated by social pressures. Firstly it showed that 25% of general surgery and up to half of plastic surgery could be carried out on day-patients without admission. Secondly, it set up a DIY centre for medical illustration, becoming a major producer of commercial medical films, photographs and slides of surgical techniques, potentially a big source of income.

Unresolved areas included allowing professors to augment their income from private practice, not allowed by the University of London in medicine, although accepted for most other faculties at Oxford and Cambridge. Surgeons allowed private practice can double their NHS income from one private patient a week, and in 1982 it was calculated they could earn five times the top academic salary. Another anomaly is that many professors were also excluded from the Merit Award Scheme.

Chapter 13

Development of The Nursing Ethic and Status

The first reference to skilled nursing as an essential ingredient of medical care relates to the Buddhist King Osaka, 264–227 BC, the royal founder of hospitals in India. He established hospitals with gardens to grow medicinal herbs and laid down strict standards and skills in nursing as one of the 'four feet of medicine', along with the physician, patient and drugs. The nurse, probably male, would be called a *Pada*, a title of honour, when he was kind-hearted without false shame, strong and trustworthy and mindful of the physician's orders. This systematic care of the sick was lost in India after the re-introduction of Brahmanism with its strict caste prejudices and inhibitions.

The Hebrews established preventative medicine and public health measures. They segregated patients with communicable diseases and, along with disinfection, burned their clothes and scraped down the walls of their houses. Strict dietary standards were laid down, together with purification after childbirth and hygiene for the new-born. Apart from midwives and wet-nurses, there are no records of nursing as a profession in ancient Greece, and in the Roman military hospitals or *valetudinaria*, any nursing care was by *medici* or first-aid dressers with little formal training.

Christianity would be the most powerful influence in the development of nursing as a profession. At first, in the pre-monastic era, it was open-minded and accepted that women could be both responsible and play a useful role; deaconesses were appointed to work alongside the male deacons as equals in a common 'brotherhood of man', with an ethic of helping the less fortunate. One of their duties was to care for the sick at home or take them into their own house, and when Emperor Constantine adopted Christianity as the official Roman religion in AD 335, many well-placed women joined the Order. One of the most famous recorded is Fabiola, who gave up her established position and wealth to dedicate the rest of her life to the care of the sick poor and is credited with opening the first Christian hospital in Rome in AD 390. In the early years many devoted their lives towards caring for the sick at home or setting up hospitals and lazar houses across Europe, and monks would leave the monastery to study at the great medical schools developing at Salerno, Montpellier and Paris. A series of edicts from the Vatican during the 11th, 12th and 13th centuries forbade the study of medicine or practise of surgery and advocated retreat into monastic isolation, treatment of disease being a matter of prayer and exorcism, laying on of hands and use of holy water and oil.

Salerno, the oldest and most famous university, located on the Italian coast near Naples, was founded around AD 1000, possibly by Benedictine monks, and many of its physicians were women. Any nursing was carried out by medical staff themselves and any patient toilet carried out by lay workers with the assistance of women. Surgery, which was of a high level, included operations that would not be possible later until Lister introduced antiseptic. Anaesthesia was induced by a sponge soaked in a mixture of opium, hyoscyamus, hemlock, mandragora and ivy placed over the patient's mouth and nose to inhale until unconscious. Healing was by first intention; wounds were washed with wine that evaporated quickly, then the edges of the wound would be brought together and covered with a linen cloth soaked with wine.

As the Church entered the monastic period this open-minded attitude towards women was short-lived and deaconesses were finally abolished as an Order by the Synod of Orleans in AD 553 'by reason of the frailty of this sex'. Women were forbidden to marry or leave their Order for any reason and their property was confiscated by the Church after death. Monks and nuns became cloistered within large abbeys and priories which were built on an increasingly grandiose scale across the Christian empire. Although Benedictine rules made a priority of providing an infirmary for the care of the sick within the monastery, this would be primarily for the clergy themselves and a resthouse for pilgrims; any outside care would become minimal.

The Hôtel Dieu was founded in Paris AD 657 and in the 15th century was brought under strict Augustinian monastic rule. The nuns had to renounce the world for life, taking vows of poverty, chastity and obedience – to the bishops. There were no servants and all the heavy and dirty work was carried out by the novices, who had to do the washing daily in the Seine, which flowed through the centre of the hospital, even in the winter after breaking the ice. The novice stage

A hospital ward in the Hôtel Dieu, Paris, from a fifteenth-century woodcut.

would last many years before they could become 'chaperon sisters' and be allowed out in uniformed pairs for nursing duties. The hospital expanded to 1,200 beds with more than half able to hold up to six patients. Nursing would consist of washing and feeding the sick, although predominantly the emphasis was on prayer. As religious exercise intensified, this brought the clergy into conflict with the medical staff over treatments such as venesection and the use of medicine, which the sisters would often countermand. Although control of the hospital passed into the hands of government authorities after the Revolution, nursing care remained under Augustinian sisters until 1908.

As the network of monasteries spread across Britain, an increasing number of monks and nuns became elderly and infirm dependants. Responsibility for their care lay within the Church and each monastery would set aside infirmary accommodation where they would be looked after by the nuns and novices, who would be quite untrained in any nursing skills. Later the infirmary might be displaced to a separate building, as at Bart's and St Thomas's, and accept outside sick poor who would come to seek help. There was little or no medical aid, and although some of the nuns might have acquired some knowledge of herbal medicine from experience and passed it on to the girls who were being educated in the monasteries, Papal doctrine prohibited monks and nuns from attending the sick at home other than for religious purposes, as it was considered pain and illness were the result of sin and could only be relieved by prayer. Any lay woman who practised herbal medicine outside her own family was likely to be labelled a 'witch', and it is estimated that over 30,000 women were tortured and burnt alive during the 15th and first part of the 16th centuries across Europe.

Any existing hospital system in Britain was decimated by Henry VIII with the dissolution of the monasteries, and it would be two centuries before the voluntary hospital system began to develop. Until then England had only two general hospitals, St Bartholomew's and St Thomas, both in London.

Across Europe by the 18th century a network of hospitals had been established independent of the monasteries, often offering a high standard of medical and nursing care. Mostly the nurses were attached to an Order of uncloistered nuns or unmarried women attracted by free board and lodging and reasonable working conditions. Many of the dedicated Orders were initiated by a single individual and developed into international movements, although the original Order in France would often be closed down by the Revolution and the centre absorbed into the State system. The Hôtel Dieu in Paris, staffed by Augustinian nurses, gave birth to a network of hospitals throughout France and the designation of nurses as 'sisters'. Ursulines from France and Austria opened a Hôtel Dieu hospital and nursing school in Quebec, and some would open centres in Britain, the best known being St Vincent's Orthopaedic Hospital at Eastcote, Middlesex, founded by the Sisters of Charity of St Vincent de Paul. It was a preliminary training school for nurses, who then went on to take their SRN finals at The Prince of Wales or National Temperance hospitals. But there was no such pool of dedicated nursing in Protestant Britain, and obtaining any standard of nurse had been a problem since the Royal Hospitals were re-established, as their early records reveal.

Matters would become worse with the increased demand for staff as the number of voluntary hospitals built up. The conditions offered were appalling and would only attract an inferior sort of woman.

Although she would retain the title of 'Sister', she would have little professional motivation, no background in nursing and be employed without any reference or character check. In 1760 a physician wrote that a character reference was never demanded from an applicant since only the lowest type of woman would undertake such disagreeable work. They would be mostly illiterate middle-aged widows or retired prostitutes unable to obtain domestic service, often dishonest and heavy drinkers with low standards of cleanliness. Hospital records of the time are full of accounts of their being brought before the committee for drunkenness, bad language, fighting, pilfering and extracting money from patients. As the voluntary hospitals opened they would be classified as servants, rated below the cook or the bug-catcher, and be treated as skivvies by a matron who was a housekeeper of little higher standing.

Florence Nightingale was to summarise the situation by stating nursing duties at the time were done generally by those too old, too weak, too drunken, too dirty, too stolid or too bad to do anything else. In fact they probably matched the appalling hospital conditions with the nature of their work as unskilled labourers scrubbing the floors and washing the patients' unclean bed linen and clothes. At Bart's and St Thomas's they had to sleep and eat in the wards after 7 p.m. in winter and 9 p.m. in summertime and in leisure time were set to some useful and profitable work, usually spinning, and were not allowed to get married or even engaged, their pay a pittance.

Initial salaries as the hospitals were founded would average £4-6s-0d p.a., with a weekly allowance for beer and food. The matron would be paid up to £15 p.a. The exception was Guy's, founded in 1725, which paid the 11 ward sisters £25 p.a. each with the threat of instant dismissal if they tried to extort money from the patients, along with night watchmen at half the pay scale – not usual at this time – compared with £80 p.a. for the chaplain and apothecary.

A typical example of the time was The London, opened in 1741. The only nursing staff employed was one living-out nurse at 5s a week, called by her surname 'Squire'. She was found to be taking money from patients and was replaced by a matron paid £15 p.a., plus 6d a day for each patient, from which she had to provide food and beer for them. She ran up heavy bills with the local tradesmen and then decamped. In 1756 the Governor issued a standing order which decreed a nurse, paid £6 p.a., reported for duty at 6 a.m. and worked until 10 p.m. with no days off duty or holiday. Duties included

An early nineteenth-century hospital scene, as depicted by Rowlandson.

Rahere Ward at St Bartholomew's Hospital in 1832.

making the beds of the servants and cleaning the rooms, passages, stairs and committee rooms.

Wages would improve slowly and in 1838 The Middlesex board found their rates compared well with the average at the London hospitals. At St Thomas's the sister received £37 p.a. and the nurses 9s 7d a week and beer, whilst at St George's the sisters were only paid £21 p.a. and the nurses £10 per annum, but all were allowed six pounds of bread and two pints of table beer weekly, with a shilling a day for board wages. Guy's remained top of the league with £52 p.a. for sisters and £30 p.a. for nurses. In 1850 conditions began to improve as the shortage forced hospital administrators to employ ward maids and scrubbers and provide better accommodation.

In 1847 an outbreak of serious illness at Guy's amongst the nursing staff – 'general disorder of nurses' health' – was attributed to excessive fatigue caused by having to perform night and day duty with only a short interval of rest in between. As a consequence 14 night nurses were employed at 1s 6d a night. By then the employment of night-watchers for a few pence a night had become general and the ward sister was allowed to sleep in a separate room at the end of the ward with a half glass window which looked onto the ward, and to eat separately, whilst assistants were brought in to take over much of the heavier cleaning duties. Practical training of nurses would only begin in 1874, followed by a course of lectures and demonstrations from the matron and members of the medical staff.

The first move towards nursing re-organisation in the British Isles was made by two sisterhoods in Ireland. The Irish Sisters of Charity was started about 1815 by Sister Mary Augustine, nursing the sick at home. She raised the money to start a hospital, but realised that first properly trained nursing staff were essential and sent three of her sisters to the Hospital of Notre Dame de la Piti in Paris, then considered the best-run hospital in Europe. St Vincent's, Dublin, was the first hospital in Britain to be founded, organised and staffed by women, and the sisterhood went on to open institutions in America and throughout Australasia, as well as St Joseph's Hospice in Hackney.

The Irish Sisters of Mercy started nursing in the Dublin hospitals during a cholera epidemic in 1832, later founding the Mater Misericordiae Hospital of Dublin. The Order was to establish hospitals in the United States and Australia, and after the Crimean War the Hospital of St John and St Elizabeth in London, which became a recognised training school for nurses.

In the middle of the 19th century conditions in England's hospitals were at their lowest level. Many of the hospitals themselves were dirty and dilapidated, medical and surgical standards low and it was not surprising that the underpaid, overworked and ill-treated nurses' morale was non-existent. Beer and whisky were amongst the main medications for the patients, and readily available to the nurses. There began to develop a wider understanding for their situation. In 1857 *The Times* commented:

> Hospital nurses have been much abused – they have their faults, but most of them are due to want of proper treatment, lectured by committees, preached at by chaplains, scowled on by treasurers, scolded by matrons, sworn at by surgeons, bullied by dressers, grumbled and abused by patients, insulted if old and ill-favoured, talked flippantly to if middle-aged and good humoured, tempted and seduced if young and well-looking, they are what any woman might be under these circumstances.

There was increasing realisation that nurses' working conditions should be improved and proper training instituted. As a first step their cleaning duties would be progressively reduced. In 1856 the Salisbury Infirmary Nursing Committee recommended that 'in future the wards be cleaned and scoured by persons engaged for that purpose and your nurses kept in every particular distinct and separate from the servants of the establishment'. This was to become generally accepted, with extra staff to cover night duty.

The first nursing organisation in England was the Institute of Nursing Sisters founded by Mrs Elizabeth Fry in 1840. Previously she had devoted herself to improving conditions for women in prison, and on a European tour visited the Kaiserwerth Deaconesses Institution. This had been founded by a Lutheran clergyman, Theodor Fliedner, in a small parish near Dusseldorf as a hospital for discharged prisoners. It had become a nursing training school for women of good character, known as deaconesses, who took no religious vows and served unpaid, but were maintained for life if they became unable to support themselves. It would expand into a network of institutions across Europe, including the Tottenham Evangelical Deaconesses Hospital in Tottenham, later the Prince of Wales General Hospital, where the original deaconesses, as guaranteed by the Kaiserwerth rule, lived out their retirement years in a private room attached to a ward.

The Institute of Nursing Sisters were literate women of good character who trained for a few months at Guy's or The London before serving as district or private nurses, paid by the Institute. They were strictly disciplined and made to wear a uniform, and this was one of the first organisations to raise the nursing image. The next significant centre was St John's House Sisterhood, founded in 1848, and the first purely nursing Order in the Church of England some 300 years after it was founded. The nurses paid £15 for a two-year practical training course at The Middlesex, Westminster or King's College hospital and were then bound to work for St John's House for five years in return for board, lodgings and a small salary. Antagonism from neighbours at the presence of nurses locally forced them to move from the original house in Fitzroy Square, but they were to take over nursing at King's College and Charing Cross hospitals for 30 years, and many accompanied Florence Nightingale to the Crimea.

The organisation was taken over by St Thomas's in 1919, when it became St John's and St Thomas's House, an institution for fully trained private nurses working on a co-operative basis. A similar organisation, The All Saints' Sisterhood, was established in 1851 and their sisters, dressed entirely in black, carried out much of the nursing at University College Hospital until 1899, when the hospital was rebuilt. St John's and All Saints' were to merge, and between them played a major role in establishing a new level of educated person in nursing, until they were progressively replaced at the hospital they served by Nightingale-trained matrons.

The figure predominantly associated with the establishment of nursing in Britain as a professional dedicated career is Florence Nightingale. She was born into a wealthy society family, but would have an unsettled early life, alternating between grand tours of Europe and periods of intense depression at her feelings of valuelessness and her need to find a worthwhile objective in life. Intensely religious, she would resolve this by her determination to become a nurse, although this led to strong family opposition – especially from her mother, who was socially ambitious – at the thought of their daughter being involved in such a degrading occupation. Attempts to train in Salisbury and in Paris, where she contracted measles, were abortive, but she was inspired by a two-month stay in Kaiserwerth and the devoted attitude of the deaconesses, although she said it was dirty, if free from the 'disgusting hospital smell' accepted in England as inevitable. Her life at home had been dominated for some years by the demanding

Florence Nightingale with her tame owl Athena, c.1850.

tantrums of her sister, who was an emotional hysteric, but in 1852, at the age of 31, she was able to spend a month in Paris studying hospital organisation and standards. On her return home she made a final decisive break from her family domination and became Superintendent of the Institution for the Care of Sick Gentlewomen in Distressed Circumstances, which was in need of re-organisation, and became resident at No. 1 Harley Street. There she was to show her latent qualities as an organiser, and her determination to establish standards.

She was engaged on the basis that she received no remuneration and would pay all the expenses of the matron she brought with her to compensate for her youthful appearance, but would have complete control of both the finances and management of the institution.

Florence Nightingale with Sir Harry Verney, Miss Crossland and nurses at Claydon, 1886.

Before, the charity had been run by two committees, a ladies' and a gentlemen's, which were in conflict with one another as well as with the medical staff. Inevitably, she herself in turn would stir up trouble by her determination to manage the committees. To save the nurses toiling up and down stairs, she installed a row of bells with flaps by which they would know which patient was calling for help and a lift to bring up their meals from the kitchen. She turned out the store rooms, to find there were no brooms or dusters and the bed-linen and furniture were dirty and neglected. Food and supplies were being bought in dribbles and she organised wholesale contracts with leading firms, including Fortnum & Mason, halving expenditure. The original staff soon left and she packed the committees with her own supporters, assuming total control within six months. She was respected by the early opposition and adored by the patients. She had even persuaded the Protestant organisation to accept Catholic patients and threatened to resign unless she could take in Jews and their rabbis to attend them. She gave the medical staff extra authority, with total obedience to them by the nurses. Her mother was to say 'we are ducks who have hatched a wild swan', whilst Lytton Strachey later described her as an 'eagle'.

In March 1854 England and France declared war on Russia and in June a British Army was landed at Varna in Bulgaria, but was

335

invalided by a cholera epidemic. The next step planned was to cross the Black Sea for Sebastopol, but lack of adequate transport forced the Army to leave behind much of its basic maintenance stores and transport. A base had been set up at Scutari, where the Turkish had given over a large barracks and general hospital, to which thousands of cholera and battle victims were to be shipped across the Black Sea in overcrowded 'hospital ships' under the most appalling conditions, with no medical aid of any sort. At the hospital, matters were no better. There were no beds and they had to lie half naked in a long line on the bare, filthy floor, wrapped in the blankets saturated with blood and excrement in which they had been lying since leaving the battlefield, with no water or food as there was no kitchen or service. Most had been ordered to abandon their packs containing a change of clothes and eating utensils before evacuation. Such circumstances were not new and had been usual in previous campaigns over the last century. The only difference was the presence for the first time of a newspaper correspondent, William Howard Russell, to send home despatches to *The Times* about the conditions and compare them with the good medical service and nursing by Sisters of Charity enjoyed by the French.

This led to a public uproar and exposed the tortuous incompetence of the three departments that divided responsibility for the British Army's medical services, which had been progressively reduced in staff and funding. The Commissariat were the bankers and store keepers responsible for supplying everything from fuel to food for the soldiers on duty or in hospital, except for invalid foods for those too ill to eat normal rations. This was the role of the Purveyor, with a staff of four; but his requirements had to be obtained through the Commissariat, and the Commissary-General at the time complained he was expected to supply the Army in the Crimea with only the help of three incompetent clerks. The Director General of the British Army Medical Service had only 12 clerks to run the entire organisation and hospitals. The staff of all three departments were poorly paid and ill qualified, and despised as not being 'gentlemen' by their Army superior officers.

Florence Nightingale had already begun to study conditions in hospitals and press for improvements in the nurses' conditions. She had been corresponding with Sidney Herbert, a long-term friend who had become Secretary at War, about this, and in October 1854 he approached her to organise and lead a team of nurses for Scutari. He had already sent out a profusion of medical stores and many more medical officers, as well as receiving offers from ladies, but he felt these would be entirely useless or worse. There was only one person who, in his opinion, was capable of organising and superintending such a scheme.

She had already made plans to take out a small private team and readily agreed to be officially appointed by the Cabinet as 'Superintendent of the Female Nursing Establishment of the English General Hospitals in Turkey' with a grant of £1,000. Eventually she chose a party of 38, of whom 24 were nuns or Anglican sisters who had to accept they must take their nursing orders solely from her above their Mother Superior. The remaining 14 were hospital nurses paid 12–14 shillings a week, with an increase for good conduct, and free board and lodging; most were stout and elderly. Miss Nightingale was to write later that in future 'fat drunken old dames of fourteen stone or over must be barred, the provision of bedsteads is not strong enough'. All signed an agreement to strict discipline, to share food and accommodation and wear a drab uniform, except for the nuns and sisters, who could wear their habits. They must never go out alone or without leave, but would be given a generous daily allowance of beer and spirits.

The party was feted on their journey across France, although problems arose as the 'ladies' refused to sit in the same railway carriage and eat with the 'hired nurses', whom they expected to act as their servants; but equality was established when they eventually arrived at Scutari after a stormy sea journey during which Florence was violently sea-sick.

She established her headquarters at the barrack hospital. The doctors at Scutari had received the news of her appointment with horror; understaffed and overcrowded, they dreaded the arrival of a pack of nurses under a society lady. The orderlies were all men and attempts to use soldiers' wives as nurses had been disastrous, because of their drinking and behaving improperly with the men. The Army Medical Department had decreed female nurses in a military hospital were 'an unwise indulgence unfavourable to military discipline and to the recovery of the patients' and they had only agreed because of Miss Nightingale's powerful political support.

The party of 40 were quartered in five small, damp, filthy rooms, with a kitchen and closet, and the only furniture was two beds and a few chairs. Nothing was offered in the way of help, and the 14 nurses were allocated to one room, ten nuns to another, whilst Florence and her housekeeper from Harley Street were in the closet. The eight Sellonite sisters were to sleep in the room above, but found it occupied by the body of a dead Russian general which had to be removed first. They all had to sleep their first night on Turkish 'divans', raised wooden platforms running round the rooms, without any bedding or food, in rooms infested with fleas and rats. Water was limited to a pint a day, obtained by lining up at a fountain in one of the corridors, and they had to use tin bowls for eating, drinking and washing.

The medical staff totally ignored the nurses and for over a week they idled away their time sorting bed-linen and any stores that arrived which the doctors refused to accept. Any patient care continued to be carried out by orderlies who were convalescents or considered too useless by the Army for any other duties. The frustrated nurses could only watch and despair.

On Sunday, 6th October, the wounded from Balaclava began to be unloaded at Scutari, most to be dumped into the adjacent Turkish Army Barracks, which had been developed as an overflow hospital, a vast, filthy building without beds or medical service. Although she allocated 28 nurses to sleep at this adjacent hospital, Miss Nightingale insisted no-one should enter a ward until invited by the doctors. There was mounting opposition amongst the nurses, as patients were dying from neglect and starvation. The situation was to change dramatically in November as the wounded poured in from the Battle of Balaclava and the sick from Sebastopol, where the Army was forced to winter without shelter or clothing. Shiploads of soldiers, hundreds at a time, poured in, and the wards and corridors of the barrack hospital were filled with men lying on bare boards, crawling with vermin, wrapped only in their soiled greatcoat from the battlefront. There was no sanitation as the privies were blocked and liquid filth from their overflow floated over the floor an inch deep. More than 1,000 men with acute dysentery had to use huge wooden tubs which were left unemptied for days.

To make matters worse, Balaclava was devastated by a hurricane that destroyed the Army base and every ship in the port was sunk, including the supply ship *Prince* loaded with the troops' winter clothing and stores. The destruction of the British Army was to be completed during the winter as thousands went down with dysentery and were off-loaded to Scutari. As many sick remained on heights above Sebastopol. Hospital administration collapsed and in despair the doctors and officials turned to Miss Nightingale for help as the shambles of their financial system made it impossible to obtain essential supplies. She purchased these locally from the £30,000 she had accumulated from *The Times* charity appeal and her own sources, and set about putting the hospital in running order, scrubbing out and equipping the wards. Depot wives who lived in squalor under the hospital had to wash their clothes, the men's clothes were to be cleaned by their wives, and the wing of the hospital that had been burnt down was rebuilt. She reorganised the cooking, which had all been carried out in 13 large copper pots at one end of the hospital, in which each unit's meat wrapped in a cloth was boiled. It was often only partly cooked, then trundled along a four-mile corridor, to be served cold and unpalatable. The tea would then be made in the same unwashed vats. She turned the kitchen in the nurses' quarter into a centre preparing special diets. By December the soldiers landed from the filthy sick transports were being well cared for with clean bedding and warm food, and the death rate was to fall from 42% to 22 per 1,000.

On 14th December she wrote to Sidney Herbert expressing her satisfaction at progress, but trouble was brewing. Some of the nursing sisters had begun to resent her discipline and above all her insistence on total subjugation to the doctors' authority – every aspect of special diets had to have their signed authorisation. Matters peaked with the unannounced arrival on 5th December of a party of 46 nurses under the leadership of Mary Stanley, a religious fanatic about to convert to Catholicism. Half of the party were more interested in missionary work than practical nursing, and the 'hired nurses', who were expected to act as servants to the 'ladies', were too old and drunk to be of any use; most had come to find a husband. There was no accommodation for them at the barrack hospital and they were to take over sole charge of a branch hospital opened at Koulali. They refused to accept Florence Nightingale's authority and she found herself in the midst of a 'Protestant howl' and 'Roman Catholic storm' as the two sects began to quarrel, not only with one another, but also amongst themselves. Conditions at Koulali deteriorated progressively and the death rate was the highest of any hospital there. In March Mary Stanley returned home when her health collapsed under the strain and the hospital eventually had to be closed. Meanwhile the mortality rate in the barrack hospital had begun to escalate. The deaths were due to 'fever contracted within the hospital'. Several of the medical and nursing staff were amongst the victims and even the officers on their rounds were afraid to go into the wards. The food remained inedible, the allowance of water still a pint a day, the building verminous and the hospital atmosphere foul.

In March a Sanitary Commission of top quality, including a medical officer from the Board of Health, and a civil engineer to survey the state of buildings used as hospitals and camps, were appalled by the conditions they were to find. The barrack hospital had been built over sewers which were choked and blew poisonous gas through the pipes of the open privies in the wards, and the water supply was contaminated. They immediately had the defects put in order and the fearful death rate fell dramatically over the next few weeks. The same month the chef from the Reform Club took charge of the catering with vast improvements, and by May 1855 Miss Nightingale reported 'the first really satisfactory reception of 200 sick men'.

By 16th June the last patient had been discharged from the barrack hospital and she returned home incognito, rejecting any offers of a public triumphal reception. Her health was shattered and she was obsessed by a sense of failure and became a recluse. In reality she had transformed the public image of the nurse from a drunken old harridan to a dedicated professional, and the soldier from a drunken brute to a man of courage and endurance under the most horrendous conditions. The rest of her life would be spent in a series of battles against the Establishment, much of it as an invalid who never left her house, remaining in bed for months at a time, until she died at the age of 90 in 1910. She accumulated a vast supply of facts and figures, which made her a formidable opponent for officials she wished to harass, as well as an invaluable source of information.

Her first target was for a Royal Commission to examine the sanitary conditions and organisation of military barracks and hospitals, and the administration of the Army Medical Department, and within six months had her way, and she moved her headquarters back to London. One of the statistics she had produced showed the death rate amongst healthy soldiers in London Army barracks was over double that of the local population and of four sub-committees established with executive powers and finance one was to put the barracks in sanitary order and another to start an Army Medical School. Miss Nightingale went into a decline and decided she was about to die, detailing her funeral arrangements, but continued to apply relentless pressure on Sidney Herbert, who was chairman of all four sub-committees. She was to become an authority on hospital structure, with a detailed knowledge of every department and piece of equipment.

She was approached by many hospitals for her advice, one of which was St Thomas's, and huge bundles of letters survive that she wrote to architects, builders and tradespeople. The hospital lay in the path of a railway line to be built between London Bridge and Charing Cross, and had to decide whether to sell the whole site and rebuild elsewhere, or to sell only part and carry on there. She went into the matter in detail and concluded the offer for the whole site should be accepted, and sent a memorandum to this effect to the Prince Consort, who was a governor. The next decision was whether to rebuild locally or move to another district, and she collected statistics that showed most patients came from outside the area and would not be affected by a change.

She became closely attached to St Thomas's and renewed her interest in nursing reform, which had been temporarily set aside by her preoccupation with Army medical reform. She had a fund of £45,000, raised by subscriptions from the public and servicemen, to found a training school and decided to establish it there. She had already written a book, *Notes of Nursing*, which had become a best seller and established her reputation as a kind, gentle and sympathetic nurse. She advocated the training of women in what they could do best, but derided 'women's rights' when they strove to emulate men, including the medical and other professions.

The decision to start a nurses' training school met with intense opposition from the medical profession's administration, to which she was well accustomed. The senior surgeon at St Thomas's, who was President of the Royal College, said nurses were subordinates 'in the position of house-maids' and needed 'only the simplest instruction such as how to make a poultice'. The objective of the school was to produce nurses capable of training others and going on to posts in other hospitals. Any scandal would have been fatal, and applicants were subjected to severe moral assessment. Fifteen were taken on as Nightingale probationers, lived in a nurses' home, a novel concept, and an upper wing of the hospital was adapted to give each a separate wing with their own bedroom and a common sitting room under strict control of the matron. The school opened in 1860 and the course lasted a year. The nurse was given £10 towards her expenses and provided with board and uniform. They had lectures from the medical staff and sisters and practical work on the wards and in the theatres. They took notes and had regular examinations. Each practitioner's progress was studied in detail, under two headings of 'Technical

Nightingale House, St Thomas's, during the 1920s. It was destroyed by bombing in 1941.

Record' with 14 sub-divisions and 'Moral Record' with 6. The latter was equally important; they were only allowed out in pairs and any flirtation with the medical students led to instant dismissal. Within months there was a flood of applicants and in 1861 a training school for midwives was opened, with six months' training at King's College, but it was closed down after six years due to an outbreak of puerperal sepsis.

With the move to the new building with eight pavilions, the pressure on the matron became too great to supervise the school and the first 'Home Sister' post was created to supervise training and the 'home life' of the probationers. Within 15 years nearly every hospital in England had at least one Nightingale nurse on its staff, many to become matron and to start their own training school. The school's selection procedure tended to be to pick rather dominant characters with confidence in their ability, excellent qualities for the new generations of matron, but which would often bring them into conflict with the administration and medical superiors.

Although she remained semi-invalid, from her 'sick-quarters' at home in London Florence Nightingale would exert a strong influence on nursing and hospital development through her extensive political and medical connections. Like a spider at the centre of her web, she would pour out memoranda on these subjects and her opinion would be sought by many faced with policy-making.

Two areas in which she was deeply involved were standards in workhouse care, and district nursing. In 1864 she was approached by William Rathbone, a Liverpool philanthropist, who had started a home visiting service for the sick poor in the district with a single nurse who had looked after his wife when she was dying from cancer, and now wished to extend this service. Miss Nightingale concluded the only satisfactory solution was to open a training school and suggested he approached The Royal Liverpool Infirmary. Within five years the first District Nursing Service had been started, with Liverpool divided into 18 districts, each under the care of a Nurse Superintendent, and paid for by a group of charitable ladies. Rathbone became concerned with the conditions in the Liverpool Workhouse Infirmary. As was standard in the workhouse scene, patients' only care was from female paupers for an extra allowance of beer and tobacco. In 1865, after lengthy arguments, the authorities agreed to a party of 12 nurses, led by Miss Agnes Jones, who had trained at the Nightingale School, as matron in charge of the infirmary, initially only for the male wards.

They faced appalling conditions, with up to 1,500 inmates sleeping up to three in a bed, surviving in filth, unwashed and with dirty clothes, food at starvation level and immorality rampant. Many were unemployed, able-bodied malingerers, deliberately festering their sores, who rapidly discharged themselves when faced with compulsory work on site. Thirty-five of the pauper nurses, many ex-prostitutes, had to be sacked for drunkenness in the first month. Agnes Jones tried to persuade some of the pauper women to take some training, but had to give up when not one proved capable and all spent their pay on drink.

Agnes Jones was a hot-tempered Irish Presbyterian and quarrelled violently with the master of the infirmary, who she considered 'lacked refinement'. Miss Nightingale was able to persuade both sides to compromise, and the venture became regarded as a great success by all concerned. Apart from the humanitarian gain, the overall maintenance costs were reduced but, unfortunately, Agnes Jones died of typhus after three years. Miss Nightingale had already started to press for legislation to improve conditions in the workhouses generally, directly approaching the Prime Minister, Lord Palmerston, as she considered the Poor Law Board impotent. She put forward a three-point programme which she labelled the ABC of workhouse reform. The first element was the separation of the sick insane, and the incurable insane, at present mixed together, into separate institutions. Secondly, there should be a single central administration and, thirdly, this should be funded by the Government from a general rate in place of the local authority. The idea was approved initially, but execution was delayed by the death of Lord Palmerston and political changes, until a Metropolitan Poor Act started the change in 1867 and funded a new infirmary at Highgate, opened two years later on plans submitted for Miss Nightingale's approval.

It would be 1897 before the employment of pauper nurses in workhouses was forbidden, but by early in the next century all of size would be under the administration of a master and matron, with a resident medical officer and adequate nursing staff. In 1929 a Local Government Act passed all the functions of the boards of guardians into the hands of the county and county borough councils, including the Poor Law infirmaries, and almost one hundred in London and throughout the provinces would be converted into general hospitals to provide acute medical and surgical care, under the control of the Ministry of Health, who would pay their maintenance costs. All aged and chronic sick were to be transferred to other institutions. Whilst central control would make it hard for the individual hospitals to develop individually with a dedicated staff, as within the NHS structure today, many of the municipal hospitals would provide a standard of care that matched any of the voluntary hospitals.

In 1868 the East London Nursing Society was founded as the first organisation in London to provide trained nurses for the care of the sick poor in their own homes. This highlighted the general need for an

A ward in St Thomas's Hospital, c.1900.

organised system and led to the development of the Metropolitan and National Nursing Association, with the target of providing a body of skilled nurses through a Central Home and Training School. Candidates had to be 'gentlewomen', and after a month at the Central

The casualty waiting hall at St Thomas's Hospital, c.1905.

A ward in Willesden Parish Infirmary, 1903.

Home they went on to train for a year in one of the London hospitals. Their duties were broad and, apart from actual nursing of the patient, would include 'putting the room in nursing order' from the dirty hovel they often found and educating the family in hygiene. Branches were opened throughout the country with local charitable support and the scheme was supported by Queen Victoria. She donated most of her 'Women's Jubilee Offering', some £70,000, and in 1888 the Queen Victoria Jubilee Institute for Nurses was instituted, with branches throughout the country, to become the 'Queen's Nurses'. In 1928 the name was changed to the 'Queen's Institute of District Nursing'. It is now a statutory authority and part of the Primary Care Services within the NHS.

Whilst Florence Nightingale was improving the quality of nurses and their standards of nursing care, others were to set about establishing a professional status, but it would take 30 years of bitter argument and debate before a Nurses' Registration Act in 1919 established a General Nursing Council with State Registration. The first steps were taken by Mrs Ethel Fenwick, who at the age of 24 had been appointed as

Matron of St Bartholomew's Hospital. She retired from active nursing when she married a doctor six years later, and started the British Nurses' Association in 1887 with a target to petition Parliament for a State Register of Nurses. There would be two categories, nurses with three years of training and a certificate of good character, or educated ladies who would only need one year. Mrs Fenwick seems to have been another domineering, stubborn self-opinionated character, a close friend of Mrs Pankhurst who was leading the campaign for the women's vote.

The council initially comprised a mix of 100 matrons, 100 doctors and 100 sisters or nurses, and although it acquired a Royal Charter six years later to become the Royal British Nursing Association, it began to fall apart from internal dissent. Mrs Fenwick herself was voted off the council, but she went on to play a leading part in the development of the American Society of Superintendents of Training Schools and the International Council of Women. At home she set up a separate society for the State Registration of Nurses and a Matrons' Council of Great Britain.

There was intense opposition to the RBNA proposals, led by Florence Nightingale, that would divide the nursing scene into two groups. She considered nursing to be a vocation as well as a profession, and character training as important as acquiring technical skills. Public examination for a certificate would attract many girls of inferior character without installing the dedication she considered essential. She was joined in her opposition by many thousands of matrons and doctors, including the superintendents of the nursing schools, and when the RBNA petitioned for a Royal Charter which would have given them the right to create a Nurses' Register, Miss Nightingale led the opposition and submitted two counter-petitions. There was an expensive legal battle by the two sides before a committee of the Privy Council, and the result was a draw. The RBNA obtained their Royal Charter, but it excluded the word 'register' and only gave them the right to maintain a 'list' of nurses who applied to have their names entered. Mrs Fenwick, meanwhile, had taken control of the *British Journal of Nursing*, which she would edit for over 50 years and use as a mouthpiece for her dominant views. She was particularly virulent in her opposition to the College of Nursing when it was established in 1916.

All the matrons at the time tended to be autocratic, which they probably had to be when facing opposition from the medical staff to the build-up of nursing status. One of these was Sarah Swift, Matron of Guy's Hospital, who was also to establish a trained nursing service in HM Prisons. She approached Sir Arthur Stanley, Chairman of the British Section of the Red Cross, for financial support to set up a nursing college, and with the backing of the Dean of Guy's Medical School and the Superintendent of the hospital, a founders' meeting was held. Amongst those attending were the Matron of The Royal Hospital, Rachel Cox-Davies, and Alicia Lloyd Still, who in turn had been Matron of The Brompton and Middlesex Hospitals before moving to become Matron of St Thomas's, where she had trained as a 'Nightingale' and established the office of 'Sister Tutor'. She was the most rigid of disciplinarians, laying down strict standards of uniform that included a regulation tight hair coiffure. The College of Nursing was registered as a limited company in 1916 and the fourth leading member of the female founders, Miss Mary Rendle, was appointed Secretary and gave dedicated service for over 17 years. The objectives of the college were to promote better nursing education, with a uniform curriculum, in approved schools, and to form a Register. Within a year it had attracted a membership of over 7,000, all meeting a basic level of training to qualify.

There ensued a clash of dominant women, all concerned with the same objective, but with different views as to how this should be achieved, and no basis of agreement could be found. Attempts to reconcile Mrs Fenwick failed and negotiations for amalgamation with

The Matron of the London Hospital with her Sisters just before a number left for the South African War.

The retirement of a matron, surrounded by her colleagues.

the Royal British Nursing Association collapsed. The First World War emphasised the shortage of trained nurses to man the service hospitals and it was generally accepted that a central authority to regulate nursing had to be established. However, Dr Addison, in charge of the newly created Ministry of Health, was presented with two contentious outline drafts for a Parliamentary Bill, from the College of Nursing Ltd and Mrs Fenwick's organisation. Fully aware of the warring factions that had frustrated all efforts to organise nursing, he is said to have ordered both drafts to be torn up. He went on to devise his own Bill, and the Nurses' Act became law on December 23rd 1919. This created a separate body, the General Nursing Council, to regulate the training and registration of nurses, with supplementary parts containing the names of male and mental nurses, and those trained in nursing sick children. Midwives had been regulated by a Central Midwives Board since 1902.

The council contained a broad cross-section of members, two thirds of whom would be elected by the nurses on the National Register. An initial decision that membership should require one year's training at an approved hospital was rescinded by Parliament as this would have excluded many experienced nurses. It was replaced by a requirement to have had three years' experience and a suitable recommendation by a hospital matron or two doctors.

One of the initial council members was Mrs Fenwick, who was appointed Chairman of the Registration Committee. Through her *British Journal of Nursing* she had forecast that the Register would be flooded with VADs who had been organised by the Red Cross and Order of St John to nurse during the war, village and cottage nurses who had never trained. She would personally check the details of every applicant, creating a long backlog, and inevitably there was a renewal of old conflicts, which led to her being voted off the council by the nurses themselves. By 1923, some 40,000 had registered, and two years later the first State examination was held. This did not prevent thousands of unregistered nurses continuing in practice, especially in private practice and nursing homes. Although the Government refused to make it obligatory, many local authorities and hospital managements tried to restrict their staff to SRNs, but with their poor levels of pay and strict disciplinarian regimes there was a great shortage of supply available and many nurses queried the value of State Registration. They would select the freedom of district nursing and the larger hospitals that could offer the comfort of a nurses' home, along with the companionship of students at an attached medical school.

The college received a Royal Charter in 1939 from King George V and seven years later it was granted arms by the College of Arms, designating the sun and stars, denoting night and day service, on a blue shield surmounted by the open book of learning and a Roman lamp as the heraldic symbol of nursing. At the base of the shield is the motto '*Tradimus Lampada*' – 'We hand on the torch'.

One of the on-going themes had been improvement in educational standards. The college took a dominant role and established a separate Educational Department to set up special training schemes for teachers in a range of areas, including midwifery, health visiting and industrial nursing. Once a Register had been established, plans for future progress would be focused on raising the status of nursing and working conditions, led by the college and joined later by the *Lancet*.

Eventually the crisis in nurses' numbers stirred the Government into action, and as the first step a committee was formed in 1937 under Lord Athens to review the problem. Over 2,000 hospitals were contacted, and their response showed conditions had changed little

350

over the previous decade and remained as unattractive. In voluntary hospitals less than 18% of nurses were fully trained, and they relied largely on probationers working a 55-hour week in the daytime and up to 75 hours on night duty. They would spend most of their time cleaning up, scrubbing and bed-panning, although cleaning staff were generally employed. Pay was £20 p.a., with free board and lodging, but a military-style discipline persisted, headed by a Nightingale-orientated matron and backed up by the ward and home sisters. Ignored by the doctors, it was a strict caste system, with the probationer at the bottom of the pecking order. The nurses' home doors would be locked at 10 p.m. and any liaison with the medical students, who were all male, was banned. However, the ward kitchen would be their meeting ground, and the teaching hospitals functioned as a matrimonial agency for the nurses. Now half the medical student intake is female.

The committee made its Report in 1939 and recommended action on most of the points raised to improve the attraction of a nursing career. These would be gradually introduced over the coming years, including a 48-hour week, with a month's paid holiday, and more domestic staff taken on to reduce the nurse's chores. The value of the role of assistant nurses was to be acknowledged and given status on a separate Register by the General Nursing Council as a State Enrolled Nurse, a measure opposed by many as being a source of cheap labour. A revolutionary proposal was that the Exchequer should fund the nurses' salary increase in the voluntary hospitals.

The next step forward was in 1949 with a Nurses' Act, when the General Nursing Council was reconstituted as the National Council of Nurses. Against strong protest, nursing schools were freed from control by hospital administration and financed separately. Male nurses would be included in the General Register and, most important, the inclusion of suitably qualified nurses from any overseas country, opening the door to the influx at the present time. Later specialist fields such as mental and child health would also be brought on to the General Register. These changes would not be endorsed by the College of Nursing until some years later, when supported by an overwhelming postal vote. The first male to be admitted to their register was a trained psychiatric nurse. In 1951 long years of conflict ended when the National Council of Nurses and the College of Nursing amalgamated under the grand title of The Royal College of Nursing and National Council of Nurses of the United Kingdom, or 'RCN' for short.

The Royal College of Nursing Headquarters, London.

The National Health Service had inherited a chaotic system of medical care, and successive Ministers would be bombarded with demands and advice from all directions, not least the nursing side, with the most vocal being the RCN. The response would be to establish a succession of Reports and Commissions, and by the time these were reported, the Minister would have been moved or another government elected. The result would be a long delay before any decision was reached, which would then be postponed because of a financial crisis. In 1961 pay and conditions had again fallen far behind and the nurses staged a massive public protest, with trained nurses supported by the RCN and enrolled nurses by their unions. This peaked with a meeting at the Albert Hall chaired by the Liberal Leader, Joe Grimond, attended by over 7,000 people. Their claim was taken to the Industrial Court and after protracted negotiations nurses obtained a $7\frac{1}{2}\%$ pay rise, with a 42-hour week, but no general overtime payment.

The Royal College of Nursing's Royal Charter.

In 1968 a new pattern of nursing administration and grading structure was rushed through, based on a Report chaired by Brian Salmon, which would destroy any existing system and itself be abandoned after a few years as impractical. It was intended to deal with the changing circumstances, with which the existing system could not cope, and the need for a radical change was evident to all.

Nursing administration and training remained in a state of chaos. Only the teaching hospital matron remained relatively secure, responsible to the board and independent of regional influences, controlling

353

nursing services and training as well as most of the services affecting the patients' environment. Her daily ward round ensured the wards were clean and the beds neat and tidy and the patients reassured. The kitchen and linen cupboards too were in her province. One sister in control of each ward was directly answerable to matron. Elsewhere, up to a dozen hospitals could be under the same management committee, composed of medical and lay administration, and the matron would not even see the minutes. The role of the senior nursing staff in management was ill-defined, and there was no path to train them in preparation.

The Salmon solution was to match the general administrative pattern by creating nursing grades. The top levels, labelled 10 and 9, reduced the matron's old functions to policy decisions, isolated from any practical aspects of control, whilst two middle grades applied these policies, the lower of which, labelled 7, would have 'hands-on' responsibility for nursing standards. This could cover several wards and specialist units. Ward sisters were graded at 6, and the more senior would abandon their wards to move up the ladder into administration.

Although nursing attracted more young female entrants than any other profession, waste was three times as high, and more would leave than entered annually. Overall they comprised half the workforce of the NHS and one third of its expenditure. The next 30 years would see a revolutionary change in training and nursing practices to match changing patterns in health care. Early mobilisation and discharge with the introduction of day surgery would disrupt the long-term relationship with ward patients. Immediate post-operative care was transferred to intensive care units, whilst specialised surgery and medical care called for highly trained nurses to form part of a separate high-powered team. The social position of the nurses themselves had changed, and many of the more experienced were married with family commitments. To meet their needs, split duties would be replaced by part-time or straight eight-hour shifts two or three days a week. Gradings were in letters A to I in place of numbers, with a sister F or G, and State Enrolled Nurses were encouraged to train to a higher level.

There was increasing disillusionment with the medical attitudes, which nurses considered were more disease- than patient-orientated. Enthusiastic nurse managers adopted a 'nursing process' that had become popular in the United States; the nurse would prepare a

354

separate 'care plan' for each individual patient based on a separate nursing history to identify the nursing needs, and a 'nursing model' to apply them.

There were equally radical changes in community nursing, where relationships between the nurses and general practitioners were much better, and the role of practice and district nurses in the primary care team steadily increased. Working conditions were more flexible, with continuity of patient relationship and care, and the number of practice nurses was to increase fivefold over ten years. They could train up to manage clinics in long-term care areas such as diabetes, asthma and hypertension, relieving the practitioner of a great deal of routine work.

In the USA, nurse practitioners had become an established intermediary, trained to diagnose and prescribe as part of a clinical team headed by doctors and often the first point of patient contact. To a reduced level this has now moved into the hospital arena, and suitably trained nurses initially assess patients in the accident and emergency departments, with great benefit to waiting times, and check patients for day surgery.

The UK was one of the last countries to conduct nursing education on an apprenticeship basis within hospitals and in 1986 the United Kingdom Central Council proposed an overall reform, termed Project 2000, which was accepted two years later by the Government. As there were too many nursing schools of variable quality and studies were interrupted by ward duties, nurses would now train at recognised colleges. They would have all the rights of other students, taking either a degree or a diploma course.

The new three-year course comprised a basic 18 months' foundation, followed by the second half in general nursing, or a specialist course in nursing children, mentally ill or people with learning difficulties. Clinical experience was through one to three days a week at a district hospital. At the end they would gain a Diploma in Higher Education and a professional nursing qualification. Enrolled nurses were able to take a conversion course to State Registration and were to be phased out as a grade and replaced by health care assistants with National Vocational Qualifications. Many universities, including former polytechnics, began to offer a BSc in Nursing Studies, although there are only a limited number of places at present. It is hoped that in future a much higher proportion will aim at a degree.

In 1993 funding of nurse training was removed from national and regional level and the number of applicants fell. With a high wastage,

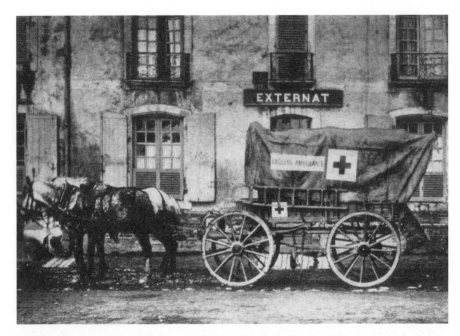

A Red Cross ambulance during the Franco-Prussian War of 1870–71.

Red Cross Hospital No. 4 in the South African War.

the shortage of trained nurses remained acute. Many trained at NHS expense could leave the profession for other work, as their skills were transferable to other better-paid positions. Temporary agencies able to offer higher salaries flourished and could supply a high level of hospital staff.

Ambitious plans have been put forward to meet a target of an extra 20,000 nurses. A fifth of nurses, who begin training, fail to register and over a half consider leaving their course – the majority because of financial hardship. Although all nursing students are exempt from tuition fees, support for living costs through student bursaries is inadequate to allow many with family commitments to complete the course.

The nursing ethic of comforting and treating the sick and aiding those unable to care for themselves has always attracted voluntary support for the professional services – the Red Cross and Red Crescent has an international organisation for this aim. Nationally, the St John Ambulance Brigade ensure first-aid is available at public events and they train a nucleus of first-aiders to attend these, along with ambulance services in support.

Chapter 14

Background to the NHS

Comment on the totally inadequate state of the medical service in Britain was recorded in early Tudor times when Sir Thomas More wrote his book *Utopia* in 1516 and visualised four large public hospitals outside each of London's city gates 'where the air would be pure with proper space for each patient and infectious cases isolated from the others'.

During the second half of the next century a number of advocates for social reform in general, and the medical services in particular, began to voice their ideas. One of the first was Hugh Chamberlen, known as the 'man-midwife' because of his efforts to reform midwifery and his introduction of the obstetric forceps. His proposal for a scheme of free well-staffed hospitals across the country, financed by a general rating levy, would have served as a model for the National Health Service today. His concept was extended and costed in 1667 by Sir William Petty, who had a chequered career across the spectrum that was common for his time. After earlier years as Professor of Anatomy at Oxford and of Music at Gresham College, he was sent to Ireland by Cromwell, initially as physician to the English Army, and then Surveyor General in charge of a survey of the country. He took advantage of this position to build up a large land holding and start a range of businesses from mining to a pilchard factory. On his return to England after the Restoration, he established himself as a political economist far ahead of his time, as well as an inventor of note. He considered the strength and wealth of a nation was related to its population and their productivity, and it was common sense to keep the workforce alive and well. Based on a population of nine million, he valued each workman at £200 and calculated free medical attention would cut the annual death rate of 360,000 by a quarter. He thought free hospital treatment should be available for all, including pregnant women and foundlings. Amongst the many inventions he patented were a double-bottomed ship, a catamaran – which sank – and the first copying machine.

Although Britain was entering an age of prosperity from industrialisation and trade, with a new middle class emerging, conditions for the general labourers who were creating this wealth remained atrocious, without any representation for their right to proper wages or social security. Towards the end of the century some social conscience began to develop and although it was considered the poor had a duty to work when able, it was also the responsibility of the rich to take care of them when incapacitated. One of the most vocal reformers was a Quaker, John Bellars, who summarised his conclusions in an essay that included 12 points. He estimated threequarters of the population lived in poverty, with more than one million sick annually, and proper medical attention could halve the death rate. He advocated a network of hospitals across the country for all who needed them. Some would be more luxurious, with one reserved for the Royalty and their families, and others confined to selective groups such as infectious diseases sufferers, the blind and those with incurable diseases. A doctor should be appointed to every hundredth of a county or parish of a city, and the State should play an active part in medical education and research. The College of Physicians and Company of Chirurgeons should draw up guidelines for all doctors to define good and bad treatments, with at least one hospital attached to the universities of Oxford and Cambridge for teaching purposes.

There would be no practical response until the voluntary hospital system mushroomed during the 18th and 19th centuries, financially dependent on charity. The first State contribution was based on the Poor Law workhouse system, originally designed to cut back on outdoor relief for the unemployed by decanting them with their families into vast institutions designed to be as inhospitable as humanely possible and force them back to work. This was largely successful and the workhouses were increasingly filled with the chronic sick and aged packed together. Public scandals over their neglect and ill-treatment led to some segregation into separate wards or institutions, but the first public hospitals to isolate patients with infectious diseases and separate the mentally ill were initiated in London by the Metropolitan Asylums Authority in 1869.

Although in theory local authorities had been empowered to take over Poor Law institutions and develop general hospitals, any response was only initiated after a Government Act in 1929 which offered to contribute 40% of the cost. Led by London and the Home Counties over the next ten years, a network of general public hospitals would be established across the country, some to achieve a standard that would match the best of the voluntary hospitals, which looked down on them and resented their competitive intrusion. One, built by the Hammersmith Borough Council, would become the Royal Postgraduate Medical School, the centre of postgraduate teaching and research in Britain today.

The hospital had been a trend-setter from the start, when Hammersmith Borough Council undertook to build its own infirmary which would set a new high standard for Poor Law hospitals. It chose a site in Du Cane Road, separated from Wormwood Scrubs prison by a narrow road called Artillery Lane and for some time these were the only two buildings for miles around.

The infirmary was a conventional pattern, with a central corridor parallel to the road, crossed by twelve 34-bedded wards. The separate workhouse of similar design was built of expensive red bricks instead of cheaper yellow ones, with a grey slate pitched roof, at a cost of £260,000. It was considered too lavish, with an entrance hall paved with mosaic and tiled dado and a dining hall of 'baronial splendour', and was dubbed the 'Pauper's Paradise' or 'Palace on the Scrubs', and the spendthrift guardians were heavily criticised. The workhouse block would hold 300 sick, mostly long-stay chronic or terminal cases under a medical superintendent, with a high standard of nursing care from 41 trained or trainee nurses, each with a single room in the nurses' home, and a training school. By 1914 it was rated one of the most modern and best-equipped hospitals in the London area, matching any voluntary hospital, with separate wards for medical, surgical and isolation cases, a ten-bedded maternity unit and a ward for tubercular children. During the First World War it became an 800-bedded military orthopaedic hospital with a comprehensive range of facilities covering all departments of treatment, a unique model of its kind.

The hospital would become included within the London County Council group and absorbed into the NHS. Initial ideas for rebuilding were shelved and replaced by plans to renovate the building to modern standards. In 1962 Enoch Powell proposed a grandiose scheme to replace the 2,800 hospitals throughout the country with 750 new modern ones, including 90 new 600-bedded units; one of these would be The Hammersmith, and his report even included a manipulated photograph of how the future hospital and medical school would look by 1971. It was to be developed in two phases, with the first to create a vast new ground floor out-patient department to deal with 100,000 patients a year, in place of the present one built in 1935 that handled

361

Hammersmith Hospital.

20,000. The second phase would comprise two modern wards on each floor designed on the 'race-track' or double corridor principle. Each floor was intended for a particular speciality, with the top one giving sterile surroundings for grafting and immunological surgery and medicine.

In 1988 Queen Charlotte's Maternity and Chelsea Gynaeological hospitals united at Goldhawk Road and many of their activities, including endocrine, pathology and in vitro fertilisation, were transferred to The Hammersmith which now includes the largest centre in Europe for research and treatment of infertility. In January 1994 The Hammersmith applied for special Trust status, with 506 multi-speciality beds, jointly with Queen Charlotte's and Chelsea Hospital, with 139 beds for obstetrics, gynaecology and neonatology, and the Acton Hospital, with 72 long-stay and rehabilitation beds. After 80 years' use and alterations, the old building survives as an eyesore, but convenient, cheap and effective. A new adjacent maternity hospital was opened in 2001.

Elsewhere, many others would achieve a high reputation. At the Central Middlesex in London Sir Francis Avery established the first specialist unit in gastro-enterology and initiated the 'sector system', whereby students would spend part of their clinical training outside the base teaching hospital. Many provincial town councils, as a matter of civic pride, created purpose-built hospitals which developed top-class specialist services. The Birmingham Accident Hospital became pre-eminent in trauma care, and the first unit for plastic surgery was established in Oxford. Only in the counties was the response poor, due to the extra cost that would be imposed on the rates.

Discussion on a unified hospital and primary health care service freely available to all dated back from the end of the First World War with a series of Reports from Royal Commissions and the British Medical Association, but without any official response. During the Second World War, in anticipation of over 600,000 air raid casualties, the first steps to co-ordinate the voluntary and municipal services were taken through an Emergency Hospital Scheme in which the country was divided into 12 regions. With the existing hospitals themselves quite unable to finance or organise the scheme, each area was controlled by a separate council, with government funding to renovate old centres, build new hospitals and set up specialised treatment

A row of Nissen huts at the Emergency Medical Service hospital at Wymondham in 1943.

centres. The ambulance service supplied by a range of agencies that included the Red Cross and St John, local authorities and individual hospitals or factories, was found to be chaotic and had to be re-organised. Although over 100 hospitals were damaged by bombing, including six direct hits on St Thomas's, casualties were far below expectations and after the war the temporary union was broken up, later to form a background for the National Health Service which all political parties had now agreed should be established. The ultimate decision on its format fell to Aneurin Bevan as Minister of Health in the new Labour Government, and he was immediately faced with the conflict of interests of all the parties concerned. On the hospital side, both the local authorities and the voluntary section wanted to retain personal control of their domains. Some Labour politicians favoured the principle of a full-time salaried medical service run by the local authorities, and this had been accepted at a Party Conference; but it was rejected when they came into power and were confronted with intense professional opposition.

In a survey by the BMA, 90% of consultants and general practitioners voted against the original proposals put forward in 1946, on the grounds these would lead to a nationalised salaried service controlled by civil servants, with loss of any professional freedom. Even the civil service rejected the scheme, which Bevan was forced to modify to bring all on board. He first overcame the voluntary consultant sector by 'stuffing their mouths with gold', allowing them to remain on a well-paid sessional basis of nine half days a week and free to practise privately outside, with a system of distinction awards for the more eminent. General practitioners were granted an independent system of payment per capita, and although they lost the right to buy and sell their practice, would receive a compensatory payment on retirement – this would be linked to an inflation level that would rapidly decline any value of their holding.

Bevan totally rejected any separation of voluntary and municipal hospitals and brought these under the control of 14 Regional Hospital Boards, overseeing some 400 hospital management committees. The only exceptions were the elite teaching hospitals, mainly based in London, which remained under the control of their board of governors, and private hospitals. Funding of the NHS would be largely central, out of general taxation through National Insurance contributions, a decision that would be set in concrete for future governments and bedevil the future financial basis of the NHS, which would be at the mercy of the general economy. This was in contrast to the general pattern throughout Europe, where a pool of health care funding would be established from a compulsory insurance levy imposed on both employer and employed, topped up by the Government. In Britain it was also originally planned to meet up to a fifth of the cost from the general National Insurance Fund contribution paid by the employer and worker. However, this level was never approached, although there was a general impression by the public that this weekly payment largely financed the NHS. The contribution was doubled to 12% in 1956 and a new insurance stamp introduced that defined the situation. By 1959 the gross cost to the NHS per head had risen to £16 from an initial £9-6s-0d, accounting for 10% of the national budget, and hospital costs which were well over half the total budget, had doubled.

The National Health Service was to inherit a complex patchwork of some 2,800 hospitals that had grown up piecemeal under separate systems unique to Britain, overlapping in some areas and leaving serious gaps in service for others. More than half were over 60 years old and had been extended and renovated over the years to try and keep them up to a standard that could cope with developments in medical technology. In both sectors, many had antiquated plumbing, heating and kitchen facilities and were in serious need of structural repairs. During the Second World War a joint study of the hospital

Halifax Union Infirmary, 1897-1901.

365

system had been sponsored by the then Ministry of Health and the Nuffield Provincial Hospital Trust. This Trust had been set up to help the development of a national health service that would embrace 'the best of public and voluntary effort' and co-ordinate hospital and ancillary services in the provinces, and it had already successfully piloted a scheme in Oxford with an Oxford and District Joint Board. Each group published a Report, together named the Doomesday Book of Hospitals. Their joint conclusions were that there was an overall shortage of hospital beds, which were unevenly distributed and badly co-ordinated due to poor bureaucratic administration.

The voluntary sector contribution was over 1,000 hospitals, many tiny, with a quarter under 30 beds and less than a hundred more than 75. Together they totalled some 77,000 beds, most offering a general acute service, but rejecting chronic and incurable cases such as tuberculosis or cancer that required long-term care, whilst some 200 confined their interest to a specialist area. Overall the larger hospitals were well run as an individual unit by a board of governors with strict discipline and financial control, but without any co-operation between themselves, and many were on the verge of bankruptcy. Any rebuilding or expansion in the past had been financed through public appeals, with some subsidy from the local authority or the Government during and after the war. They were run on a shoestring adminis-

The All Saints Convalescent Hospital, Eastbourne.

District General Hospital, Eastbourne.

tratively and staffed at consultant level by an elite honorary staff who gave their services free in return for the benefits of private practice. In London especially this had dictated the central location of the hospitals for convenience of access by the doctors rather than the patients. At the teaching hospitals, junior resident staff were paid a pittance of £50 for a six-month house job, essential for their future career, whilst on duty night and day and at best with only a weekend off between each post. Patient charges had been brought in with 'means testing' by lady almoners, and many would have pay-beds or a private wing, to replace the 'begging bowls' which were placed on a chair in the ward during visiting hours in early days.

Included in the NHS takeover were around 140 general municipal hospitals, adding another 70,000 beds to match the voluntary sector contribution. The Government had funded 40% of the cost, with the balance provided from the local authorities, who were obliged to means-test for a contribution towards their upkeep from the patients or their family. Overall development had been as uncoordinated as in the voluntary sector, with each administered as a separate unit by a medical superintendent with largely full-time paid consultants and resident staff. Standards varied from bad through indifferent to some as excellent as the best voluntary hospital. A few, as at The Archway Group in London, were co-ordinated into a group offering specialist as well as general services, but many had become a decanting site for chronic and incurable cases. Any co-operation between them and the voluntary system was unique, with a few successful exceptions as at Newcastle and Oxford, and generally the municipal area resented the arrogant attitude taken towards them by the voluntary group. Alongside these general hospitals run by local authorities was a range confined to special needs. There were still several hundred isolation hospitals in existence, many minuscule and most redundant after the control of infectious diseases. Within a few years the majority would either be closed down or converted into sanitoria for the tubercular and homes for the elderly. Government aid for the tubercular had been extensive and there were a hundred sanitoria offering over 30,000 beds.

Besides these were two 'Cinderella' areas of care, the mentally ill or backward, along with the elderly and chronic. Altogether at the time of take-over there were nearly a hundred public asylums housing over 120,000 mentally ill and subnormal. Run by the local authorities, these mostly dated back to Victorian times and were mainly vast isolated sites in the country, many with over 2,000 beds, and farmed by the patients to support their keep. Acute mental care was haphazard, with little available within the general hospital system, and the afflicted were despatched to the asylums, where there were few facilities to enable them to cope.

The other large deprived group was the elderly and chronic sick, who were rejected by the general municipal and voluntary hospitals. Especially in the poorer areas they would be decanted into the Poor Law and Assistance hospitals that remained, to end their days in discomfort and neglect, with as many as 60 patients in a single ward. Most of the buildings were patched-up workhouses described as 'ill designed, deficient in sanitation, often isolated, bare, bleak and soulless' in a *Times* editorial. Medical and nursing attention was minimal, with little or no remedial and occupational therapy.

This diversity of hospitals had to be unified under the NHS, and Bevan set up a structure in which the country was divided into 14 regions. All the hospitals within each region were under the control of a Regional Hospital Board, which in turn was under direct control by the Ministry of Health, and it was planned that each region would include a university medical school. The board was composed of 20 to

30 members from a cross-section of professions and business who met once a month and served on a voluntary basis. A board would control up to 200 hospitals within its region and inevitably this led to working committees and expensive levels of headquarters staff, who totalled over 4,000. Sheffield Regional Board created seven standing committees, six standing sub-committees, many advisory committees and some 24 committees of consultants.

Beneath the regional boards were some 400 Hospital Management Committees each in charge of up to 20 hospitals. The basic principle was to form a self-sufficient unit that offered an overall range of clinical services, although specialist services such as mental or children's hospitals might be separated. The members were a cross-section of representatives serving on a voluntary basis, whilst the lay administration was in the hands of a group secretary and finance and supplies officers, whose areas of responsibility would often be ill-defined and lead to conflict.

The new structure would dislocate the existing pattern of control in both sectors. Previously in the municipal hospitals this had been in the overall hands of a medical superintendent, who would now be replaced by a separate lay administration in charge of all services and non-medical staff, and a medical committee only responsible for its own field. In the voluntary area control passed from the governors to management committees, except for the teaching hospitals. The biggest loss of status was by the former matron, who ceased to have any authority over catering, cleaning and domestic staff – in some cases even the nurses' home – to become merely a 'nursing administrator'.

The result was a breakdown of management within the individual hospital, with loss of discipline and standards in all the non-medical areas and an overall loss of morale and *esprit de corps*. The local house committees had little jurisdiction and even the management committees had to pass trivia such as the appointment of a cleaner or an office promotion up to regional level.

The original concept on which the NHS was based envisaged a fixed amount of ill health in the community which would be reduced as general health improved with a free service, holding the cost level. In reality this escalated as people queued up for free teeth and glasses. The great demands on finances would come from the pent-up demand for hospital services, whilst the pharmacy bill would treble over the first two years. The result was a limitation on capital expenditure to £10 million p.a. and no new hospitals were built during the first ten years. In spite of this, there was a great improvement in the overall situation and the NHS was generally respected across the world. Surveys over the next ten years showed over 80% of people considered it a good service, although the cost of medical care remained under 4% of national income tax, less than the average for Europe. The standards of the existing hospitals were upgraded with new operating theatres and improved X-ray and pathology services, and waiting lists were brought under control. Up-to-date hearing aids and surgical appliances for the handicapped were readily available, although some charges were introduced for prescriptions, dental care and glasses, which led to Bevan's resignation in protest.

Within ten years 30% more patients were admitted annually than when the NHS began, due to better use of beds and an increase in the number of nurses. Although medical records were less accurate than today, the inherited waiting list of 500,000 fell slightly and one estimate concluded 60% of surgical cases were admitted within three months, in complete contrast to today. The Emergency Bed Service run by the King Edward VII's Hospital Fund co-ordinated vacant beds in the London area and ensured general practitioners could obtain immediate admission for urgent cases even at times of 'red alert'. The main pressure fell on maternity units as the proportion of hospital deliveries rose steadily, in some cases to over 80%, and there was a shortage of midwives.

The escalating cost of the NHS was of increasing government concern, and led to a Committee of Enquiry under the chairmanship of a Cambridge economist, Claude Guillebaud, which reported in 1956. It concluded there was no evidence of extravagance or inefficiency and the cost of the NHS as a proportion of national income had fallen from 3.75% to 3.25%, well below the European average. It also concluded that more money was needed to build new hospitals, as the profession was trying to practise 20th-century medicine in 19th-century buildings. No immediate action was taken, but six years later plans were made to extend the hospital services over the next ten years through a range of new 600-800-bedded District General Hospitals and to upgrade others at a cost of half a billion pounds. These hospitals would offer a wide range of general services alongside measures to increase co-operation with general practitioners and improve local health services.

It became increasingly evident that the existing three-legged basic structure of control was divisive. General practitioners, along with pharmacists, dentists and opticians, were under the authority of 134 Executive Councils and felt isolated from the hospital services, whilst locally based welfare services were controlled by 174 Local Health Authorities. After lengthy discussions and a succession of government 'green papers', the service was re-organised in 1974 in an attempt to unify and co-ordinate all three services and bring them under one authority. The end result was to superimpose a further administrative layer of 14 Regional Health Authorities overseeing 90 Area Health Authorities. These lacked any professional representation and each area was further split into Health Districts, with local management teams responsible for hospitals. General practitioners remained a separate contractor under Family Practitioner Committees and Community Health Councils were set up.

The outcome was an increase of 16,700 administrative staff within a year, with higher costs and further loss of morale. It was at once evident that there was one administrative layer too many, but it would be eight years before the Conservative Government introduced any change under the banner 'Patients First'. Area Health Councils were abolished and replaced by 192 District Health Authorities, each covering a population of around 250,000, which would delegate power to management units that ranged in scope from all hospital services in their area to a single large hospital. Twenty separate Special Health Authorities were set up, mostly to run the teaching hospitals in London, whilst general practitioner services were detached from the mainstream of NHS administration and placed under Family Practitioner Committees, and Community Care Councils were retained.

Overall there was a significant reduction in administration costs, but the hospitals continued to absorb over 70% of the total NHS budget. Increasingly, cash limits were imposed but, although where possible prescribing and other costs were off-loaded onto the general practitioners' budget, the annual shortfall increased steadily through advances in medical technology, rising patient expectations and demands from an ageing population. The deficit approached £400 million annually. As a result the authorities were forced to restrict admissions, temporarily close wards and reduce staff. By 1987 the financial state had reached a pitch where the BMA and Royal Colleges joined forces to issue a statement that the NHS had almost reached breaking point.

Earlier the Government had initiated a far-reaching review of the

NHS and taken measures to try and stem expenditure. These included a programme of efficiency savings under the label 'cost improvement programmes' that would reduce expenditure by almost a billion pounds a year throughout the health services by the end of the decade. 'Performance indicators' were introduced to compare hospital levels of cost per patient and length of stay, and there was now competitive tendering from outside contractors for catering and domestic services. Sales of staff residential accommodation, including nursing homes and closure of the large mental hospitals, raised capital, whilst local income was raised through car parking charges and turning the entrance to hospitals into retail areas, housing everything from banks and mini-supermarkets to holding a weekly market in the entrance foyer. Glossy brochures and logos advertising their services matched annual reports of major public companies, and private patient units were re-opened.

Although the principle of 'free-for-all' was to remain sacrosanct in theory, the Thatcher Government initiated measures to stimulate the growth of private care, which was to rise to a billion pounds annually by the end of the decade from £10 million in the 1970s. Under Barbara Castle the Labour Government had closed down NHS pay beds and banned new private hospitals, but with new incentives by 1988, led by non-profit making Nuffield Hospitals and with-profit groups such as BUPA, there would be over 200 hospitals within the private sector offering 90,000 beds. With tax incentives for the elderly and business, over 6 million people, 11% of the population, would carry private insurance, which covered 17% of all elective surgery, including 15% of all hip replacements and 20% of cardiac surgery – the areas where waiting lists are worst today. Higher benefits for the elderly from a change in supplementary benefit regulations led to a rapid expansion in private residential and nursing home provision, charity home and hospice care. Increased charges for dental and ophthalmic care, as well as higher prescription fees, would cover nearly 5% of total costs.

In spite of these changes, without any fresh cash injection, conditions within the NHS continued to deteriorate, public dissatisfaction rose steadily and by 1989 reached 80%. The hospital service still absorbed over 70% of total costs and strict cash limits had been imposed, leaving an annual shortfall approaching £400 million. Beds and wards had to be closed at times; aggravated by industrial action, the waiting list rose to over 685,000 in the five major areas of surgery.

In orthopaedics alone this was over 142,000, with nearly half waiting more than a year for admission.

In an attempt both to improve efficiency and respond to patient dissatisfaction, radical changes in the management of the NHS were introduced in 1990 under the banner 'Working for Patients'. A separate Department of Health with its own Minister was created to take overriding responsibility for the NHS, with direct management at a non-political level by an executive under a former health service manager.

Although the source of funding remained central and the money passed over to the 14 RHAs, these would lose any responsibility for hospital management and focus on assessment of the patient needs for their district, which they then purchased by a contract that laid down the extent and quality of care that was required. The supplier was self-governing NHS Trusts, to be created by the acute general hospitals and larger general practitioner groups. This 'internal market' tended to divide management into two competitive teams with opposing responsibilities and led to a surge of extra staff to obtain the necessary information and negotiate and monitor contracts that would cost an extra £1.5 billion annually. The eventual outcome was to merge the regional health offices into a central NHS Executive Headquarters.

At Trust level there would be major managerial changes towards an industrial pattern with a board of directors, including non-executives with an emphasis on their business skills at the expense of professional and public representation. The committees were under a general manager and took over appointments and terms of service for staff, including consultant appointments with a defined job plan as well as the allocation of distinction awards.

Medical audit control was also introduced to make doctors more accountable for their performance. Such audits became a routine part of clinical work and showed up immense discrepancies between hospitals. Surgeons especially regarded this as an intrusion on their clinical judgement and management. Whilst an average surgeon's waiting list was 2,000 patients, some were ten times as great, and the turnover for orthopaedic surgery ranged from 100 to 750 operations a year. District hospital bed turnover could vary threefold, with a tenfold multiple in support staff.

The new proposals caused concern at all levels, especially the medical profession, and the British Medical Association, which had not been consulted beforehand, labelled the changes as an 'infernal bazaar' rather than an internal market, but the freedom from bureaucratic control gradually overcame both professional and management resistance. Initially the minimum unit size for a Trust was set at 250 acute hospital beds or a practice size of 11,000 patients, but these limits were progressively reduced and within the first five years over 400 Trusts were set up.

The District Health Authorities were answerable for the standard of services available, which were monitored by regional outposts set up by the overriding Management Executive, whilst separate Clinical Standards Advisory Groups would assess standards of care in a wide range of conditions from emergency admissions and neo-natal intensive care to diabetes and coronary by-pass surgery. Wide variations in patterns of care were to be revealed, as well as the gaps between demand and resources.

The benefits from the changes were subject to ongoing analysis by researchers, with variable conclusions due to difficulty in defining standards of measurement that could distinguish between the 'internal market' and the extra funding that was being made available. One highly respected analyst concluded there was 'little change for the better or for worse'. At primary care level, there was an improvement that included extra services from general practitioners and a better relationship with consultants. At hospital level, benefits were less evident as waiting lists mounted and the waiting time for elective surgery increased from lack of beds and shortage of nurses and general staff due to low pay and poor morale, as well as increased pressure from emergency admissions. These issues would become a political football as successive governments promised, for electoral purposes, targets that would prove impractical to deliver.

The only clear-cut result was the increase in management costs for extra staff to negotiate contracts and supply information, amounting to £1.5 billion, leading to a restructure of the management arrangements at all levels in 1996. The separate Regional Health Authorities and NHS Management Executive regional outposts were merged, as were the separate District Health and Family Health Service Authorities. These changes streamlined the services, reducing paperwork and regulation. After 50 years the Regional Authorities which had regulated the NHS had been disbanded and replaced by eight regional outposts of the Department of Health with reduced staff, no role in funding and little power except quality control. The 105 District Hospitals and 90 Family Health Authorities were merged into 100

374

single Health Authorities, saving over £150 million a year in administration charges.

There had already been a shift in policy to reduce the competitive elements that had developed in the earlier stages of 'Working for Patients' towards overall closer co-operation between the areas of health care, and the earlier intense opposition from the Labour Party was modified when 'New Labour' came into power. Under their banner of 'Renewing the NHS' they flagged a balance between their former extremes of State regulation and a competitive internal market. The principle of separation of purchaser and provider was accepted, but the length of their contracts was extended, a process already under way and used as a means of assessing providers' performance. Primary Care Groups were established in England, with varying arrangements for the rest of Britain, composed predominantly of general practitioners with nursing and social service representation. These would be free-standing bodies accountable to one of a hundred Health Authorities in charge of the money available, with the responsibility to provide and fund community and general practitioner services in their area as well as commissioning hospital services. Their money could be moved freely between primary and hospital Trusts at will, with a radical change in the allocation of services. General practitioner services would be extended; a new level of specialised nurse practitioner would be introduced who would enable local care for especial groups of patient with diabetes, asthma and hypertension, and consultants would hold specialist clinics within a group practice. Even more fundamental were the changes within the hospital system.

The acute services were coping remarkably well with the increasing pressures imposed on their limited facilities and shortage of staff at all levels. Accident and Emergency Departments faced increasing numbers of patients from an ageing and more demanding population and there were improvements in techniques of treatment for life-threatening conditions, such as heart attacks, which made up to 90% of all medical admissions. Defensive medicine was becoming an increasing problem and patients would be referred for X-rays and tests where these were not clinically necessary to avoid legal exposure. More patients were being seen in hospital, but public attention was focused on the time spent in Casualty before medical attention, waiting lists and admission delays, all of which rose steadily.

Studies by the Audit Commission showed great variation in the efficiency with which hospitals used the beds available, from admission procedures through bed allocation and length of stay in hospital, operating theatre use and clinical practice, to discharge procedures. These would lead to changes, with improvement across all areas, led by management and medical teams and stimulated by the competitive atmosphere for the supply of contracted services to the Purchasing Trusts. There was a general overhaul of procedures, from the assessment of patients on arrival at the A & E Department by a nurse who could judge urgency, through operating theatre management to unblocking beds by arrangements for district care after discharge and improved facilities for the chronic sick and elderly.

Another trend was for District General Hospitals to extend their range of services and develop specialised units beside their general ones. These extended services, as with cardio-vascular surgery, could offer great advantage locally and save some patients a great deal of the dislocation that having to travel long distances for their treatment could cause. As specialist care became increasingly complex, demanding a high level of skill and costly equipment, as with cancer therapy, there was a danger of this becoming duplicated and under-utilised at the local level. The result has been a review of the allocation of specialist care between local secondary care hospital units and larger hospitals with highly specialised services serving large areas.

Chapter 15

The Independent Sector

At its initiation the NHS would acquire some 3,000 hospitals and 'disclaim' 230, which were allowed to remain independent. Most of these were small and either started by workers' co-operatives and friendly societies in the 19th century with subscriptions from their members, or run by religious groups. They covered a wide range of interests from unions to freemasons and professional groups, that included the Manor House, Royal Masonic and St Luke's Hospital for the Clergy. The Catholic orders were given dispensation and their hospitals included The Retreat at York managed since 1792 by the Society of Friends and St Andrew's, Northampton, established in 1838.

One of the more select elder independents was the King Edward VII's Hospital for Officers, established in London in 1899 by two sisters, Agnes and Fanny Keyser, who turned their home at 17 Grosvenor Crescent into a hospital for wounded officers returning from the Boer War. They established the hospital from their own funds, and raised subscriptions of £100 per annum for five years from a private appeal to 24 friends, followed by an appeal to serving officers to contribute five shillings a year. It became a charity in 1930 and moved to its present site in Beaumont Street in 1948. It has always enjoyed Royal support, and generous donations from Friends, and a wide range of sources which have enabled it to give the highest standards of medical care. Besides Service personnel and their families it now accepts civilian patients.

The London Clinic had been opened in 1932, as the most luxurious and expensive hotel in the world, built on a site located between the Regent's Park end of Harley Street, the mecca of English medicare, and Devonshire Place, planned to combine the latest resources of an up-to-date 175 bedded hospital with the comfort of a first class hotel. It would soon face bankruptcy and after three years would be transferred to a non-profit making company that would become a charity in 1963. Staffing has included many of the eminent physicians and surgeons of their time, and patients included royalty, business and

King Edward VII's Hospital Sister Agnes, London.

political leaders alongside stars who have always featured intense publicity as they leave.

Altogether these 'disclaimer' beds would total some 18,000, to which could be added around 8,000 private beds within the NHS, which would form the basis for continued private practice. Before the NHS some half of the population had not been covered for medical care by government schemes, and many of these had taken out insurance for hospital treatment through a range of small societies that they wished to continue without dependence on the NHS. The bulk of these blended together under the banner of the British United Provident Association (BUPA). The main insurer, the Hospital Service Plan, which offered an annual subscription of £2 12s 0d, elected to remain independent and would become the Private Patients' Plan (PPP) in 1962.

During the first twenty years of the NHS there was little change in the pattern of private use, which was small units offering limited facilities, but there would be increasing professional and political conflict between the interests of the two sectors. The hospitals in the independent sector were mostly small with limited facilities, whilst the NHS pay beds were under used. There was increasing criticism in Parliament and amongst staff unions and junior doctors of these being misused by the private sector at the expense of NHS patients. This would lead to a

378

cutback in pay beds and stricter costing for the use of NHS facilities by the private sector.

The Nuffield Homes Charitable Trust had begun to develop larger independent hospitals in the late 1950s, initially funded by BUPA private care and expanding rapidly to total 29 modernised or newly built up-to-date acute hospitals each with up to fifty beds by 1978. By then BUPA itself had begun to create a chain of similar hospitals across the country that offered reduced rates to its own subscribers. At the time, however, independent care largely remained a cottage industry with 95% in the hands of small religious or non-profit groups with 30–40 beds at most in each.

In the early 1980s changes in government policy were to accelerate further growth in the private hospital sector. Tax allowances were introduced for group and business subscribers to insurance schemes and now accounted for over half of all members. Changes to consultant contracts within the NHS encouraged many to give up full-time and move towards more private work.

Restrictions on the development of private hospitals would also be relaxed and this led to a number of hotel groups and others entering the field. These included overseas companies, initially investors from the United States. In all eight American companies concerned with private health would take initial steps and two have developed a dominant role in Britain.

The first was American Medical International (AMI) which entered the British market in 1970 when it bought The Harley Street Clinic, followed by The Princess Grace Hospital in 1977 and by 1983 it owned thirteen hospitals through purchase or building and challenged Nuffield as the largest private supplier. It is now the largest private bed provider in the UK owning 47 hospitals. In America it has created a well-publicised image for personal patient care by a 'properly packaged employee who looks and feels good' from a 'personalised image workshop'. In Britain it has extended into specialist areas, including a psychiatric division formed in 1984 and later centres for brain injury and learning disabilities under the banner Partnership in Care. Many of the individual hospitals that are concerned with acute medical and surgical care have also focused on a specific area of interest that include a transplant centre at the Clementine Churchill Hospital and a range of in vitro fertilization units.

Subsequent developments in the ownership of AMI have been complex. It was floated on the London Stock Market in 1988 for three

379

BMI Esperance Hospital, Eastbourne.

years, but was then involved in a succession of acquisitions. The first was by a French company Generale de Sante, which became the General Health Group with the British hospital unit run as a separate operating company, BMI Healthcare. This acquired the fifteen hospitals built up by the Compass hotel and catering group under the name Amicus, to form the largest private hospital group in Britain. All these groupings were brought together under one heading, Cinven Ltd, which has now passed the management into the hands of a group of funds controlled by a European private equity fund, BC Partners, which has diverse interests across the financial centres in America.

The other major entrance to the United Kingdom market was the Hospital Corporation of America (HCA), the largest with-profit hospital company in the world. It began as merely a recruiting agency for its Middle East operations and acquired The Wellington Hospital which had been built in 1974 as a purpose built 250 bedded unit to match The London Clinic in quality care by a luxury hotel and liner group, The British & Commonwealth Shipping Company. HCA has focused on London, where it now owns six of the largest clinics that include the specialised Portland Hospital for Women and Children.

The largest private centre in London is The Cromwell, opened in 1981, handling 70 specialities covered by over 500 specialists offering

Portland Hospital, London.

the widest range under one roof in the private area. One of its assets is a fixed price system for patients without insurance cover that enables them to establish the cost of their treatment for specified surgical procedures, excluding the surgeon's fees. It even offers high security suites with bulletproof windows and steel doors.

The Wellington Hospital, London.

The reception area of the Princess Grace Hospital, London.

One of the European companies to enter British healthcare was Capio Sweden by acquiring 21 hospitals through The Community Group and psychiatric care through The Florence Nightingale Hospitals. It has also been appointed as preferred bidder for establishing the initial treatment centres within the NHS. These will offer diagnostic, general and orthopaedic surgery facilities through newly built, refurbished or existing facilities designed to speed up investigation and treatment.

There are now 253 independent acute care hospitals in Britain, roughly the same number as when the NHS was established, but now very different in quality of service. The sector has been changed from a cottage type industry into one with over 10,000 beds that offers a high standard of care. Over half of these are controlled by BUPA, Nuffield or charity and other independent groups in equal numbers, with any profit ploughed back into the business; whilst the rest are owned by with profit organisations that have to pay stockholders.

The sector now carries out over 20% of all elective surgery, over a million operations a year, a quarter of which is of major calibre which includes a third of hip replacements and hysterectomies and 15% of cardiac surgery. It covers a much higher proportion of lesser procedures such as cataract surgery and stripping varicose veins. Around 70% of patients are now covered by private health insurance, the majority middle-class working males whose subscriptions are paid through their employer, although now many are trade union members. The rest pay their own fees and are from overseas or the elderly, who would otherwise face a lengthy waiting time for NHS treatment. At one time overseas patients were dominant, but the development of hospital services locally, especially in the Middle East, and criticism of overcharging by the profession, has greatly reduced this source. Insurance cover is now provided by a range of major companies. Whilst BUPA remains independent, PPP has been absorbed into the Axa empire and publishes a designated list of hospitals that offer private care.

The with-profit sector has been criticised for putting the interests of their stockholders before the patients and creating a two-tier system of care. This has been especially levelled at companies based in America, where the level of hospital admissions and surgical intervention is the highest in the world, with by-pass surgery at ten times the European incidence, some of which has been criticised as unnecessary, whilst the rate of investigation such as CT scans is over double.

There has been no evidence of such trends here and the NHS has increasingly taken advantage of independent facilities for investigation and surgery, whilst the availability of compact, conveniently located modern facilities has proved popular. The independent sector is now subjected to the same level of quality controls and investigation as the NHS hospitals. It was claimed that the units in the independent sector might be too small to offer sufficient expertise and back-up support, but experience has shown it has been careful to restrict its range and ensure adequate out-of-hours patient cover. Professional standards were also challenged, as to whether direct payment would buy extra time and personal attention as with other professions, but overall this does not appear to have been a major source of criticism.

Many of the larger units have focused on one or more specialist areas, offering overall as wide a range of service as is available within the NHS. BUPA has built up a chain of 300 care and retirement homes in addition to its 35 hospitals.

The private sector has always been alert to offer services where the NHS could only provide restricted facilities. One of these was abortions, many of which were carried out through non-profit organisations such as The British Pregnancy Advisory Services. With the 1967 Abortion Act demand increased greatly and a number of commercial organisations entered the field and over half of all abortions, many on patients from overseas, were carried out in with-profit clinics and accounted for up to a quarter of all private hospital work during the early 1980s.

In direct contrast, more recently there have been established a number of private facilities for infertility treatment, in particular in vitro fertilisation, based in specialised centres as at Bourn Hall in Cambridge, or units within private hospitals as at The Wellington, Cromwell and The Esperance, as well as separate full fee paying units in NHS hospitals as at Nottingham and St Thomas's.

Most recently has been the development of cosmetic surgery facilities for which there has been an unprecedented increase in demand. This has been met by many of the existing independent hospitals, but in addition a number of clinics confined to this field have been opened.

The independent area as a whole has greatly extended services to cover health screening for individuals and industrial groups, both through its hospitals and mobile units.

Chapter 16

Money Matters

The original hospitals were more than self-supporting. The early Temples of Aesculapius and medical centres symbolised by the name of Hippocrates were far from charitable and kept their priests and medical practitioners in comfort, if not luxury. The early British hospitals developed as appendages of the monasteries and enjoyed equal profitability, building up large land-holdings and property rental incomes. Located on the main pilgrimage routes, they derived income from collecting boxes outside the hospital and paid care for long-term residents. Indulgences and pardons were sold to wealthy local landowners and licensed out-riders, called proctors, would travel around the country offering forgiveness for the penitent. A valuable source of money would be royal grants of levies and tolls from local farmers and merchants, ranging from imports of wine to production of grain. Amongst the largest beneficiaries were St Peter's at York and St Bartholomew's and St Thomas's in London, which built up individual incomes approaching £250,000 annually at today's values, to make them a natural target for Henry VIII along with the monasteries.

When the London hospitals were re-established to relieve the vagrancy that their closure had caused, they were refunded by the Crown, with the City of London meeting half the running expenses and exerting over-ruling supervisory control through a Court of Governors. Whilst their financial security allowed them to rebuild with a quality of construction that would match the highest today, the wards having large windows, high ceilings and ample water supply, there were no funds available for any new hospital development until the beginning of the 18th century and the so-called 'voluntary hospital' era.

Over the next 150 years over 200 general and specialist hospitals would be opened offering free medical care, entirely dependent financially on charity. The origins were often of the humblest level, with the initial premises, as at The Westminster Hospital, soon condemned as insanitary. The charitable aims appealed to the social conscience of the emerging middle classes of tradespeople and manufacturers. For an annual subscription of a few guineas they could become a hospital governor with the right to put forward a patient for admission and to vote at all meetings. Equally attractive was the opportunity to mix socially with the 'Establishment' and 'nobility' who began to support the hospital movement, which was patronised later by members of the Royal Family and many hospitals were designated as 'Royal'.

As these hospitals developed their long-term reputation, they would be faced with increasing financial demands which the income from subscribers could not meet and they were often on the verge of bankruptcy. Saturday Clubs would help to raise funds by block subscriptions from the lower-paid workers and Sunday Clubs were supported by the clergy with church appeals. More desperate measures ranged from a begging bowl placed on a chair in the ward during visiting hours, to employing travelling salesmen who would go around door-to-door selling household goods on commission. Competition amongst the hospitals for charity was intense and advertising in the press and on posters extensive.

Fund-raising fêtes and dinners were common, and Moorfield's Eye Hospital even held annual dinners where patients were exhibited. As today, the entertainment world contributed freely to fund-raising through concerts and special performances. Hogarth and Handel set the pattern initially for the Foundling Hospital and their example was followed by successive generations of artists and entertainers, with Charing Cross a major beneficiary due to its location in the heart of London theatreland, and overall the hospital was to retain a lead in showing initiative for fund-raising over the years.

By the start of the 19th century many of the voluntary hospitals were in serious financial trouble from falling subscriber numbers, and in 1798 Worcester Royal Infirmary had published the names of those late with their donations and had begun to charge accident admission of 7s 6d a week. Administration through cumbersome voluntary subscriber groups was increasingly realised to be impractical and incompetent, and the hospitals began to appoint a paid hospital secretary and committees to control expenditure and medical management.

Patient charges had been introduced to some extent from earliest times, with deposits to cover return to the patient's parish or burial, and charges by the nursing services, but as costs and demand rose, more effective action had to be taken and admission charges became general. The initial movement would relate to the outpatient departments of the general hospitals which were becoming overwhelmed with patients.

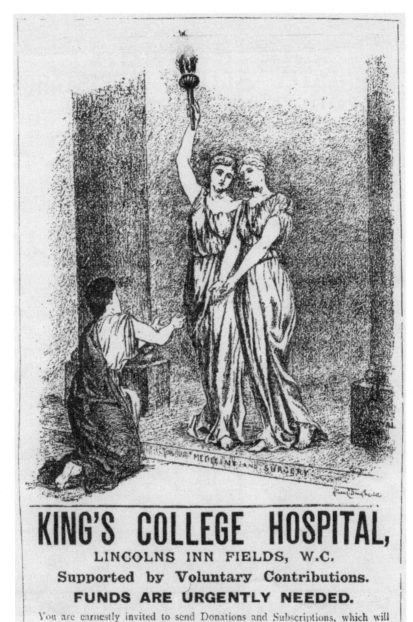

KING'S COLLEGE HOSPITAL,

LINCOLNS INN FIELDS, W.C.

Supported by Voluntary Contributions.

FUNDS ARE URGENTLY NEEDED.

You are earnestly invited to send Donations and Subscriptions, which will be gratefully received and acknowledged.

N. BROMLEY (REV.), *Warden.*

Some examples of hospital advertising to bring in funds.

387

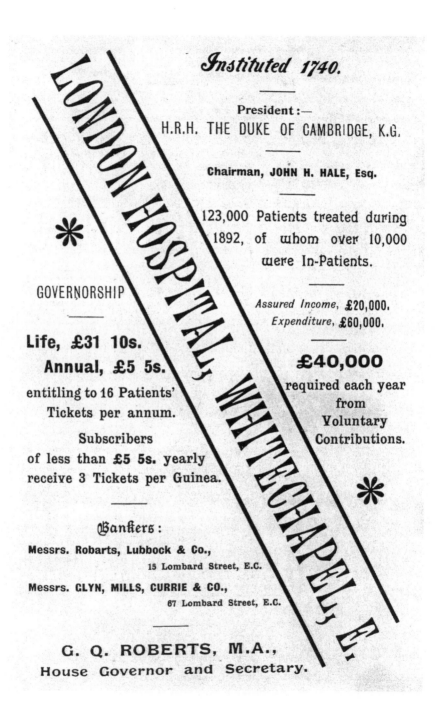

Instituted 1740.

President:—
H.R.H. THE DUKE OF CAMBRIDGE, K.G.

Chairman, JOHN H. HALE, Esq.

123,000 Patients treated during 1892, of whom over 10,000 were In-Patients.

Assured Income, £20,000.
Expenditure, £60,000.

£40,000
required each year
from
Voluntary
Contributions.

LONDON HOSPITAL, WHITECHAPEL, E.

GOVERNORSHIP

Life, £31 10s.
Annual, £5 5s.

entitling to 16 Patients'
Tickets per annum.

Subscribers
of less than £5 5s. yearly
receive 3 Tickets per Guinea.

Bankers:

Messrs. Robarts, Lubbock & Co.,
15 Lombard Street, E.C.

Messrs. GLYN, MILLS, CURRIE & CO.,
67 Lombard Street, E.C.

G. Q. ROBERTS, M.A.,
House Governor and Secretary.

26

MERSEYSIDE
VOLUNTARY
HOSPITALS

are associated with
the Merseyside
Hospitals Council

Royal Liverpool United
Hospital :—
  Royal Infirmary
  David Lewis
    Northern Hospital
  Royal Southern
    Hospital
  Stanley Hospital
Bootle General Hospital
Hahnemann Hospital
Waterloo General
    Hospital
Lourdes Hospital
Royal Liverpool
    Children's Hospital
Royal Liverpool
    Babies' Hospital
Women's Hospital
Liverpool Maternity
    Hospital
Croxton Recovery
    Hospital
Liverpool Eye, Ear
   and Throat Infirmary
Heart Hospital
Liverpool Radium
    Institute
St. Paul's Eye Hospital
Sir Alfred Jones
    Memorial Hospital
Birkenhead General
    Hospital
Birkenhead Maternity
    Hospital
Birkenhead and Wirral
    Children's Hospital
Ellesmere Port and
    District Hospital
Hoylake and West Kirby
    Cottage Hospital
Neston and District War
    Memorial Cottage
    Hospital
Victoria Central Hospital
    Wallasey
Wallasey Cottage
    Hospital

You Can rebuild

MERSEYSIDE
VOLUNTARY
HOSPITALS!

In Victorian times there was little State support for the sick, unemployed or those unable to work. Their only relief was the meagre, harsh Poor Law aid and the needy had to turn to charity. Many charities had been long established to serve their parish or trade, but until a universal Charity Organisation Society was founded in 1869 their distributions were piecemeal and more to the plausible than the needy. The society orbit included the voluntary hospitals as well as the dispensaries and dreaded infirmaries, and one of the major problems was the build up of out-patient volume. Initially all hospital applicants for treatment as an out- or in-patient had been vetted by duty members of the board of governors, but numbers had become far too great. As early as 1678 the out-patient problem at Bart's had been described as 'burdensome' and this would mount over the decades.

The problem was to select the genuine poor sick from the unemployed who sought food and shelter and wandered from hospital to hospital. Others merely sought free advice at the expense of their local general practitioner, whom they would have had to pay, but could well afford. Distinction was to prove a source of great debate ranging from the serious concern by the BMA in 1870 to the *Lancet*, who expounded 'there could be no abuse of out-patients as conditions [were] so appalling, crowds so intolerable and treatment necessarily so cursory, that no-one who could possibly avoid it would enter such a department.'

An attempt to resolve the problem was the effort to develop Provident Dispensaries to which the hospitals were linked; patients would pay a small weekly charge whilst fit and at work, with the benefit of free treatment when ill. As their financial problems mounted, the hospitals had to face the need to assess out-patients' contributions. At St Mary's there was an inquiry officer, often a retired policeman, who had the authority to reject anyone he considered unsuitable, but this was no satisfactory solution to the increasingly chaotic state of out-patients' departments and deciding who could really afford to contribute.

In 1895 the Charity Organisation Society paid the salary of a social worker, Mary Steward, to work in the out-patients of The Royal Free Hospital for a trial period of three months as the first 'lady almoner'. 'Almoner' was a title that had been given in the past to the official at the monastery who would dispense charity to the poor, and later to the governors of the Royal Hospitals who selected patients for admission. Initially, Miss Steward's role was deeply resented by the medical

Delegates attending the Convention on Social Science, held in Toronto in June 1924.

staff, who refused to refer any patients, and she had to work in a screened-off area in the corner of the out-patients' department with a radiator the only seat for a visitor. She managed to interview enough patients prepared to discuss their circumstances, and discover many could afford to contribute towards a provident society. Medical opposition was gradually overcome and from merely a source for medical appliances and convalescence, the lady almoner's role steadily expanded to become an integral part of the hospital staff and a member of a recognised professional body that laid the background to Social Services today. Without offering direct relief, they established contacts with charities and clergy that could help patients where necessary and increasingly became involved with all aspects of patient welfare, as well as assessing their financial contribution for treatment.

At the turn of the century many workers lived in overcrowded, insanitary housing with a high incidence of tuberculosis. Maternity and child welfare were in their infancy and infant mortality was high, with most deliveries at home as there were no maternity wards in any general hospital. Almoners began to persuade the authorities to develop ante-natal clinics and home visits, with advice for mothers through maternity clubs and post-natal care – an attitude against the general feelings of the time. Their work received a great boost from generous funds provided by a Trust set up by a benefactor, Stafford Northcote, in memory of his sister, for research at St Thomas's into the social causes of ill health and their relief. The work extended into maternity and infant welfare, as well as tuberculosis, through the energies of a lady, Anne Cummins, who had been appointed in 1905 as the first lady almoner at St Thomas's. The status of the lady almoner in the establishment matched that of Florence Nightingale in nursing and the value of almoners' work became generally realised by the medical staff, subscribers and administrators. Their role was primarily educational and required a general training in the social sciences, leading to a diploma course run by the London School of Economics.

In 1920 Parliament authorised voluntary hospitals to charge patients for a contribution towards their costs. A flat rate was considered unfair for the poorer and after long discussions the almoners at St Thomas's agreed to act as assessors for a means test. This role was gradually introduced across the country and in turn the municipal hospitals were obliged to charge patients or their families where possible. Inevitably their work became more administrative, but within the NHS their role as an assessor of a patient's 'needs' rather than 'means' would be restored.

Bevan had to make two vital decisions on the infrastructure of the National Health Service that would make it a political football for the future. The first was to remove hospital management from the local authority or voluntary board of governors and bring them all under central control by the Minister of Health through Regional Hospital Committees.

The second concerned the financing of the NHS, which it was agreed should be 'free for all'. There were two main alternatives. One was by direct taxation and the money allocated from a general national insurance fund, as in Sweden and Denmark. The alternative was some form of social insurance, with payments contributed by employees and employers into an independent fund, the standard pattern elsewhere in Europe, where payments could reach 6% of salary. Details of cover varied greatly from country to country, but contributions were related to income, with the higher earners and singles subsidising the lower paid, largely families. The State would cover the cost of the unemployed and chronic sick and often new hospital construction, mounting to around 10% of the fund in France and Germany. Although the right to health care is universal, the patient may be required to meet part of the cost of a general practitioner consultation or hospital care, which in France and Belgium may reach 25%, which can be covered by personal or group private insurance.

There is some form of government regulation in all countries, usually with annual negotiations between all concerned on premiums to be paid by the workers and fees to doctors and hospitals, but the governments avoid any form of control in the direct running of the hospital or practitioner services, even where it was meeting the bulk of their cost from central funds, as in Spain and Italy.

Bevan's final decision was to finance the service out of general taxation, but the calculations on which this was based would be undermined through basic misconceptions by the economists of the time, including Beveridge. They advised there would be a falling need for healthcare after an initial backlog had been cleared, due to the improved health of the nation. In reality demand would accelerate, with the cost in the first year double that anticipated, and continue to rise by 5% per annum in real terms. The main pressure would fall onto the inherited hospital services, which were already in a poor state and badly in need of additional funding. Instead, a financial crisis imposed a government standstill on all non-essential services. This included capital spending on hospitals, which fell to a third of the level before nationalisation. No new hospital would be built within the first ten years of the National Health Service and any money spent would be on a patch-and-mend level.

All alternative sources of finance on which both voluntary and municipal hospitals relied had dried up. Guy's had been founded by the generosity of a single donor and most of the major voluntary hospitals contained a wing, nurses' home or ward that carried the name of a benefactor. Rebuilds, as at St Thomas's move to Westminster in 1871, would be the result of a general money-raising project from the public, or a specific fund such as Florence Nightingale's, which was diverted to the establishment of her nursing school, or Queen Victoria's Anniversary Fund.

In the municipal sector the local authorities, supported by a 40% contribution from the State, had previously funded the running costs from the rates. Equally important was the loss of the means-tested contributions from patients or their relatives for treatment in both voluntary and municipal hospitals. Another was the fund-raising activities of all the performing arts for the voluntary hospitals, dating back to Hogarth and Handel's support for the Foundling Hospital. Large individual charity donations and artistic fund-raising continued, but the money was diverted from support for hospitals to education, international relief for famine and children's charities.

From the start the Treasury's allocation was only a fraction of that needed to develop the NHS, and the gap would widen over the years. In the rest of Western Europe, led by France and Germany, expenditure would rise steadily by 10% per annum to reach over 8% of gross national domestic product, in 1989 £1,500 per head of population, compared with under £1,000 in Britain, most of which was on running costs, with less than 4% going into capital investment in new hospitals and stock. As an end result the number of hospital beds and doctors per 100,000 of population was half the Western Europe average, lengthening waiting lists for hospital appointments and treatment and putting limitations on the range of services that could be provided.

Far from the theory that health service expenditure would become reduced, it steadily rose during the first 50 years to over £50 billion a year – 20 times the initial cost after allowing for inflation – and a further boost of £20 billion is planned over the next few years. One reason has been the steady overall increase in life expectancy, with more people living longer to take advantage of the major advances in medical and surgical treatment for the ageing. Half of overall expenditure is on the acute services, hospitals remaining the main source in spite of some transfer to the primary practitioner care. The biggest single item, accounting for two thirds overall, is salaries for staff, half of which are nurses and midwives.

Another major source of expenditure for the NHS is pharmaceuticals, which now account for over 15% of the overall budget and half the family health cost. In the 19th century, as medical duties were separated, the hospital apothecary had become a pharmacist within his own department, purchasing the raw materials to make up prescriptions for the patients, who would queue up in hundreds in a waiting hall and often pay a few pence. Behind the pharmacy front would be a manufacturing background with all the machinery and equipment to make up all their tablets, pills and potions. Some would publish their own pharmacopoeia containing many complex formulations. At the time of the establishment of the NHS many of these pharmacies continued and much of the medication that passed across the pharmacist's or GP's counter was a placebo with little active content. There was a limited range of active drugs derived from plants, such as morphia and digitalis, or from animal tissues, such as insulin or thyroid.

Synthetic medicinal chemistry began in the later part of the 19th century and led to the first sulphonamides in 1935. By 1948 penicillin and streptomycin were in use and during the next decades there was a flood of new drugs that would control many of the common medical conditions such as asthma and blood pressure. Medical control of psychiatric illness would lead to the emptying and closure of the large asylums, whilst a wide range of antibiotics and vaccination to control infectious diseases resulted in the closure of fever hospitals.

The new drugs were expensive, forcing rising prescription charges, and the pharmaceutical industry flourished amid increasing criticism as drugs bills rose by 10% per annum. Although there was a voluntary Pharmaceutical Regulation Scheme with which the industry co-operated, it was considered ineffective in price control by the House of Commons Public Accounts Committee. The industry's defence was the cost of research and development, which accounted for 10–15% of costs, and the vast extent of clinical trials to try out new drugs. In fact these were often merely developments of old ones for which the patent had expired, thus allowing unbranded generic forms. Alongside the rising cost of pharmaceuticals was the development of investigation techniques such as scanning, endoscopy and laboratory tests, which would increase the cost of patient-screening.

There has always been a big difference in the running costs of individual hospitals. In 1857 the annual level per patient ranged from 18s at Guy's to 4s 4d at the Royal Free and University College. Within the NHS, initially there was considerable criticism of the cost and the numbers in hospital management, which ballooned out of hand under the earlier administration of Regional Hospital Boards. The changes in the administrative structure have reduced the increase, which in 2001 was 4.2% of the total budget, down from 5% two years before, and a fraction of the cost of running the medical system in the USA, where there is major private involvement.

One major change has been the relationship with the private financial sector, which has become steadily closer over recent years. Initially the association was in non-clinical services such as cleaning and catering, but now this is being extended. As an alternative to direct State finance, hospitals are being added to the list of public sector capital projects such as schools and transport which are financed by the banks and other groups under the term 'Private Finance Initiative'. As well as the capital involved, developmental and management services are becoming included.

Overall, the NHS budget grew by 21.5% to £51 billion between 1999 and 2002, although critics point out the number of managers has risen by 3,000 alongside an increase of only 1.5% in the number of patients treated. There has also been increased referral by the NHS of patients to the private sector for treatment within areas where facilities do not exist, as in acute mental illness, or have become overwhelmed, as in orthopaedic and cardiac surgery. Patients are being diverted to private hospital facilities or even to hospitals in France and elsewhere in Europe for joint replacements and by-pass operations. Mobile units are being brought over from South Africa and elsewhere to undertake simpler procedures, confining the home facilities to the more complex cases.

Chapter 17

The First 50 Years

During its earlier years the NHS was regarded with respect by the rest of the world for offering high-quality care economically. Now it is subject to general criticism, not least internally, led by its own medical and nursing staff; some consultants refer to the hospital system as a bureaucracy on the point of collapse.

At the onset standards of health care available across the country were very variable, ranging from excellent to deplorable, and the NHS gave the chance to level upwards. Instead there has been a general lowering of standards compared with other leading industrial countries, and the United Kingdom has drifted towards the bottom of the health care league. Overall, national spending is only two thirds of the average, with the number of doctors and hospital beds available as low as half the ratio elsewhere. This is reflected in the worst recorded figures for deaths from heart disease and breast and overall forms of cancer.

One outstanding feature remains, the immense variation in standards of care and outcome across the hospital board. An independent organisation that has focused on the analysis of these differences is Dr Foster's Ethics Committee, established to provide information on the performance of health bodies and professionals. Members, including leading professionals in all aspects of health care, prepared a *Good Hospital Guide*, which was published in *The Mail on Sunday* in March 2002. They assessed a wide range of criteria to award each hospital a star rating for its overall performance, compiling their information from a range of sources, including questionnaires to both NHS and private hospitals, who co-operated fully.

The criteria were comprehensive and the guide covered over 400 hospitals in a detailed individual analysis of best standards, showing up great variations across the board in waiting lists for surgery and outcomes. One particular feature was the death rate index across a six-year period, allowing fully for age, sex and condition, to give a national average, and this found the level in the worst hospitals to be double that in the best. There would appear to be a range of reasons, with the main one insufficient financing resulting in inadequate levels of medical and nursing staff. This would lead to low care standards, with longer trolley waits before admission for emergency surgery and administration of anti-coagulant treatment for coronary thrombosis. Upgrading staffing levels and intensive care facilities with extra beds and up-to-date equipment could bring about a great improvement and reduce death rates by over a third. The use of day-case surgery, which is of much greater convenience to patients, could range from 2% to 81% for hernia operations, whilst patients' complaints about their level of care ranged from one to seven per 1,000. The guide ends by giving ten tips as to how to get the promptest and best treatment from the NHS.

Only 2 out of 218 NHS hospitals achieved a ten-star rating, both run by the Bart's and Royal London Trust. Of the 14 others awarded eight or nine stars, 5 teaching hospitals and the Central Middlesex were also London-based. Only single star status was achieved by 17 hospitals, and in some of these the death rate was double that in the best. The evident explanations were underfunding and lower staffing levels; however, some had a high local incidence of social deprivation and ill health and a lack of hospices in the area.

These results have to be compared with the quality control system of star awards introduced by the NHS itself two years before and reviewed annually. The best performers would receive a three-star rating, whilst those reaching reasonable standards overall would be awarded two stars. One- and zero-rated Trusts would be giving cause for concern. There were nine key targets initially, with failure in any one leading to loss of a star. These included a maximum waiting time of 18 months for any surgery and below 15 months average, which were largely achieved within a year, as was reduction of a maximum trolley wait of 12 hours before a patient was dealt with in the casualty and emergency department. Less successful was the target of a two-week maximum wait for a patient to be seen for cancer screening and cancelled operations.

The approach has been a carrot-and-stick one, with three-star hospitals to be awarded an extra million pounds a year in their budget to extend their services, and low performers given three months to improve or be faced with a management takeover from within the NHS or the private sector. A hit team has been formed, with eight private companies asked to bid competitively with NHS teams to run zero-rated hospitals for performance-related bonuses. This has already

'Waiting to see the Doctor', a study at the Seamen's Hospital Dispensary, Well Street, London Docks.

An engraving from 'The Graphic' showing patients in the new Out-Patients room of UCH in January 1872.

led to the private sector being accused of recruiting NHS managers who take early retirement.

The review after the first year showed little overall change, although the hospitals were now assessed on a total of 37 yardsticks. Of 166 acute hospitals, half remained unchanged, although the number with two or three stars had improved slightly, whilst 8 remained zero-rated against 12 the year before.

The emphasis on politically sensitive waiting times inevitably led to distortion of figures by some hospital managements exposed by the Audit Commission, who carried out spot checks. It found up to a third had made 'inappropriate adjustments', a synonym for 'massaging their books'. Firstly a hidden waiting list emerged in three stages. The first was ballooning the waiting time for the general practitioner to obtain an outpatient consultation for his patient, followed by a delay in the essential diagnostic tests such as endoscopy or tomography or magnetic resonance imaging. There could be a variation from a few weeks to over a year from district to district, along with delay in radio-therapy after cancer surgery. Alongside this was the management pressure on consultants to give priority to simpler procedures, such as cataract operations, and criticising surgeons for devoting too much attention to complex long-term cases. The result was a temporary reduction of 100,000 in the waiting list, but this was short-lived and soon rose back above a million.

There was a big exercise in damage limitation to reassure patients that a low star rating for their local hospital did not mean their standards were low or care and services unsafe. Whilst the staff might be personally doing a good, conscientious job, it was organisational services that were in need of improvement. In an effort to try and improve overall performance and equalise standards across the country, an extra £20 billion pounds was poured into the NHS from 2000 to 2004, to bring expenditure up towards the average for Europe as a whole, but critics have emphasised that in itself this is not a solution. Expenditure has increased fourfold since the 1960s with little improvement in patient turnover; most of the money has been swallowed in wage increases and management charges as a result of centrally imposed targets.

The promised extra money was accompanied by a wave of new high targets affecting all areas, from correcting the shortage of doctors and nurses to the ambulance services, all generally criticised by their professional bodies. The BMA Consultants Committee considered the flood of performance measures would destabilise the service, and the Royal College of Nursing that a rating which did not assess nursing care would do more harm than good.

In an attempt to control the use of the extra money, a new Commission for Health Care Inspection was established, given powers similar to the Schools Inspectorate, to inspect all hospital and health care practices and present a report on their efficiency.

A feature during the first 50 years of the NHS has been the changes in management systems brought about by alterations in political mood, but retaining central control and financing by the Ministry of Health remain the dominant features. In time the emphasis moved towards improved performance, with any new developments in the service having to be funded by overall cost savings in place of extra money.

Although doctors became involved in management, this also meant they became answerable for their use of resources. Another cause for resentment has been increasing intrusion on judgement of their clinical standards as a number of cases of failure were highlighted, leading to the establishment of a National Institute for Clinical Excellence to supervise the quality of clinical services throughout the NHS, covering individual illness, such as cancer and heart disease, to overall care for children and the elderly.

After the creation of NHS Trusts an initial period of competition developed into a longer-term relationship between the Trusts and the purchasing authorities, co-operating in programmes to modernise the service and improve overall quality and availability. Under the banner 'The New NHS', the emphasis was to move away from competitiveness towards co-operation in research and a development programme in health care and a broader assessment in relation to access and delivery, along with patient experience and health outcome across the board. The Trusts had considerable financial freedom to hire and fire staff and borrow money, but overall had to balance their books, which could lead to individual crises through mismanagement, as in the commercial world.

As local management accumulated increasing powers, relationship with the medical and nursing staff within the hospitals became increasingly strained, with many consultants dissatisfied with their conditions of service and lack of up-to-date facilities deserting the NHS in favour of the private sector. Another cause for discontent has been the increase in paperwork for administrative demands that could take up

403

to half a consultant's time, whilst internal inefficiency leading to missing notes and hunting for test results could take up half the time of 8.2 minutes allotted for each consultation.

The financial freedom for Trusts led many to extend their range and District General Hospitals to develop local specialist services such as cardiac and urological surgery or radiotherapy which would previously only have been available at more distant regional or university hospitals. Teaching Hospital Trusts, because of high overheads and managerial complexity, would face increasing competition and were especially vulnerable, but remained essential for training junior doctors and had to open their doors more widely and develop highly specialised areas.

Some Acute Hospital Trusts would develop private patient units on site in competition with private hospitals, but overall the bed shortage and waiting times ensured more NHS patients were referred into the private area by fund-holders.

In spite of the extra money being poured into future development of the NHS, financial restrictions became inevitable as the demand increased. One of the restrictions would be rationing of services in some areas of both surgery and medicine, with the decision in the hands of regional authorities, leading to variations in selection. In the surgical field, infertility treatment availability varies widely, whilst cosmetic treatment is generally excluded from the plastic surgery area. Even more prolific had been the expansion of the pharmaceutical industry, which now accounts for over 15 per cent of overall expenditure within the NHS and half of that within the family health services. As the budget accelerated, Bevan had noted within a few months of the initiation of the NHS that he 'shuddered to think of the ceaseless cascade of medicine which is poured down British throats at the present time', and this was when effective medicines were restricted to a narrow range. Now this is limitless and constantly expanding at increasing cost, so that the availability of some, such as drugs for impotence, being restricted.

One overall result of the partial diversion of management from central to the periphery was an immense increase in local managers, who now outnumber hospital beds and approach the total of the million nurses employed within the NHS. At all levels there are now eight managers employed to every ten nurses, four times the level within the private sector, and overall 5% of total expenditure. Some idea of the waste can be estimated from a government target to free a billion pounds from bureaucratic expenditure over a five-year period.

There is also considerable criticism of management for the standard of services such as cleaning and catering, and the use of facilities. The deficiencies include utilisation of operating theatre time and supply of the necessary nursing and intensive care staff, organisation of out-patients, admissions and investigation services and supply of adequate equipment. They are also vulnerable to outside pressures ranging from central directives to failures in local community services. A recent release by the National Audit Office, which acts as a public police force, showed 4,000 acute hospital beds were blocked daily by elderly people who were fit for release, but could not be found care homes by their local authority at a cost of £1 million a day.

Overall, the 50 years would end with the politicians and the professionals at loggerheads as to the best programme for the future of the NHS, with a wealth of advice for the future.

Chapter 18

Hospitals in the Future

The NHS treats over one million patients a day and faces the future with a Government guarantee to raise the level of funding towards the European average. There has been no shortage of advice in the Minister's in-tray from well-intentioned sources, covering all aspects from financing to overall control and local management, as to how to restore its initial reputation for high-quality health care.

One overriding theme has been the need to reduce the role of Government control right down the line. The NHS has been through a series of phases since its initiation. It began in a post-war period when food and fuel were rationed, with a general shortage of housing and an economic crisis. For the first time all aspects of health care had been brought together and from the beginning Bevan realised, in spite of the beliefs of the economic pundits of the time, that there would be no limit to public demand, which almost always exceeds capacity. There were no funds to meet the increases, and the facilities would remain unchanged, to leave a widening gap that has faced the politicians ever since. As a nationalised monopoly, it remained vulnerable to political pressure and exposed to media publicity over any incidents of unsatisfactory care.

Criticism has been general and widespread from the professional bodies, such as the British Medical Association and Royal Colleges and a number of independent 'think-tanks' that have reviewed the overall situation. One source of condemnation has been the heavy central hand of authority issuing reports and targets, but in practice the NHS has remained a wasteful and inefficient organisation.

One of the review bodies was the Health Policy Group of the Centre for Policy Studies, which invited a team of experts with a range of interests to review the situation. The main conclusion was that the extra money in itself was not the only answer, but there had to be a radical change from a nationalised bureaucracy to a system of self-governing specialist and community hospitals. There could be a choice for patients to transfer part of their NHS entitlement into the private sector if preferred, raising standards all round. Increasingly they drew attention to the build-up of management at all levels, and at a recent review the Centre expressed fears that the extra money would be wasted in extra administration. Department of Health statistics indicate health service managers have already increased by over 30% over the past 13 years, whilst hospital beds have dropped by 20%, halving the number per administrator to under six. Now the number of managers matches that of trained nurses and the total of management staff at all levels accounts for a quarter of the total work force.

The Adam Smith Institute, an organisation concerned with an overall review, advocated everyone should be covered for health care by insurance through a range of providers, with the premiums of those on low incomes covered by the Government, whose role would be reduced to a regulator policing policy standards and ensuring a fair balance between the purchasing insurance companies and hospital providers.

The King's Fund is a think-tank specifically concerned with health affairs, especially in London, and characterised the NHS as suffering from the 'dropped bedpan' syndrome, with even the minutest details of care subjected to overall Whitehall oversight and interference. It attacked the 'torrent of pledges, policy documents, regulations and advice and guidance that has issued from the Department of Health since 1977' which wasted time and resources on the front line and demoralised doctors and nurses.

This chorus of criticism was joined by all the bodies representing doctors and nurses. In December 2001 the President of the Royal College of Surgeons described the NHS as a second-class service where the demand for surgery outstripped capacity, which was restricted by the shortage of beds and operating theatres, surgeons and anaesthetists, whilst much of their equipment was out of date. Government plans to increase the number of consultants by 7,500 within the next four years could not be met because of lack of places for training and the shortfall would have to be met from overseas recruits. He forecast a change in pattern with smaller elective surgery, such as hernia and varicose vein repairs, carried out in smaller district hospitals, whilst major surgery would have to move to larger regional centres and surgeons move between the two.

One particular area of debate has been the background of funding the service. The King's Fund alone was supportive of the existing system of payment through general taxation as being most efficient and fairest, but considered the role of central government should be restricted to funding and overall policy for strategy and ethical framework for health care. Local care provision and day-to-day management should be separated and passed across to the front line staff and the community they served.

There has been a great deal of support for a change in the funding system towards the commoner practice across Europe, where the money for health care is collected from the employer and employee on a national insurance scheme, deducted at source, by which each pays an equal percentage of salary. This would be 'ring-fenced' under separate management, and unemployed and pensioners would be covered by the State. Advocates claim people are prepared to pay more where they can 'identify the benefit', but the cost can be high. France is considered to have one of the best medical systems in the world, with a high ratio of doctors and beds and no waiting times, but the national insurance takes up to 20% of salaries and is held accountable for a high level of unemployment. There are also gaps in cover, which is only some 70% of health care. It includes surgery and hospital care almost completely, but only one third of the cost of visits to the GP or specialist when the patient is free to choose their doctor. However, patients must pay in advance and then reclaim from the fund, and dental and optical care is not covered. The balance may be covered by 'mutually' private insurance paid by the employer or individual, but overall the system is the most expensive in the world to run, with high administration costs, excessive red tape and unrestrained demand.

In Germany the pattern is similar, with some 14% of salaries diverted into a separate fund by equal contributions from employer and employee, although higher earners can opt to divert to a private insurance scheme. Social insurance covers some 60% of cost, with 21% paid direct by the taxpayer, and another 11% for 'hotel' and prescription charges. Unemployed and disabled are covered by the State and it is possible to take extra insurance to cover the choice of specialist and a single room. The patient can choose their hospital, to induce competition, but the system is expensive as it carries an unnecessary layer of specialists based in their own offices, rather than hospitals, whom the patient can contact direct. Conditions in hospitals are of the highest standards of cleanliness, with an over-capacity of doctors and beds and no waiting times, and they are equipped with the latest IT, allowing details of individual patients to be mapped onto a central nurses' station.

The hospitals themselves may be funded from the national insurance funds or receive State support, but are managed locally through the fund, or by traditional charitable or church organisations which take out 'not-for-profit' contracts as suppliers, with standards and fees regulated by a National Health Tariff Authority, but again the system is expensive to run. The health services of Sweden and Denmark are largely centrally tax funded, but power is diverted to the periphery, where hospitals and trusts compete.

The Adam Smith Institute went further and advocated an overall social insurance scheme, of which health care would form part. Everyone would be required to buy this from one of a number of providers and the cost would be met by a tax deduction equal to the present payment towards the NHS, with the contribution from low-income earners paid by the Government. Such a system would increase competition between insurers and providers to supply the most cost-effective treatment.

The NHS Plan in July 2000 promised a 6.3% increase in funding over five years and an action plan ten years ahead, with an ambitious range of targets from extra hospitals and beds, with more doctors and nurses to shorten waiting times at all stages of care. Hospital facilities would be raised, with better food and cleaner wards and more attention given to the patient. The changes would be led by a Modernisation Board that would include leading members of health care institutions such as the Royal Colleges, NHS managers and patient representatives, and be headed by the Health Secretary. There would also be ten 'task forces' to focus on individual areas of improvement.

Two years later, Derek Wanless, a banker commissioned to examine the trends that could affect the health service over the next 20 years, published a review estimating the resources that would be required to catch up and continue to match the services in other leading countries and meet Government targets for improvement. It estimated the increase in resources required would average 7.1–7.3% over the next five years, double the level over the previous 20 years. It also reckoned overall an extra 62,000 doctors and 108,000 nurses would be required, and half of these would not be provided by the training facilities. The problem was aggravated by the programme to restrict the excessive time worked by junior doctors to 48 hours a week and the need for doctors and nurses to more than double – to 10% – the limited time spent on clinical governance to ensure up-to-date best practice.

A great deal of thought and planning has gone into measures to cope with the forecast shortfall in key front-line staff, causing considerable controversy within the professions. Although forecasts for nurses starting training were optimistic with Project 2000, loss overseas to the USA and Australia for improved conditions and pay are proving high, the overall number has increased from overseas immigrants; up to a quarter of nurses in London hospitals are from abroad. The problem to meet the shortage of doctors is more intractable.

One plan is to adjust the barriers between the front-line professionals. Extra training would allow nurses to prescribe some medicines and carry out minor surgery to relieve the general practitioner and casualty officer. Already Accident and Emergency waiting times are being reduced through an initial assessment of casualties by a higher-trained nurse who can categorise their urgency and need for medical care. In turn, care assistants can learn new skills and take on some nursing duties. At consultant level, there are proposals to reduce training time from six to five years before the Royal College issues a certificate entitling a doctor to apply for consultant posts; at present this is a year longer in the UK than on the Continent or in the USA. Currently the overall training time for the highest specialist levels can be as long as 13 years, and there have been proposals to reduce this, although there is total opposition to the creation of a junior 'sub-consultant level'. It may, however, be possible for a trained general practitioner to develop the ability to carry out some surgical or specialist medical duties, as was commonplace in the days of the local cottage hospitals. There are also plans to increase the number of overall vacancies at medical schools, reduce training time through an allowance for previous study courses and restrict the number of overseas students who return home after completion of training.

The Government has committed itself to a range of targets to bring the NHS back to high standards of quality care and has undertaken a lot of measures towards this. One of the main ones is a reduction in waiting times across the board, from a GP visit through to specialist consultation and investigation at hospital, admission for surgery and trolley times in Accident and Emergency. To a great extent these are in the hands of the management teams and medical staff concerned. With more co-operation and cuts in red tape to monitor performance, significant reforms could be made.

The consequences of delay in treatment can range from a year or more of pain and discomfort for those in need of orthopaedic care to a fatal outcome for those awaiting cardiac surgery or cancer treatment. Besides a waiting list of over a million for in-patient treatment, another quarter of a million are waiting for MRI and CT scans or diagnostic endoscopy through lack of the necessary equipment or skilled technicians, and the solution to waiting times is not entirely extra hospital beds. In the USA, the number of beds relative to population is much lower than in the UK, but there is no delay in screening due to the diagnostic facilities outside the hospital service. This is because of the predominant private sector, where health care expenditure is double, although some 15% of people have no insurance and are dependent on some form of medicare.

In a recent annual report the Department of Health has emphasised the amount being spent on the new equipment necessary for clinical investigation. Another area of equal importance for the future is the use of day surgery. Advances in surgery and anaesthesia and keyhole surgery through a laparoscope have extended the list of operations where this is possible, ranging from removal of cataracts and gall bladders to hernia repairs, bladder and gynaecological investigations and orthopaedic exploration. The use of these day techniques varies widely from region to region, as high as 65% of operations in some, down to much less elsewhere. It is thought the figures could be raised to 75% of all surgery, and up to 19 specialist 'fast-track' diagnostic and treatment centres are about to be opened which could treat an extra 25,000 cases a year.

To attract doctors towards a career within the NHS, new terms of service for both GPs and specialists have been proposed. However, the proposals for consultants have proved especially controversial. At present their hospital sessions and on-call days are fixed, leaving them free to organise the rest of their time for private work and make their own arrangements for overall cover. The new plans would require consultants to increase their weekly hours and give the NHS first call on weekends and evenings, with loss of personal control. The intrusion is considered aggressive micro-management and has led to a proposal that consultants should organise themselves into barrister-like chambers and form groups that would compete for work from the Trusts.

A proposal put forward by the Government in the Queen's Speech in November 2002 is the creation of a new class of Foundation Hospital as not-for-profit public interest companies, on the model of those providing a range of other services from housing and education to care homes and prisons. It was originally planned to open the first 12 by April 2004, funded by borrowings from banks and other investors through the Private Finance Initiative – or the issue of bonds by the local authority or hospital itself, as is common in the USA, which allows more freedom of movement. However, any borrowing arrangements would attract ultimate Treasury control, and responsibility for repayments would remain on the public sector balance sheet and be funded from the Department of Health capital budget. This gives Whitehall the power to limit overall borrowing, and the individual hospitals would have to approach an independent regulator as to the amount they could safely borrow.

The hospitals will be given an operating licence that makes their primary purpose as serving the needs of NHS patients, but also includes an unspecified 'wider public benefit duty' which could cover such matters as cancer screening facilities or health care for specific conditions. The running of the hospital would be by local management, which would be free to innovate and adapt to local needs, to engage and sack staff, buy new equipment and create new specialist treatment centres. The running would be 'overseen' by a 'Stakeholders Council' that had representatives of the local community and staffing at all levels and was not directly accountable to the Department of Health.

Some doubt has been expressed as to the number of managers capable of coping with the increased responsibility, as their funding would still depend on achieving targets in relation to waiting times and numbers. This would leave management exposed to temptation to 'adjust their book-keeping', which one in twelve admitted doing on at least one occasion; however, under a new code they would be liable to be sacked for manipulation of waiting lists. This new code also contracts chief executives and senior managers to a formidable range of responsibilities across the board, from acting with integrity to accepting responsibility for their own decisions and the performance of their staff, with whom they should co-operate in a team relationship. Of great importance is the safety of patients and developing a good relationship down the line with their relatives and carers in the community. There has been anxiety that the new Foundation Hospitals would become elite and create a two-tier level of care.

Another area of closer communication has been with the private sector. In its programme to reduce waiting times the Government has introduced a pilot scheme in London, whereby after an operation waiting time of six months, the patient can opt whether to continue on the list in their own area, move to a Trust with a shorter time lag, or be treated in a private or overseas clinic through the NHS. Agreement has been reached with the Belgian health authorities to treat 1,000 patients at a fixed tariff, similar to an agreement with the French medical service. The scheme covers some 65% of surgical procedures including hip replacements, cataracts, coronary by-pass and other routine procedures. The scheme was to be extended throughout the South-East and was planned to become general by 2005. One possible proposal is for each patient to be given a voucher which can be used across the board in the NHS or discounted within the private sector.

Overall radical changes are planned in the hospital scenario, although these are unlikely to affect central funding as the Treasury insists on ultimate control of expenditure.

There is increased acceptance that more direct control has to be passed down the line to the hospital level with the authority to manage their services through Trusts. This has led to fears that the extra money to be pumped into the NHS will be squandered on increased expenditure on staffing at all levels rather than more hospital beds or improved services. Local management in particular has greatly increased under a range of labels from information analysts and service planners to collaborative facilitators and patient access managers. Overall, managers and their support staff now outnumber qualified nurses. The central authority has retained overall responsibility for standards.

Measures to improve these have ranged from the award of Foundation status to a restricted number of hospitals to a star system of awards based on a limited range of assessment criteria applied to all. The star system has been shown to have limitations and is likely to be modified. Particular problems have arisen as services have been passed on to outside contractors, particularly in relation to hygiene standards and the level of hospital infection.

Audits have shown a great variation in medical performance across the board, especially in surgery that has led to new contracts that define a level of performance. This has led to increasing professional antagonism with many consultants leaving the NHS to spend all their time in the private area. This has exaggerated an overall shortage in certain specialities, especially the orthopaedic, cardio-vascular and cataract surgery which are increasingly being filled from overseas.

Hospitals and GP's will soon be able to instantly exchange medical information about their patients through advances in information technology. As business practices become more integrated into the NHS, healthcare provision is expected to improve significantly.

Bibliography

Abel-Smith B. *The Hospitals 1800–1948* (Heinemann, 1964)

Allderidge P. *Bethlem Hospital 1247–1997. A Pictorial Record* (Phillimore, 1997)

Allderidge P. *The Bethlem Royal Hospital. An Illustrated History* (The Bethlem & Maudsley NHS Trust, 1995)

Ayres G.M. *England's First State Hospitals and the Metropolitan Asylum Board 1867–1930* (Wellcome Institute, 1971)

Baly M. *Nursing* (Batsford, 1977)

Barnes P. *The Royal Manchester Children's Hospital 'Pendlebury' 1829–1999* (Churnet Valley Books, 1999)

Barnes S. *The Birmingham Hospitals Centre* (Stanford & Mann, 1952)

Bell *The Story of Hospital Almoners* (Faber & Faber, 1961)

Best S.H. *The Story of the British Red Cross* (Cassell & Co, 1938)

Birmingham *The Diana Princess of Wales Children's Hospital. A Special Place* (Assorted Images, 2000)

Blomfield J. *St George's 1733–1933* (The Medici Society, 1933)

Boulay S. *Cicely Saunders* (Hodder & Stoughton, 1984)

Bowman G. *The Lamp and the Book: The Story of the RCN 1916–1966* (Queen Anne Press, 1967)

British Dental Association *The Advance of the Dental Profession.* (1979)

BMA *History of the British Medical Association. 2 vols: 1832–1932; 1932–1981* (BMA,1982)

Brockbank W. *Portrait of a Hospital: Royal Infirmary Manchester 1752–1948* (Heinemann, 1952)

Brown K. *St Mary's Hospital, An Illustrated History* (London 1991)

Browne O.T.D. *The Rotunda Hospital 1745–1945* (E & S Livingstone Ltd, 1947)

Buckstone-Browne *University College Medical School* (Common Room, 1937)

Cameron H.C. *Mr Guy's Hospital 1726–1948* (Endowments Committee, 1954)

Cholmeley J.A. *History of the Royal National Orthopaedic Hospital* (Chapman & Hall, 1985)

Clark-Kennedy A.E. *The London, 2 vols: 1740–1840; 1840–1948* (Pitman Medical, 1962)

Cope Z. *History of St Mary's Hospital Medical School* (Heinemann, 1954)

Crompton F. *Workhouse Children* (Sutton Publishing, 1997)

Davidson M. & Rouvray F.G. *The Brompton Hospital* (Lloyd-Luke, 1954)

Donnison *Midwives and Medical Men* (Heinemann, 1988)

Evans A.D. & Howard G.R. *The Romance of the British Voluntary Hospital Movement* (Hutchinson, c 1930)

French C.H. *The Story of St.Luke's Hospital 1750–1948* (Heinemann, 1951)

Frischauer W. *The Clinic: A Case History of the London Clinic* (Cape, 1967)

The Governors *Saint Bartholomew's Hospital 1123–1961 (1961)*

Granshaw L. & Porter R. *The Hospital in History* (Wellcome Institute, 1989)

Granshaw L. *St Mark's Hospital, London* (King Edward's Hospital Fund, 1985)

Graves C. *The Story of St Thomas's 1106–1947* (Faber & Faber, 1947)

Gray J.D.A. *The Central Middlesex Hospital* (Pitman, 1963)

Grey-Turner E. & Sutherland F.M. *History of the BMA 2 vols.* (BMA, 1982)

Guy's Hospital *250 Years* (Guy's Hospital Gazette, 1976)

Haggard H.W. *Devils, Drugs and Doctors* (Harper & Brothers, 1929)

Hall F.M. et al. *The Kent and Canterbury Hospital 1790–1987* (Kent Postgraduate Medical Centre, 1987)

Harrison A. and Dixon J. *The NHS Facing the Future* (King's Fund, 2000)

Hart F. *The Roots of Service, A History of Charing Cross Hospital 1818–1974* (Trustees, 1985)

Higgins T.T. *Great Ormond Street 1852–1952* (Oldhams, 1952)

Hough R. *Sister Agnes* (Murray, 1998)

Humble J.G. and Hansell P. *The Westminster Hospital 1716–1966* (Pitman, 1966)

Ives X. *British Hospitals: Britain in Pictures* (Collins, 1948)

Jameson E. *The Natural History of Quackery* (M. Joseph, 1961)

Jewsbury *The Royal Northern Hospital 1856–1956* (H. K. Lewis, 1956)

Jones T.B. and Collins W.J.T. *History of the Royal Gwent Hospital* (Trustees, 1948)

Kosky J. & Lunnon R.J. *Great Ormond Street and the Story of Medicine* (Hospitals for Sick Children, 1991)

Langdon-Davies J. *Westminster Hospital 1719–1948* (J. Murray, 1952)

LCC Hospitals *A Retrospect* (Staples Press, 1949)

—— *London Hospital Illustrated, 250 Years* (Batsford, 1990)

MacManus E. *Matron of Guy's* (Melrose, 1956)

Masters A. *Bedlam* (Joseph, 1977)

McInnes E.M. *St Thomas's Hospital* (Allen & Unwin, 1963)

McMenemey W.H. *Worcester Royal Infirmary* (Press Alliances, 1947)

Medvei V.C. and Thornton J.L. *The Royal Hospital of Saint Bartholomew 1123–1973* (1974)

Merrington W.R. *University College Hospital and Its Medical School* (Heinemann, 1976)

Minney R.J. *The Two Pillars of Charing Cross* (Cassell, 1967)

Moore N. *History of Saint Bartholomew's Hospital,* 2 vols. (Pearson, 1918)

—— *Moorfields Eye Hospital. A Century of City Road* (1999)

Morris E.W. *A History of the London Hospital* (Edward Arnold, 1910)

Nuffield Provincial Hospitals Trust *Medical History and Medical Care* (1971)

O'Neill C. *A Picture of Health* (Meadow Books, 1990)

Orme N. & Webster W. *The English Hospital 1070–1570* (Yale University Press, 1995)

Ormrod & Walker *The National Health Service* (Butterworth, 1950)

Parsons F.G. *The History of St Thomas's Hospital* 3 vols (Methuen & Co., 1932)

Pavey R. *The Growth of Nursing* (Faber & Faber, 1938)

Porter R. *Man Forged Manacles* (Athlone Press, 1987)

Porter R. *Madness* (OUP, 2002)

Power D'Arcy & Waring H.J. *History of Saint Bartholomew's Hospital 1123–1923* (1923)

Poynter F.N.L. *The Evolution of Hospitals in Britain* (Pitman Medical, 1964)

Railton M. and Barr M. *The Royal Berkshire Hospital 1839–1989* (Royal Berkshire, 1989)

Ranger D. *Middlesex Hospital Medical School* (Hutchinson, 1985)

Rhodes P. *Dr John Leake's Hospital* (Heinemann, 1950)

Richards T. *Medicine in Europe* (BMJ, 1992)

419

Richardson *The English Hospital 1660–1948* (Royal Commission on the Historical Monuments of Britain, 1998)

Ripman *Guy's Hospital 1725–1948* (Hospital Gazette Committee, 1951)

Rivett G. *From Cradle to Grave* (King's Fund 1997)

Robertson E. *The Yorkhill Story* (Board of Management, 1972)

Robinson *Hospital Administration* (Butterworth, 1966)

—— *St George's Hospital and Medical School and Associated Hospitals 1933–1983* (Trustees, 1983)

Sandwich F. *Compassionate Surgeon, Story of Dr William Marsden* (Davies, 1960)

Saunders H. St G. *The Middlesex* (Max Parrish, 1949)

Saunders C. *Hospice, The Living Idea* (Saunders, 1981)

Shepherd J.A. *A History of the Liverpool Medical Institution* (Library, 1979)

Shepherd M.P. *Heart of Harefield The Story of the Hospital* (Quiller Press, 1990)

Skinner E.F. *The Sheffield Royal Hospital 1832–1932* (Board of Management, 1932)

Spurgeon P. *The New Face of the NHS* (RSM, 1998)

Stancliffe F.S. *The Manchester Royal Eye Hospital 1814–1964* (University Press, 1964)

Stoddard D.D. *The Hospice Movement* (Cape, 1978)

Talbot *Medicine in Medieval England* (Oldbourne, 1967)

Trevelyan *English Social History* (Longmans, Green & Co. NY 1942)

Thompson C.J.S. *The Quacks of Old London* (Brontano's, 1928)

Vaughan P. *Short History of The BMA* (Heinemann, 1959)

Wallis *Story of the School of Pharmacy* (Pharmaceutical Press, 1964)

Watkin *Documents on Health and Social Services* (Methuen, 1975)

Whitteridge G. & Stokes V. *A Brief History of the Hospital of Saint Bartholomew* (The Governors, 1961)

Wiltshaw B. *History of the Royal Marsden Hospital* (Altman Publishers, 1998)

Wise A.R.J. *Your Hospital: Heritage and Future* (Heinemann, 1949)

Yeo *Climate and Health Resorts* (Chapman & Hall, 1885)

Index of Illustrations

All Saints Convalescent Hospital, Eastbourne 366
Ambulance, horse-drawn, 1886 170
Ancient methods of hastening labour 239
Antiseptics surgery 141
Apothecary 303

Bethlem Mental Hospital 281, 283, 284
Birmingham Asylum for Destitute Children 160
Birmingham Children's Hospital 271, 272, 273
Birmingham General Hospital 99, 100, 101
Birmingham, Queen's Hospital 100
Birmingham Union Workhouse 155
Blackheath Hospital 299
BMI Esperance Hospital, Eastbourne 380
Bristol Royal Infirmary 88, 89
The Brompton Hospital 192

Canterbury Cathedral, Monastic Infirmary 1
Canterbury, St Nicholas Harbledown 10
Casualty Waiting Hall at St Thomas's Hospital 345
Charing Cross Hospital 111, 113, 116, 117, 118, 388
Charing Cross Hospital Medical School 115
Chelsea Hospital 180
Chelsea Hospital for Women 207
City of London Lying-in Hospital 240
City Orthopaedic Hospital 197
Colney Hatch Asylum 290
Cornerstones of Eighteenth Century Medicine 143
Cranleigh Village Hospital 220

Dublin Lying-in Hospital 236

Eastbourne District General Hospital 367
Edinburgh Medical School 307
Edinburgh Royal Infirmary 94, 306

Edinburgh, Surgeons' Hall 95
Eighteenth Century Hospital Scene 330
Elizabeth Garrett Anderson Hospital 131
Examination Hall of Medicine and Surgery 317

Foundling Hospital 252, 253

Glasgow Royal Infirmary 94
Gosport Hospital 179
Great Ormond Street Hospital for Children 256, 257, 258, 259, 260
'Great Surgeon, A' (Dr Bland Sutton) 318
Greenwich Hospital 178
Guy's Hospital 38, 46, 49

Halifax Union Infirmary 365
Hammersmith Hospital 362
Harefield Hospital 207, 208, 209, 210
Hospital for Diseases of the Throat 389
Hotel Dieu, Paris 327

Kent and Canterbury Hospital 92
King Edward VII's Hospital Sister Agnes, London 378
King's College Hospital 130, 387

Leicester Royal Infirmary 93
Liverpool Royal Infirmary 95, 96, 97
Lock Hospital 187
London Chest Hospital 195
London Homeopathic Hospital 205, 389
London Hospital 74, 76, 78, 390
London Hospital, a matron and sisters 348

Maidstone, Boniface Hospital 6
A man-midwife 232
Manchester Children's Hospital 263, 264
Manchester Royal Infirmary 97, 98, 99
Matron, the retirement of a 349
A mentally ill patient restrained 282

421

Merseyside Voluntary Hospitals 391
Middlesex Hospital 79, 80, 81, 82
A midwife going to attend a labour 233
Moorfields Eye Hospital 189
Mundesley Sanatorium 193

National Hospital for the Paralysed and
    Epileptic 203
National Orthopaedic Hospital 198
New Hospital for Women 389
New out-patients room of UCH in
    January 1872 401
Nissen huts 363

Obstetrical chairs 229, 230
'Orthodoxy' (Sir William Henry
    Broadbent) 319

Petersfield Cottage Hospital 221
Physician and patient of the sixteenth
    century 302
Portland Hospital for Women and
    Children 381
Princess Alice Memorial Hospital,
    Eastbourne 223
Princess Grace Hospital 382

Queen Charlotte's Hospital 247
Queen Victoria Hospital, East Grinstead
    225

Rahere Ward at St Bartholomew's
    Hospital 330
Red Cross ambulance during the Franco-
    Prussian War 356
Red Cross Hospital No.4 in the South
    African War 356
The Reward of Cruelty 310
Roehampton Priory 298
Rotunda Hospital 237, 238
Rowlandson: Nineteenth century hospital
    scene 137
Royal College of Nursing HQ, London
    352

Royal College of Nursing's Royal
    Charter 353
Royal Free Hospital 107, 108, 109, 110
Royal Hospital for Sick Children,
    Glasgow 267, 268, 269
Royal Hospital for Neuro-disability 211,
    212
Royal Marsden Hospital 201, 202
Royal National Orthopaedic Hospital
    199

St Bartholomew's Hospital 22, 50, 51, 53,
    54
St Edmundsbury Hospital 17
St George's Hospital 69, 70, 71, 72
St Luke's Hospital 287
St Mary's Hospital 121, 122
St Mary's Hospital Medical School 119,
    120
St Pancras Infirmary 163
St Thomas's Hospital 24, 34, 35, 36, 43,
    45, 48, 342, 345
St Thomas's Hospital, a ward in 345
Salisbury, St Nicholas Monastic
    Infirmary 2, 89, 90
Savoy Palace 16
Seamen's Hospital dispensary – waiting
    to see the doctor 401
Sheffield, Royal Infirmary 93
Social science, delegates attending a
    conference on 393
A student's certificate of attendance at
    lectures 309
Surgery before anaesthesia 140

University College Hospital, London 124,
    125, 126, 128, 129, 389, 401

The Wellington Hospital 382
Westminster Hospital 61, 63, 64, 65
Westminster Lying-in Hospital 243, 244
Willesden Parish Infirmary, a ward in
    346
Worcester Royal Infirmary 91

General Index

Abernethy, John 52, 53, 308, 309
Act of Settlement 1662 154
Adam Smith Institute 408, 410
age of hospitals, the 57
almshouses 15, 53
American Medical International 379
anaesthesia 44, 127
Anatomy Act 1832 312
antiseptic surgery 127, 140
Apothecaries, Society of 40, 57
Apothecary Act 1815 40, 304
apothecary, terms of service 41, 302, 304, 305
Armstrong Dr 253
asylums, private 285, 286, 287, 289, 291
Audit Commission 402
Augustine, St 2;
  Brothers of 14

Barber-Surgeons' Company 301
Bellers, John 133, 360
Benedict, St 2
Berry,James 308
Bevan, Aneurin 364, 365
Blizard, Dr 77
BMI Healthcare 380
Board of Lunacy Commissioners 175
Bonsor, Sir Cosmo 46
Borchardt, Dr 262
Bristowe and Holmes 139, 147
British Journal of Homeopathy 149, 150, 151
British Medical Association 363
British Medical Journal 186
British National Formulary (BNF) 142
British Postgraduate Medical School 320
British Pregnancy Advisory Services 384
British United Provident Association (BUPA) 378, 384
Burdett, Sir Henry 222

calomel purges 142
Canterbury 1
  Archbishop of 2
Capio Sweden 383

Chadwick, Edwin 156, 161, 162, 265
Chamberlen family 230, 231, 359
'chancery' priests 7
  chantry priests 5, 6, 9, 14
Charing Cross Railway Bill 42
charity fundraising 85
Charles II 142
Chatham Chest 178
Cheseldon, William 60
children's dispensaries 261, 262
children's surgery 273, 274, 275
cholera 77, 106, 134
Cholera Board 135
Conjoint Examinations Board 1884 316
Cooper, Sir Astley 39, 40, 312
Coram, Captain Thomas 252
corrody 7, 8
cottage hospitals 219 - 226
Cranleigh village hospital 220
Criminal Lunatic Act 1800, 1845 288, 289
Curie, Marie - Cancer 213
Cygnet Health Care 299

Davis, John Bunnell 254
Darenth 170, 171, 172, 175
Domesday Book 3
Dreadnought Hospital Ship 167
Dr Foster's Ethics Committee 399, 400

East London Nursing Society 344
Edinburgh Surgeons' Hall 95
Edinburgh University: foundation 306
Emergency Bed Service 370
Emergency Medical Service 363

Fabiola 325
Farr, William, Registrar-General 147
Fenwick, Ethel 346, 347, 348, 349, 350
Fleming, Sir Alexander 122
foundation hospitals 226
French hospital system 148, 149
Fry, Elizabeth 332
fundraising 85, 115

Galen 58, 183, 302
General Medical Council, medical
    register 1858 305
General Nursing Council 351
George III, porphyria 286
Golding, Benjamin 110, 111, 112
Goodenough Report 320
Grainger, Richard 41
Guillebaud Committee 370
Guinea Pig Club 225
Guy, Thomas 37

Hahnemann, Samuel 205
Halle, John 301
Hammersmith postgraduate medical
    centre 247, 320, 321
  rebuilding 321
  finances and management 321, 322, 323
Hardy, G 164, 165
Harrison, Benjamin 46
Henry VIII 17, 18
Help the Hospice, charity 213
Hislop, Dr T. P. 270
hospitals
  admissions policy 146, 147
  cleanliness 12
  diet 13
  diseases 137
  endowments 7
  financial corruption 14, 15
  funding 6, 7
  hospice 3
  hospital mortality 138
  Hospitum 3
  inspection by King's Chancellor 8
  landowners 13
  medical care 13
  patient care 12
  patronage 8, 9
  patrons 8, 9
  proctors 7
  religious establishement 5
  rents 44
  residential 5
  secretary 'receiver' 42
  tolls 14
Hospital Corporation of America 380
Hospital Management Committee 369
Hospital Plan 1962 296
  1975 Better Services for the Mentally
    Ill 297

hospital ships 170
Howard, John 136

indulgences 7
infection, surgical 135, 136, 138
infectious diseases 86, 134, 165, 172, 275
infirmarer 3
Inman, John 117
Institute of Child Health 260
Institute of Nursing Sisters 332
Institute of Psychiatry 294
Institute of Urology 191
Irish Sisters of Mercy 331

Jones, Agnes – Sister 343, 344
Jones, Sydney – surgeon 139
Justices of the Peace 154, 292

Keyser, Agnes and Fanny 377
King Edward VII Hospital Fund 184,
    408
Knox–surgeon 311

Labourers Revolt 155
Lady Almoners 392, 393, 394
Lancet 158, 185, 313, 314, 316
lazar houses 9
Lazarus, St 10
Leake, John 245
leeches 145
leper hospitals 12
leper houses 10
lepers 11, leprosy 9, 11, 12
Lefranc, Archbishop 4
Leiden University 87, 306, 310
Linde, James 133
Lister 140, 141, 142, 307, 308
Little, Dr William 196
Lock Hospitals 12, 187
London Pharmacopoeia 1746 142
Lunacy Act 1890 175, 294

management, hospital 87
Mappa Mundi 5
Marsden, William 105, 106, 200
Marshall, F.S. 70
matron 87, 353, 354
Maudsley, Henry 294
McIndoe, Archibald 225
McKeown and Brown 133
Mead, Richard 39
Medical Act 1886 305

medical audit 373, 374
medical care 13
Medical Register 1858 305
medical schools 308, 314, 315, 316
medical students fees 313
Mental Health Tribunal 298
mental hospitals 279-298
Mental Treatment Act 1930 295
Metropolitan and National Nursing
    Association 345, 346
Metropolitan Asylums Board 166, 167,
    168, 169, 172, 173, 174, 175, 176,
    177, 292, 360
Metropolitan Board of Works 164
miasma 275
midwives
    Central Midwives Board 234, 235,
        349
    licencing 231
    lying-in hospitals 231
    men-midwives 231, 232
    Midwives Act 1936 235
monasteries
    decay in standards 15
    dissolution of 17, 18
    hospitals 5
    infirmaries 1, 2
Monroe, Dr 306
Mosse, Bartholomew 236
Munro family 281

Napper, Albert 219
National Health Service 364, 365, 366,
    367, 368, 370, 371, 372, 373, 375,
    394, 395, 396, 398, 404, 405, 412
NHS Trusts 373, 374, 400, 403, 404, 414,
    415
National Spinal Injuries Centre 211
Nightingale, Florence 139, 159, 160, 234,
    329, 333, 334, 335, 336, 337, 338,
    339, 340
    Kings College 342, 343
    workhouse reform 344
Nuffield Homes Charitable Trust 379
Nurses' Act 1919 349
nursing 327, 328, 329, 331, 332
    care plans 355
    matron 87, 353, 354
nursing conditions 350, 351
nursing school 341, 342, 343
    Sister Tutor 348
    Nurse Practitioners 355

obstetrical chair 228, 229
Obstetrical Society 234
Order of the Garter 9

paediatric hospitals, criticism of 276, 277
Pare, Ambroise 184
Parsons, Dr Leonard 277, 278
patient care 12, 13
Petersfield Cottage Hospital 221
Petty, Sir William 359
plague 13
Platt, Sir Henry 278
Poor Law Act 1601 154
Poor Law Amendment Act 1834 155
Poor Law Board 160, 161, 164, 166, 168
Postgraduate Medical Federation 319,
    320, 361
Primary Care Trusts 375
Pringle, James 133
Priory Hospital Group 299
private finance initiatives 397, 413
private medical schools 87, 308, 313
Private Patients Plan 378
proctors 7
Project 2000 355, 357

quacks, quack treatments 58
Quakers 84
    York Retreat 286, 290
Queen's Institute of District Nursing 346

Rahere 19
Red Cross 357
Regularis Concordia 1
restraint 281, 282, 290
'resurrection men' 309, 310, 311, 312
Ryder, Sue – Care Centres 213
Roman field hospital 1
Royal British Nursing Association 347
Royal College of Nursing 348, 350, 351,
    352
Royal College of Physicians 302, 304,
    305
Royal College of Surgeons 305

Salerno 326
Salmon Report 353, 354, 355
Sanitary Act 1866 163
Saturday funds 85, 386
Savoy Palace 16
School of Hygiene and Tropical Medicine
    317

Semmelweis 238, 239
Simpson, Professor 307
smallpox 168, 169, 170, 173
Society of Apothecaries 40
Speenhamland 154
stagiarii 4
St John's Ambulance Brigade 357
St John's House Sisterhood 333
Stanley, Mary 339
Sunday funds 85, 386
sunshine hospitals 276
surgical standards 139
Surrey Hall 106

Tait, R. L. surgeon 141
Times, The 157, 162
trade guilds 4, 15
typhus 133, 134

University of London 117, 123, 124, 317

Vagrancy Act 1714, 1744 285
venereal disease 12, 86
Victoria History of the Counties of
   England 15
Vienna hospital system 149
   Vienna Obstetric Hospital 238
voluntary hospital financing 386–392,
   397

Walter, John, *The Times* 157
Wanless, Derek 410, 411
West, Dr Charles 254, 255
workhouses 160
   medical officers in 158, 159

Yacoub, Sir Magdi 210

Index of Hospitals

Aberdeen Infirmary 134
Addenbrooke's Hospital, Cambridge 83
Andover Union Workhouse 157
Atkinson-Morley Hospital 73

Bethlem Mental Hospital 280
  conditions 282, 283, 284
  Moorfields 280, 281, 282
  Southwark 284, 291
Birmingham Children's Hospital 270
  Broad Street 271
  Ladywood 270, 271, 277
  Steelhouse Lane 270, 272
Birmingham General Hospital
  initiation 83, 99, 100, 101, 102
Birmingham Queen's Hospital 100
The Brompton Hospital 192, 193, 194,
  195, 196
Brownlow Hill Infirmary 159
Bridewell House of Correction 280
Bristol Royal Infirmary 88, 89, 96
British Lying-in Hospital 239

Charing Cross Hospital
  Fulham Palace Road 117, 118
  fundraising 115
  initiation 110
  nursing 114
  rebuilding 113, 115, 116, 117
  staffing and regulations 113
  Suffolk Street Institute 111
  Villiers Street 112
Charing Cross Medical School 114, 115
Chelsea Royal Hospital 177, 180, 181
Chelsea Hospital for Women 207
Chester General Infirmary 134
City Orthopaedic Hospital 196, 197
Claybury Hospital 294
Clementine Churchill Hospital 379
Colney Hatch Asylum 290, 291
Cranleigh Village Hospital 219
The Cromwell Hospital 380, 381

District General Hospitals 370, 376
Dublin Lying-in Hospital 236, 237

Dublin, National Children's Hospital
  251

Edinburgh Medical School
  foundation 1720, Dr Monroe 306, 307,
  311
Edinburgh Royal Infirmary 94, 233, 306
Elizabeth Garrett Anderson Hospital 131

Fever Hospitals 166, 167, 168, 169, 170,
  171, 172, 173
Florence Nightingale Hospital 383
Foundling Hospital London 85, 252, 253

Glasgow Hospital For Sick Children
  Garnethill 266, 267, 268
  Yorkhill 269, 277
Glasgow Infirmary 135, 140
Glasgow Royal Infirmary 94
Gosport Hospital 179
Great Ormond Street Hospital For
  Children 51
  Cromwell House 259
  Hospital in the Garden 256, 258
  initiation 255
  Nursing School 258
  rebuilding, Variety Club Builing 260
  'Tertiary Referral Hospital' 261, 274
Greenwich Hospital 178
Guy's Hospital
  amalgamation 47
  foundation 37
  future plans 49
  nineteenth century 331
Guy's Hospital Medical School
  dental school 40, 47
  student fees and dress 39, 40

Hammersmith Hospital 361, 362, 363
Hammersmith Medical School 320, 321,
  322, 323
Harefield Hospital 207, 208, 209, 210
Harley Street Clinic 379
Haslar Hospital 178, 179
Hotel Dieu, Paris 13, 138, 326, 327, 328

Inchtuthill, Roman Field Hospital 1
Infants Hospital, Vincent Square 261

Kent and Canterbury Hospital 92
King Edward VII's Hospital, Sister
    Agnes, London 377
King's College Hospital
  establishment 130
  rebuilt 132, 141
King's College Hospital Medical School,
    establishment 132

Leeds General Infirmary 86
Leicester Royal Infirmary 93
Liverpool Seaman's Hospital 95
Liverpool Royal Infirmary 92, 95, 96, 97
London, City of, Chest Hospital 195
London, City of, Lying-in Hospital 239,
    240
The London Clinic 377, 378
London Fever Hospital 165, 166
London Homeopathic Hospital 206, 208
London Smallpox Hospital 165

Maghull Hospital 293
Manchester Children's Hospital 262
  Pendlebury 264, 265
Manchester Royal Infirmary 83, 97, 98,
    99, 134
Marsden Cancer Hospital 105, 108
Central Middlesex Hospital 363
Middlesex Hospital, initiation 79, 80,
    239, 315
Middlesex Hospital Medical School 80
Middlesex Infirmary
  initiated 78
  staffing problems 78, 239
Millhill Emergency Military Hospital
    295
Moorfields Eye Hospital 188, 189

Napsbury Hospital 296
National Hospital for Neurology and
    Neurosurgery 203, 204
National Heart Hospital 196
National Orthopaedic Hospital 196, 198
National Temperance Hospital 130
Normansfield Hospital 296, 297

Papworth Hospital 210
Portland Hospital for Women and
    Children 380

Princess Alice Memorial Hospital,
    Eastbourne 223
Prince Grace Hospital 379, 380
Princess of Wales Children's Hospital,
    The, Birmingham 272, 273
Queen Charlotte's Hospital 241, 242, 244,
    245, 246, 362
Queen Victoria Hospital, East Grinstead
    224

The Radcliffe Infirmary 83, 87
Roehampton Priory 298
The Rotunda Hospital 236, 237
Royal Asylums, Scotland 288
Royal Edinburgh Hospital for Sick
    Children 265
Royal Free Hospital
  cholera 106, 107, 200, 392, 393
  initiation 105
  rebuilt 106
Royal Free Medical School 108, 110
Royal Hospital for Sick Children,
    Glasgow 265, 266, 267
Royal Hospital for Neuro Disability 211,
    212, 213
Royal Liverpool Children's Hospital,
    Alder Hey 265
Royal Liverpool Infirmary 343, 344
Royal Marsden Hospital 108, 200, 201,
    202, 203
Royal National Othopaedic Hospital 196,
    199, 200
Royal Orthopaedic Hospital 196
Royal Postgraduate Medical School 319,
    320, 361
Royal Victoria, Bournemouth 223
Rye, Winchelsea & District Memorial
    Hospital 224

St Bartholomew's Hospital
  appointment of surgeon 184
  'box carriers' 51
  extension of boundaries 21, 26
  fees 27
  foundation 19, 20
  medical school 52, 53
  nurses' training scheme and
    accommodation 55
  nursing sisters 28, 29
  physician, water supply 31
  plan 22
  politics 26

property donations 23
public right of way 51
rebuilding 32, 47, 50, 51, 52, 53, 54
restoration 25
specialist departments 54, 55
surgeon 30
Tomlinson Report 55, 56
water supply, burial grounds 32
St Bartholomew's Hospital Medical
    School
incorporation in the City of London 53
initiation 52
rebuilding 53
redevelopment 54
St Christopher's Hospice 213
St George's Hospital
    initiation 60
    Lanesborough House 67
    management 70
    modernisation 72
    rebuilding 68
    specialist services 72
    staff 68
St George's Hospital Medical School 72,
    73
St Luke's Hospital 286, 287
St Mark's Hospital 185, 187, 189, 190,
    191, 192
St Mary's Hospital
    Clarence Memorial Wing 121, 122
    consultant staff 119
    initiation 118
    Queen Mother Wing 122, 392
St Mary's Hospital Medical School 119,
    120
St Paul's Hospital 191
St Peter's Hospital 191
St Thomas's Hospital
    amalgamations 47
    burial grounds 32
    dissection room 37, 39
    foundation 20, 21
    future plans 48
    hospitaller, hospital regulations and
        fees 27
    Nightingale School of Nursing 44
    nursing changes, surgery 29
    physician, sanitation 31
    politics 26
    rebuilding 23, 24, 33–6, 43, 44, 45, 50,
        51, 52, 139, 145, 150, 184, 333, 341
    restoration 25, 26

surgery 30
Surrey Gardens 42, 43
war damage 45
St Thomas's Hospital Medical School
    dissection room 37, 39
    museum 40
    staff fees 40
    staff disagreements and disruptions 40,
        41
Salisbury Hospital 134
Salisbury Infirmary 88, 89, 90
Salisbury, St Nicholas Infirmary 2
Scutari Hospital 336, 337, 338, 339, 340
Sheffield Royal Infirmary 93
Stoke Manderville Hospital 211

Tavistock Clinic 294
The London Hospital
    decays 75, 76
    rebuilding, development 75, 76, 77
    redevelopment 77
The London Infirmary 73

United Hospitals 37
Universal Dispensary for Sick Children 254
University College Hospital London
    future development 129
    initiation 80, 123
    Institute of Obstetrics 127
    new building programme 127
    rebuilding 125, 126, 127
University College Hospital Medical
    School 81, 127, 130

The Wellington Hospital 380, 382
Westminster Hospital
    Broad Sanctuary site 62
    Chelsea and Westminster Hospital 65
    conditions and renovations 63, 64
    Petty France 62
    St John's Gardens 65
Westminster Infirmary 3, 58
    initiation, staff 59
    patients 60
    Petty France 62
    relocation 60, 61
Westminster Lying-in Hospital 243, 244,
    245
Westminster Hospital Medical School
    development 66
    Imperial College of Medicine 67
    initiation 65

Winchester Hospital 83, 88
Worcester Infirmary 83
Worcester Royal Infirmary 91, 386

York Retreat 286, 290
York Asylum 287
York, St Leonard's 7, 14